HANDBOOK OF NUMERICAL METHODS AND APPLICATIONS

LOUIS G. KELLY
Applied Physics Laboratory
Johns Hopkins University

ADDISON-WESLEY PUBLISHING COMPANY
Reading, Massachusetts · Menlo Park, California · London · Don Mills, Ontario

TO MARY

PREFACE

This book was in preparation over a period of about ten years. The selection and organization of material is based on the author's experiences in computation centers associated with industry and research as well as in university teaching. It has developed from material written and revised many times in connection with the above experiences. In fact most of the material has been used the past several years in lectures given by the author in a university course and in special courses for computing personnel and various groups of engineers. Numerous requests have been made for the author to combine all of the material in one volume.

The book has been designed as a handbook, but can be used as a text as explained in the next paragraph. In supervising and working with analysts and computer programmers in industry and research, the author felt the need for such a book. Much of the material on numerical methods can only be found in many different books on numerical analysis. Much of the material related to applications can only be found in books of an engineering nature, and are of particular interest to scientists, physicists, and engineers. The author has felt a definite need for a book which brings all of these topics together in one volume with ample references to other sources of the material, and believes it would be a valuable addition to the personal library of every programmer of scientific and engineering problems. The references to other sources of material are given in three different ways. The Bibliography in the back of the book is a basic set of references with a sequenced numbering system. In addition, most of the chapters have a set of supplementary references for greater emphasis. Finally, many references, particularly recent ones, are contained in the running text itself for even greater immediate emphasis and in Appendix F on keeping up with the literature.

The book can be used as a text if the chosen material is accompanied by appropriate lectures given by the instructor. The author has found the majority of the students in his university course majoring in engineering, physics, chemistry, and fields other than mathematics, and has used much of the material very success-fully in the above manner. Chapters 1 through 9 could be used as the foundation of a basic course in numerical methods. The instructor may vary his course con-siderably, depending on the interest and level of his class, by choosing topics from the first 9 chapters and supplementing with appropriate topics from the remaining 16 chapters. The author has found this approach gratifying since it affords a great deal of flexibility in the breadth and depth of material covered and provokes questioning from the students, thereby encouraging class participation.

Chapter 11 on complex variables and Chapter 12 on the Laplace transform serve one purpose only, that is, to present a few special definitions and theorems as background for much of the material to come later. The last half of the book contains topics of special interest to scientists and engineers and should be quite useful to computing personnel working with them.

The author wishes to acknowledge the valuable suggestions, criticisms, and contributions given for various parts of the manuscript by Dr. L. W. Ehrlich, Dr. R. P. Rich, Professor John R. Sullivan, Mr. Harry Shaw, Mrs. Frances Akridge, Mr. James Kuttler, Mr. George Lindamood, Miss Janet Bramhall, and Mrs. Patricia Stamper. The author also wishes to express his gratitude to Mr. J. G. Monteabaro for his untiring effort in editing the entire manuscript, and Mrs. Betty Hess for her meticulous typing of the manuscript. Finally, the author wishes to express his appreciation to Dr. D. C. Sheldon, former teacher, colleague, and friend, for his interest, counseling, and encouragement over the years.

Silver Spring, Maryland   L. G. K.
May, 1967

CONTENTS

Chapter 1 Introduction 1

   1.1 Numerical computation: art and science 1
   1.2 Historical development 2
   1.3 Computer mathematics 3
   1.4 Problems and difficulties 3
   1.5 Formula derivation 5
   1.6 Source and types of errors 9
   1.7 Truncation–roundoff error curve 9
   1.8 Examples of truncation error, roundoff error, and instability . . . 11
   1.9 Significant figures, relative error, and accuracy 17
  1.10 Error in polynomial approximation 19
  1.11 Iteration and convergence 20
  1.12 Summary remarks 21
       Exercises 22

Chapter 2 Finite and Divided Differences 23

   2.1 Introduction 23
   2.2 Calculus of finite differences 23
   2.3 Related differences and operators 25
   2.4 Differencing of discrete data 27
   2.5 Forward differences 27
   2.6 Backward differences 28
   2.7 Central differences 29
   2.8 Relationship between forward, central, and backward differences . 29
   2.9 Divided differences 30
  2.10 Differentiation of divided differences 30
  2.11 Relationship between finite and divided differences 31
  2.12 Finite differences of polynomials 32
  2.13 Errors in a tabular entry 32
       Exercises 33

Chapter 3 Basic Interpolating and Approximating Polynomials 34

   3.1 Introduction 34
   3.2 The cardinal function of interpolation 34
   3.3 Newton's fundamental formula 36
   3.4 Newton's forward difference formula 37
   3.5 Newton's backward difference formula 38

3.6   Linear interpolation   39
3.7   Higher-order interpolation   40
3.8   Aitken's method   40
3.9   Gaussian formulas   42
3.10 Lagrange's interpolation formula   43
3.11 Other special formulas   45
3.12 Supplementary references   46
        Exercises   47

Chapter 4   **Differentiation and Integration**   48

4.1   Introduction   48
4.2   Lagrangian differentiation formulas   48
4.3   Derivative formulas from finite difference operations   51
4.4   Lagrangian integration formulas   52
4.5   Integration formulas involving finite differences   55
4.6   Gaussian integration formulas   57
4.7   Other methods of numerical integration   61
        Exercises   62

Chapter 5   **Curve Fitting and Data Smoothing**   63

5.1   Introduction   63
5.2   Principle of least squares   63
5.3   Polynomial curve fitting   66
5.4   Orthogonal functions   66
5.5   Orthogonal polynomials   67
5.6   Forsythe method   68
5.7   Legendre polynomial approximation   71
5.8   Laguerre polynomial approximation   71
5.9   Hermite polynomial approximation   72
5.10 Other types of approximations   73
5.11 Fourier approximation   73
5.12 Chebyshev approximation   76
5.13 Exponential approximation   80
5.14 Rational functions   82
5.15 Smoothing of data   84
        Exercises   84

Chapter 6   **Nonlinear Algebraic Equations**   86

6.1   Introduction   86
6.2   Types of problems associated with solution   86
6.3   Method of bisection   88
6.4   False position; linear interpolation   89
6.5   Parabolic interpolation   89
6.6   Newton-Raphson method   90
6.7   Iterated synthetic division   91
6.8   Lin's method   92

6.9   Synthetic division with quadratic factors   93
6.10   Lin's method for quadratic factors   93
6.11   Bairstow's method   94
6.12   Modified Newton-Raphson method   97
6.13   Graeffe's method   97
6.14   Systems of nonlinear equations   98
6.15   Newton-Raphson method for system of equations   99
6.16   Minimizing methods   100
6.17   Rich-Shaw method   100
6.18   Matrix methods   101
6.19   Comparison of several methods   101
       Exercises   102

Chapter 7   **Matrix Algebra and Operations**   103

7.1   Introduction   103
7.2   Matrix and vector notation   103
7.3   Special types of matrices   104
7.4   Addition and multiplication of matrices   105
7.5   Determinant value, singular matrices, and rank   106
7.6   Inversion of matrices   106
7.7   The eigenvalue problem   107
7.8   Hermitian matrices, positive definite matrices   108
7.9   Orthogonal matrices, unitary matrices   108
7.10   The Jordan canonical form   109
7.11   Similarity transformations   109
7.12   Vector norms and matrix norms   110
7.13   Triangular matrices   111
7.14   Tridiagonal matrices   113
7.15   Supplementary references   113
       Exercises   113

Chapter 8   **Linear Algebraic Equations**   115

8.1   Introduction   115
8.2   Method of determinants   115
8.3   Elimination, pivoting, and scaling   116
8.4   Iterative improvement   117
8.5   Gauss elimination   118
8.6   Crout reduction   119
8.7   Triangular matrices from Crout reduction   121
8.8   Inverse method   122
8.9   Jordan elimination   123
8.10   Iterative methods   123
8.11   Gradient methods   125
8.12   Orthogonalization methods   125
8.13   Comparison of methods   125
       Exercises   126

Chapter 9   Eigenvalues and Eigenvectors 127

9.1   Introduction 127
9.2   The characteristic polynomial 128
9.3   Methods 128
9.4   Jacobi method for real symmetric matrices 129
9.5   Givens' method 131
9.6   Muller's method 133
9.7   Power method and inverse power method 133
9.8   Laguerre's method 137
9.9   Householder's method 139
9.10   Supplementary references 141
       Exercises 142

Chapter 10   Scaling of Matrices 143

10.1   Introduction 143
10.2   Scaling matrices on a digital computer 143
10.3   Methods of scaling matrices 144
10.4   Scalar multiplication 144
10.5   Equilibration 145
10.6   Linear program method 145
10.7   Osborne's method 148
10.8   Modified Osborne's method 149
10.9   Comments and supplementary references 149

Chapter 11   Introduction to Complex Variables 150

11.1   Definitions 150
11.2   Elementary functions of a complex variable 151
11.3   Limit, continuity, and analyticity of functions of a complex variable   152
11.4   Line integrals of complex functions 154
11.5   Cauchy's integral theorem 155
11.6   Cauchy's integral formula 156
11.7   Taylor's series 157
11.8   Laurent series 157
11.9   Singularities 158
11.10   Residues and Cauchy's residue theorem 159
11.11   Supplementary references 162
        Exercises 162

Chapter 12   Introduction to the Laplace Transform 163

12.1   Definition 163
12.2   Existence of Laplace transforms 163
12.3   Transforms of simple functions 164
12.4   Transforms of derivatives 165
12.5   The inverse transformation 166
12.6   Inverse transform by method of residues 167
12.7   Certain properties of the Laplace transformation 168

12.8   Certain basic functions 169
12.9   Shifting theorem in the t-plane   170
12.10   Supplementary references 170
        Exercises 170

Chapter 13   Difference Equations   172

13.1   Introduction 172
13.2   Simple difference equations and their order 172
13.3   Solution of first-order difference equations 174
13.4   Solution of second-order difference equations 175
13.5   Convergence and order of accuracy 177
13.6   Examples of difference equations 178
13.7   Partial differential equations and finite differences 179
13.8   Simple wave equation 180
13.9   Simple heat equation   180
13.10   Supplementary references 181
        Exercises 181

Chapter 14   Ordinary Differential Equations   182

14.1   Introduction 182
14.2   Picard's method of successive approximation   182
14.3   Finite difference schemes   183
14.4   Open type formulas 183
14.5   Closed type formulas   185
14.6   Euler's method   185
14.7   Modified Euler or Heun method 185
14.8   Adams' method 186
14.9   Modified Adams or Adams-Bashforth method 186
14.10   A simple predictor-corrector method 186
14.11   Milne methods   186
14.12   Runge-Kutta methods 187
14.13   Nordsieck's method   187
14.14   Higher-order equations 188
14.15   Linear equations with variable coefficients 188
14.16   Unstable finite difference schemes   189
14.17   Boundary-value problems 190
14.18   Matrix form of a system of second-order equations   193
14.19   Second-order reduction   193
14.20   Matrix exponential method   194
14.21   Survey of nonlinear ordinary differential equations 195
14.22   Supplementary references 197
        Exercises 197

Chapter 15   Transfer Function Computations   198

15.1   Introduction 198
15.2   Matrix transform equation   198

15.3   Transfer function analysis 202
15.4   Time response from transfer functions 202
15.5   Frequency response from transfer functions 204
15.6   Automatic monitoring 204
15.7   Minimum phase and nonminimum phase transfer functions . . . 206
15.8   Stability 206
15.9   The stability and phaseness test 207
15.10 Frequency response computations 208
15.11 Bode plots and Nichols plots 209
15.12 Static and root locus gain constants 212
15.13 The root locus curve from transfer functions 213
15.14 Supplementary references 214
        Exercises 214

Chapter 16   Partial Differential Equations 215

16.1   Introduction 215
16.2   Examples of well-posed problems 215
16.3   Classification of partial differential equations 216
16.4   Finite difference methods, convergence, and stability 218
16.5   Numerical solution of parabolic equations 220
16.6   The maximum principle 222
16.7   Convergence and stability 223
16.8   Numerical solution of elliptic equations 224
16.9   Boundary equations for elliptic problems 225
16.10 Matrix form of the finite difference problem 226
16.11 Iterative solution of $Av = B$ for elliptic equations 228
16.12 Numerical solution of hyperbolic equations 229
16.13 Method of characteristics 230
16.14 Finite difference method for hyperbolic equations 231
16.15 Supplementary references 231

Chapter 17   Harmonic Analysis 232

17.1   Introduction 232
17.2   The Fourier series 233
17.3   Harmonic analysis of equidistant data 233
17.4   Chebyshev approximation 234
17.5   The Fourier integral 234
17.6   Applications of Fourier transform 238
17.7   Supplementary references 238

Chapter 18   Special Functions and Integrals 239

18.1   Introduction 239
18.2   Bessel functions 239
18.3   Sine, cosine, and exponential integrals 242
18.4   Numerical integration of Fourier transform integrals 242
18.5   Supplementary references 244

Chapter 19 Sampled Data and Digital Filtering 245

19.1 Introduction 245
19.2 Sampled data and the cardinal function 245
19.3 Folding frequency and sampling level noise 246
19.4 Digital filters 247
19.5 Substitution rule 247
19.6 Transient response 248
19.7 Example of a discrete analog for a continuous filter 249
19.8 Supplementary references 251

Chapter 20 Numerical Solution of Integral Equations 252

20.1 Introduction 252
20.2 The Fredholm equation of the second kind 253
20.3 Method of solution 253
20.4 Difference correction technique 256
20.5 Approximation and correction 256
20.6 The Fredholm equation of the third kind 262
20.7 Method of solution 262
20.8 Computing the eigenvalues 265
20.9 Computing the eigenvectors 266
20.10 Supplementary references 270

Chapter 21 Numerical Solution of Vibration Problems 271

21.1 Introduction 271
21.2 The equations of motion 273
21.3 Analogs of linear, torsional, and electrical systems 275
21.4 The transformed equations of motion 276
21.5 Other vibration type problems 280
21.6 Supplementary references 280

Chapter 22 Padé Approximation to a Function 281

22.1 Introduction 281
22.2 Generating the approximation 281
22.3 Accuracy of the approximation 283
22.4 Applications of approximations 285

Chapter 23 Gram-Schmidt Orthogonalization Procedure 286

23.1 Introduction 286
23.2 Numerical computation 286
23.3 Comments on numerical computation 287
23.4 Supplementary references 289

Chapter 24 Computer Methods of Functional Minimization 290

24.1 Introduction 290
24.2 Criteria for comparing minimization procedures 290

24.3   Definitions and function evaluations 290
24.4   Direct mathematical approach   291
24.5   Gradient methods of minimization   291
24.6   Other methods of minimization   293
24.7   Conclusions 294
24.8   Supplementary references 294

Chapter 25   Elementary Statistics   295

25.1   Introduction 295
25.2   Measures of central tendency and dispersion   295
25.3   Probability distributions   296
25.4   Fisher's maximum-likelihood estimation 298
25.5   Method of confidence intervals   299
25.6   Testing of parameters 300
25.7   Regression and analysis of variance 301
25.8   The Monte Carlo method 309
25.9   Supplementary references 310

Bibliography   311

Appendix A   Mathematical theorems   321

Appendix B   Formula derivation by matrix methods 323

Appendix C   Theorems of interpolation function theory 325

Appendix D   Test matrices with known inverses and eigenvalues   331

Appendix E   Table of Laplace transforms 333

Appendix F   Keeping up with the literature   337

Answers to Selected Exercises 341

Index 347

CHAPTER 1

INTRODUCTION

1.1 NUMERICAL COMPUTATION: ART AND SCIENCE

Classical or "pure" analysis deals with infinite processes. Undergraduates in most of our colleges and universities are guided through the channels of pure mathematics with its elegant theorems, lemmas, corollaries, and rigorous proofs. The academic atmosphere is often not conducive to the development of an intellectual curiosity as to the relation of these facts to the physical world and its many problems. Many students may find later that many of these channels do not lead to adequate preparation for basic research in various branches of physical science. They may find that many of the theorems, proofs, etc., which they have mastered, can seldom be applied to specific problems, and that, indeed, many mathematical models defy the use of any known formal methods.

Many physical phenomena lead to linear differential or integral differential equations and can be solved by classical methods. However, most physical phenomena lead to nonlinear equations and the classical methods of analysis fail altogether. An awareness of these facts in "practical" analysis should reach all students of applied science and engineering at the junior or senior level.

Lanczos [89]* objects to the word "practical" with its popular connotations and coins a new word which he considers more adequate. He uses the Greek word "parexic" which means "nearby." He speaks of parexic methods, parexic expansions, and parexic viewpoints.

In addition to *pure* and *practical* analysis a new expression, *numerical analysis*, has come into usage during the last few years. Lanczos [89] says this deals with translation of mathematical processes into operations with numbers, truncation errors, roundoff errors, etc. Kopal [86] says that numerical analysis as a scientific discipline represents much more than a collection of formulas. It stands for the mastery of processes for developing numerical methods that are best suited for any particular problem. Hamming [65] says the purpose of computing is *insight*, not numbers. Forsythe [44] defines numerical analysis as that branch of applied mathematics which uses mathematical ideas to devise and evaluate numerical techniques for employing computers to solve problems, and to study their convergence and errors.

---

* Numbers in brackets are keyed to the references at the end of the text.

A numerical method cannot furnish a general solution but leads to a particular solution. This had not been appreciated by some mathematicians, but a family of particular solutions may throw light on a general solution.

The physical background of his problems alone makes the task of the applied mathematician different from that of the pure mathematician. The numerical analyst may be more interested in particular solutions satisfying his requirements, and in attacking problems closed to formal approaches. In many cases he operates by intuition and analogy, hoping the methods and results are correct and reliable enough to use. In these cases he is practicing the art of numerical analysis. When he uses proven algorithms with precise error bounds, etc., he is practicing the science of numerical analysis. Like any science, the science of numerical analysis has grown very gradually. There are relatively few practical problems which the practicing numerical analyst really knows how to solve. Numerical analysis is still almost as much an art as it is a science. There are many challenges and opportunities in its development as a science.

1.2 HISTORICAL DEVELOPMENT

The roots of numerical analysis go back many thousands of years. Progress was slow in prehistoric times due to the variety of symbols and many different numerical systems. Records show systems using quinary (Greek, Roman), decimal (Egyptian, Sanskrit), or vigesimal (Aztecs, Mayas) base. All of these were based on finger counting.

The Babylonians were the first numerical analysts. They used a number system with a base of 60, and gave us the concepts of 360° in a circle, 60 minutes, and 3600 seconds. They gave us the first great discovery of the positional principle or positional meaning of numbers.

About 2000 years later the concept of zero and negative numbers was introduced, probably by the Hindus. They were the first to apply the positional principle to the decimal system and to express all numbers by ten symbols.

The ancient Egyptians were apparently the first to use the method of false position in solving nonlinear algebraic equations.

The ancient Greeks also made significant contributions. About 200 B.C. Archimedes approximated the value of π. Heron, the elder, about 100 B.C., used the iterative process $\sqrt{a} \sim \frac{1}{2}(x_n + a/x_n)$ usually attributed to Newton. The Pythagorean school summed series. Diophantus, about 250 A.D., worked on indeterminate equations and introduced an arithmetical method for the solution of quadratic equations.

The basic concepts of modern day computers were introduced by Charles Babbage with his analytical engine in 1834 and Kelvin with his differential analyzer in 1876. Of course some of the reasons for delay in this area were technical. Mercury delay lines, vacuum tubes, and transistors had not been developed.

The most profound influence on numerical analysis was probably exerted by men working in the field of astronomy. Men such as Newton, Gauss, Laplace, and Bessel made significant contributions working in this area.

1.3 COMPUTER MATHEMATICS

Modern high speed digital computers are very powerful and useful instruments for solving complex problems. However, there are certain difficulties and pitfalls associated with digital computing equipment and numerical techniques. Everyone who uses a digital computer should be aware of these problems and develop a basic understanding of them.

The number system used by a digital computer is not the real number system. It is a finite, bounded set of rational numbers. That the set of numbers used by a digital computer is finite is a direct consequence of the fact that the number of digits which can be stored internally in the computer is also finite—an inherent physical limitation of the machine. Such a finite set of rationals does not possess certain properties of the real numbers—properties such as density, existence of multiplicative inverses, and algebraic closure—which are essential for a complete theory of limits. Hence, in most digital computer operations, we are attempting to do classical mathematics in a number system quite different from the one on which the mathematics is founded, and in many cases the operations themselves may be pseudo-operations.

The classical solution of many problems in mathematics depends on the basic principle of a limiting process and on the theory of continuity. With numerical methods, however, we are concerned with discrete and finite quantities. We approximate numerical derivatives by finite differences instead of a limiting process. The solution of a differential equation is a set of values obtained at discrete points instead of a continuous function.

Numerical methods for a computer must involve formulas of finite length. A formula for differentiation may be obtained from a truncated Taylor series. Many elementary functions are evaluated by using truncated infinite series.

Accurate and reliable approximation is the keystone of numerical computation. Most of the fundamental approximations in numerical analysis are based on polynomial approximations. This follows naturally from the famous and powerful Weierstrass approximation theorem, one of the cornerstones of modern analysis. This theorem, along with several other important mathematical theorems is given in Appendix A for quick reference.

1.4 PROBLEMS AND DIFFICULTIES

Numerical methods are involved in solving the following types of problems on a digital computer:

1. Approximations:
   a) interpolation
   b) integration
   c) differentiation
   d) summation of series
   e) smoothing data and curve fitting

2. Functional equations:
   a) ordinary differential equations
   b) partial differential equations
   c) minimization
   d) integral equations
   e) simulation

3. Algebra:

   a) root finding

   b) linear equations

   c) nonlinear equations

4. Matrix problems:

   a) linear equations

   b) determinant

   c) inverse of a matrix

   d) eigenvalues and eigenvectors

One may find a number of methods available for solving a particular problem, with one method giving better results than another method. For example, to solve a system of linear equations one may use Cramer's method, Gauss' elimination method, Crout's method, or Gauss-Seidel's iteration method. Cramer's method is not a satisfactory method for computers. The iteration method is usually satisfactory if the matrix is strongly diagonal and generally sparse.

Even though theory and a numerical procedure may be very straight forward, challenges continue to present themselves and may vary from problem to problem, even problems of the same type. Order of operations may affect a computation drastically. Overflow or underflow, due to finiteness, can lead to a completely unreliable result. Repeated or equally spaced roots may cause no end of trouble. Near singular matrices can render a computation worthless. Single or multistep methods of integration may lead to inaccuracies or instability. One method of finding eigenvalues and eigenvectors may give excellent results, while another method fails miserably. Widely spaced elements of a matrix can present problems. Scaling may improve results in one case and give worse results in another. Fixed-point, floating-point, single-precision, and multiple-precision arithmetic may give widely varying results.

Curve fitting a set of data may turn out to be more "art" than science in many cases. Convergence and stability may be very important questions in certain numerical solutions.

The convergence problem is characterized by the question, "Does the numerical solution approach the true solution as a chosen numerical procedure is applied?" The convergence problem may arise from such procedures as the truncation of an infinite series or the use of an iterative process.

The stability problem is characterized by the question, "Do small errors occurring early in a computation give rise to errors of increasing magnitude or possible oscillations during the remainder of the computation?" The stability problem may arise in such procedures as the numerical integration of a differential equation.

After we choose a method, we must obtain and analyze results for accuracy and reliability. The various types of errors may be so interlaced in a sequence of computations that a complete error analysis is impossible. However, we may run special check cases and do a local error analysis at certain check points within the sequence of computations. Then we may make decisions as to changing methods, using fixed-point instead of floating-point arithmetic, or using double-precision arithmetic.

1.5 FORMULA DERIVATION

There is sometimes a tendency to think of numerical methods as being composed of a large collection of unrelated formulas with many different derivations. However, it is the purpose here to show that we can derive most of these formulas by a standardized method.

If 0 is some linear operator operating on $f(x)$, we assume a form

$$0\{f(x)\} = W_1 f(x_1) + W_2 f(x_2) + \cdots + W_n f(x_n). \qquad (1.5.1)$$

If 0 is an operation such as integration or differentiation, then the weighting coefficients W_i are determined for a given class of functions $f(x)$.

An exact error analysis of a complex and lengthy sequence of computations is usually extremely difficult or impossible. Extensive theoretical investigations have been carried out related to the different types of errors and particular numerical computations. For certain numerical formulas a theoretical estimate of the error is given. In many cases this error estimate involves higher derivatives. These higher derivatives may be extremely difficult or impossible to find. Therefore, these estimates may be of theoretical value but useless in actual practice. In practice the best one can do is a somewhat limited and isolated or local error analysis.

The aim here is to develop a basic understanding of errors with as practical an approach as possible. We will give a brief incomplete discussion with some of the formulas being derived in this section. The next section in this chapter will give a general discussion of errors as a background for error estimates associated with particular numerical formulas developed in future chapters. Only basic theory will be given, with some extensions in the appendices and with ample references to extensive and elegant developments.

We shall illustrate this with several examples. The simplest examples elucidating the method involve the operation of integration and polynomials as the class of functions.

Example 1. Determine the numerical integration formula

$$\int_{-1}^{1} f(x)\,dx = W_{-1} f(-1) + W_0 f(0) + W_1 f(1), \qquad (1.5.2)$$

such that the W_i give an exact formula for $f(x) = 1$, x, and x^2. [In general $f(x)$ may be an arbitrary set of functions. The set chosen here is for simplicity and convenience.]

Solution. For
$$\begin{aligned}
f(x) &= 1, & W_{-1} + W_0 + W_1 &= 2; \\
f(x) &= x, & -W_{-1} \quad\quad + W_1 &= 0; \\
f(x) &= x^2, & W_{-1} \quad\quad + W_1 &= \tfrac{2}{3}.
\end{aligned}$$

Solving this system of equations, we have

$$W_{-1} = W_1 = \tfrac{1}{3}, \qquad W_0 = \tfrac{4}{3}.$$

Therefore

$$\int_{-1}^{1} f(x)\,dx = \tfrac{1}{3}[f(-1) + 4f(0) + f(1)].$$ (1.5.3)

This is the celebrated *Simpson's rule* with $h = 1$. Formula (1.5.3) is written as

$$\int_{-1}^{1} f(x)\,dx = \tfrac{1}{3}[f(-1) + 4f(0) + f(1)] + E_m,$$ (1.5.4)

where E_m is the error for the special functions $f(x) = 1, x, x^2, x^3, \ldots, x^m$. Hamming [65] in Chapter 10 and Hildebrand [73] in Chapters 5 and 8 give a very rigorous and elegant derivation of the following formula for determining the general error estimate for arbitrary $f(x)$:

$$E = \frac{h^{m+1}f^{(m)}(\theta)}{m!} E_m, \qquad -1 < \theta < 1.$$ (1.5.5)

Applying (1.5.4) to $f(x) = x^3$, we obtain

$$\int_{-1}^{1} x^3 \cdot dx = \tfrac{1}{3}[-1 + 0 + 1] + E_3, \qquad E_3 = 0.$$

Therefore, the formula is exact for x^3.
    Using $f(x) = x^4$, we have

$$\int_{-1}^{1} x^4\,dx = \tfrac{1}{3}[1 + 0 + 1] + E_4, \qquad E_4 = -\tfrac{4}{15}.$$

Therefore

$$E = \frac{h^5 f^{(4)}(\theta)}{4!}\left(-\frac{4}{15}\right) = -\frac{h^5 f^{(4)}(\theta)}{90}, \qquad -1 < \theta < 1,$$ (1.5.6)

which is the commonly known error estimate given for Simpson's rule. The general form of Simpson's rule with error estimate is written

$$\int_{a}^{a+2h} f(x)\,dx = \frac{h}{3}[f(a) + 4f(a + h) + f(a + 2h)] - \frac{h^5 f^{(4)}(\theta)}{90}.$$ (1.5.7)

Example 2. Given the values of the function and its derivative at the end points, find the formula

$$\int_{0}^{1} f(x)\,dx = W_0 f_0 + W_1 f_1 + W_2 f_0' + W_3 f_1',$$ (1.5.8)

which is exact for $f(x) = 1, x, x^2, x^3$.

Solution.

$$W_0 + W_1 = 1,$$
$$W_1 + W_2 + W_3 = \tfrac{1}{2},$$
$$W_1 + 2W_3 = \tfrac{1}{3},$$
$$W_1 + 3W_3 = \tfrac{1}{4},$$

where

$$W_0 = \tfrac{1}{2}, \qquad W_1 = \tfrac{1}{2}, \qquad W_2 = \tfrac{1}{12}, \qquad W_3 = -\tfrac{1}{12}.$$

Substituting these into the formula, we have

$$\int_0^1 f(x)\,dx = \tfrac{1}{2}[f_0 + f_1] + \tfrac{1}{12}[f_0' - f_1'] + E_m. \tag{1.5.9}$$

For

$$f(x) = x^4, \qquad W_1 + 4W_3 + E_4 = \tfrac{1}{5},$$

and hence $E_4 = \tfrac{1}{30}$.

The general error estimate for arbitrary $f(x)$ is

$$E = \frac{E_4 h^5 f^{(4)}(\theta)}{4!} = \frac{1}{720} f^{(4)}(\theta), \qquad 0 < \theta < 1. \tag{1.5.10}$$

Example 3. Given the value of the function at three points, find the formula

$$\left.\frac{dy}{dx}\right|_{x=1} = W_0 f_0 + W_1 f_1 + W_2 f_2. \tag{1.5.11}$$

Solution. Using $f(x) = 1,\ x,\ x^2$, we get

$$W_0 + W_1 + W_2 = 0,$$
$$W_1 + 2W_2 = 1,$$
$$W_1 + 4W_2 = 2,$$

where $W_0 = -\tfrac{3}{2}$, $W_1 = 0$, $W_2 = \tfrac{1}{2}$. And we obtain

$$\left.\frac{dy}{dx}\right|_{x=1} = \tfrac{1}{2}[f_2 - f_0]. \tag{1.5.12}$$

In the previous examples the abscissa values were specified. Now we consider an example in which this is not the case.

Example 4. Determine the following formula where the abscissas x_1 and x_2 are not specified:

$$\int_{-1}^1 f(x)\,dx = W_1 f(x_1) + W_2 f(x_2). \tag{1.5.13}$$

Solution. Using $f(x) = 1,\ x,\ x^2,\ x^3$ in Eq. (1.5.13), we get

$$W_1 + W_2 = 2, \tag{a}$$
$$W_1 x_1 + W_2 x_2 = 0, \tag{b}$$
$$W_1 x_1^2 + W_2 x_2^2 = \tfrac{2}{3}, \tag{c}$$
$$W_1 x_1^3 + W_2 x_2^3 = 0. \tag{d}$$

From (b), $W_2 x_2 = -W_1 x_1$, and

(d) $W_1 x_1^3 - W_1 x_1 x_2^2 = 0$, $W_1 x_1 \neq 0$,

$x_1^2 - x_2^2 \quad = 0$,

$x_1 \quad\quad = -x_2$ (+ sign gives only 1 point);

(b) $W_1 x_1 - W_2 x_1 = 0$, $W_1 = W_2$;

(a) $2W_1 = 2$, $W_1 = 1 = W_2$;

(c) $x_1^2 + x_1^2 = \frac{2}{3}$, $x_1^2 = \frac{1}{3}$, $x_1 = \pm 1/\sqrt{3}$.

If $x_1 = -1/\sqrt{3}$, then $x_2 = 1/\sqrt{3}$ and therefore

$$\int_{-1}^{1} f(x)\, dx = (1)f(-1/\sqrt{3}) + (1)f(1/\sqrt{3}),$$

or

$$\int_{-1}^{1} f(x)\, dx = f(-1/\sqrt{3}) + f(1/\sqrt{3}). \tag{1.5.14}$$

This type of formula in which we do not assign the values of the abscissas is known as a Gaussian formula.

Example 5. Determine the weighting coefficients for the formula

$$\int_{0}^{1} f(x)e^{-x}\, dx = W_0 f(0) + W_1 f(1). \tag{1.5.15}$$

Solution. Using $f(x) = 1, x$, we calculate

$$W_0 + W_1 = 1 - e^{-1},$$

$$W_1 = 1 - 2e^{-1}, \quad W_0 = e^{-1},$$

$$\int_{0}^{1} f(x)e^{-x}\, dx = e^{-1}f(0) + (1 - 2e^{-1})f(1)$$

$$= 0.367879\, f_0 + 0.264242\, f_1. \tag{1.5.16}$$

The method does not depend on the properties of e^{-x} and will apply to any integral of the form

$$\int_{a}^{b} K(x)f(x)\, dx, \tag{1.5.17}$$

although the weighting coefficients W_i will depend on the $K(x)$ chosen.

A general approach, using matrix methods, for solving the system of linear equations

$$\sum_{i=1}^{n} W_i x_i^k = m_k, \quad k = 0, 1, 2, \ldots, n - 1,$$

is given in Appendix B.

A quite lengthy and rigorous development of formula derivation is given by Hildebrand [73] in Chapters 5 and 8 and by Hamming [65] in Chapter 10.

1.6 SOURCE AND TYPES OF ERRORS

The determination of error in the result of a complicated sequence of calculations is a vexing problem not easily solved. One may run test cases and check the intermediate calculations at certain chosen points. However, there is no complete check for all cases. We may perform a so-called *local* error analysis on certain numerical formulas that are used. We may make estimates of rounding errors for specified ranges of numbers in doing certain calculations. Bounded estimates of the overall error may then be attempted. When we understand the different types of errors, and how these may be interlaced in a lengthy sequence of computations, we realize why an accurate calculation of the total error in a result may be prohibitive or impossible.

There are four major sources of error as distinguished by Von Neumann and Goldstein:

1) Mathematical formulations are seldom exactly descriptive of any real situation, but only more or less idealized *models*.

2) Most mathematical formulations contain parameters, such as length, time, mass, temperature, etc., whose values can be had only from *measurement*. Observed data quite often contain inaccuracies, and one cannot expect to obtain accurate results from inaccurate data.

3) Many mathematical equations have solutions that can be constructed only in the sense that an infinite process can be described whose limit is the solution in question. By definition, the infinite process cannot be completed, so one must stop with some term in the sequence. This results in a type of error called the *truncation* error.

4) The decimal or binary representation of a number is made by writing a sequence of digits to the left, and a sequence to the right, of an origin which is marked by the decimal point. In digital computation we only can take account of a finite number of digits. The error due to dropping the others and rounding off the number is called the *roundoff* error.

The above errors are distinguished from human errors or mistakes, which can be eliminated. However, there is another type of error that is very subtle and extremely difficult to evaluate. Operations may sometimes be approximate. For example, the operation of division may be inexact. This is a *generated* error.

1.7 TRUNCATION–ROUNDOFF ERROR CURVE

We approximate a first derivative by the formula

$$\frac{dy}{dx}\bigg]_{x=x_0} = \frac{y(x_0 + h) - y(x_0)}{h}, \qquad (1.7.1)$$

or in simpler notation as

$$y_n' = (y_{n+1} - y_n)/h, \tag{1.7.2}$$

where $h = x_{n+1} - x_n$.

A more basic understanding of Eq. (1.7.2) is obtained from a Taylor series expansion about x_0. We write

$$y(x) = y(x_0) + (x - x_0)y'(x_0) + \frac{(x - x_0)^2}{2!} y''(x_0) + \frac{(x - x_0)^3}{3!} y'''(x_0) + \cdots.$$
$$\tag{1.7.3}$$

Letting $x = x_0 + h$, we see that Eq. (1.7.3) becomes

$$y(x_0 + h) = y(x_0) + hy'(x_0) + \frac{h^2}{2!} y''(x_0) + \frac{h^3}{3!} y'''(x_0) + \cdots. \tag{1.7.4}$$

If $y(x_0) = y_0$, or in general $y(x_n) = y_n$, $n = 0, 1, 2, \cdots$, then we may write Eq. (1.7.4) in a simpler, more general form:

$$y_{n+1} = y_n + hy_n' + \frac{h^2}{2!} y_n'' + \frac{h^3}{3!} y_n''' + \cdots. \tag{1.7.5}$$

When we truncate this series after the second term in the right member, an error is committed equal to $(h^2/2!)y_n'' +$ (a series of small terms). Thus, using the truncated formula

$$y_{n+1} = y_n + hy_n' \tag{1.7.6}$$

for computational purposes, we say that a *truncation error* of the order of h^2, usually written $0(h^2)$, is committed.

Formula (1.7.6) is a simple example of a *first-order difference equation*. If we solve it for y_n', we get

$$y_n' = (y_{n+1} - y_n)/h,$$

which is the same formula as (1.7.2). By analogy we could write

$$y_{n+1}' = (y_{n+2} - y_{n+1})/h. \tag{1.7.7}$$

Corresponding to Eq. (1.7.5) we write the Taylor expansion for y_{n+1}':

$$y_{n+1}' = y_n' + hy_n'' + \frac{h^2}{2!} y_n''' + \frac{h^3}{3!} y_n^{(4)} + \cdots. \tag{1.7.8}$$

Substituting for y_n' from (1.7.2) and y_{n+1}' from (1.7.7), we write (1.7.8) as

$$y_{n+2} = 2y_{n+1} - y_n + h^2 y_n'' + \frac{h^3}{2!} y_n''' + \cdots. \tag{1.7.9}$$

Truncating after the h^2 term on the right gives the *second-order difference equation*

$$y_{n+2} = 2y_{n+1} - y_n + h^2 y_n'' \tag{1.7.10}$$

with a *truncation error* of $0(h^3)$.

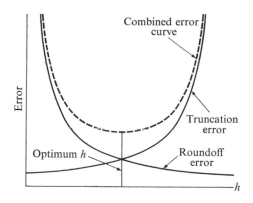

Figure 1.7.1

When we assume that the higher derivatives are small, it is evident that the *truncation error* is decreased by using a smaller computation interval h. (Although not evident at this time, the truncation error may sometimes be decreased by using higher-order difference equations. However, the matter of stability then becomes a problem. This will be illustrated later.) Decreasing the step size h, however, increases the number of computations and thereby increases the roundoff error. Thus, the truncation error and the roundoff error behave conversely as the interval size h is changed. This is illustrated in Fig. 1.7.1. The optimum h would be that value where the minimum of the combined error curve occurs. Unfortunately, it is very difficult to determine the optimum h in advance.

1.8 EXAMPLES OF TRUNCATION ERROR, ROUNDOFF ERROR, AND INSTABILITY

Example 1. Given the following ordinary differential equation, find its discrete solution which approximates its analytic solution:

$$y' = y, \qquad x_0 = 0, \qquad y_0 = 1, \qquad y_0' - 1. \qquad (1.8.1)$$

Solution. The analytic solution is $y = e^x$. Using the truncated formula (1.7.6), called *Euler's formula*, we find that

$$y_{n+1} = y_n + hy_n',$$

and substituting $y_n' = y_n$ from the given differential equation, we get the simplified first-order difference equation:

$$y_{n+1} = y_n + hy_n = (1 + h)y_n.$$

Using a stepsize h equal to 0.1, we get

$$y_{n+1} = 1.1y_n.$$

Starting with the initial conditions $x_0 = 0$, $y_0 = 1$, we get the discrete solution from $x = 0$ to $x = 1$ at intervals of 0.1.

Table 1.8.1

		y-values	
x	True value	$h = 0.1$	$h = 1$
0	1	1	1
0.1	1.10	1.10	
0.2	1.22	1.21	
0.3	1.34	1.33	
0.4	1.49	1.46	
0.5	1.64	1.61	
0.6	1.82	1.77	
0.7	2.01	1.95	
0.8	2.22	2.16	
0.9	2.45	2.38	
1	2.71	2.62	2
2	7.38		4
3	20.08		8

Using $h = 1$, we have the first-order difference equation $y_{n+1} = 2y_n$. Starting with $x_0 = 0$, $y_0 = 1$, we get the discrete solution from $x = 0$ to $x = 3$ at intervals of 1.

These two discrete solutions are shown in Table 1.8.1 along with the true values. As a matter of convenience, only two decimal places were used in computing the values in Table 1.8.1. Therefore, some roundoff error is involved causing a deviation from the true values. However, the prime consideration here is the very significant increase in truncation error in going from $h = 0.1$ to $h = 1$.

Example 2. Solve the following second-order differential equation with given initial conditions by using an appropriate finite difference formula for the derivative:

$$y'' = -(\pi^2/4)y, \qquad x_0 = 0,$$
$$y_0 = 0, \qquad y'_0 = \pi/2. \tag{1.8.2}$$

Solution. Note that the true analytic solution to this problem is $y = \sin \pi/2x$. This problem will be used to illustrate a number of important points. It will indicate the extreme care with which the finite difference formula and stepsize h must be *chosen* and *used* to avoid unacceptable truncation error or even instability and to obtain convergence to the true solution.

In order to simplify the presentation and get a clearer understanding of the total picture, several finite difference forms of the derivative y'' will be given. The corresponding difference equations will be obtained, and the computed results of using these equations for various stepsizes will be presented in a single table for comparison.

a) If we choose to represent y'' by Eq. (1.7.10) in the form

$$y''_n = (y_{n+2} - 2y_{n+1} + y_n)/h^2,$$

we have a second-order difference formula called a *forward difference* formula, since it approximates the derivative at y_n in terms of y_n and the two succeeding points y_{n+1} and y_{n+2}.

Substituting this into (1.8.2), we get

$$(y_{n+2} - 2y_{n+1} + y_n)/h^2 = -(\pi^2/4)y_n. \tag{1.8.3}$$

We would use Euler's formula (1.7.6) to get the starting value at y_1 and then switch to Eq. (1.8.3) to continue. The computed results, which use this formula with $h = 0.1$, 0.5, and 1, are shown in Table 1.8.2.

b) Instead of using the forward difference formula (1.7.10), if we choose to use the second-order *central difference* formula

$$y''_n = (y_{n+1} - 2y_n + y_{n-1})/h^2, \tag{1.8.4}$$

we get a different difference equation.

Central, forward, and backward difference formulas will be explained in detail in the next chapter. Let it suffice at this time to say that we choose to let the right member of (1.8.4) approximate the derivative at the middle point, instead of at the first of three points.

Substituting (1.8.4) into (1.8.2), we get

$$(y_{n+1} - 2y_n + y_{n-1})/h^2 - (\pi^2/4)y_n$$

or

$$y_{n+1} = (2 - 2.48h^2)y_n - y_{n-1}. \tag{1.8.5}$$

Again we use Euler's formula (1.7.6) to get the starting value at y_1, and then switch to (1.8.5) to continue. The computed results, which use this formula with $h = 0.1$, 0.5, and 1, are shown in the Table 1.8.2.

c) The effects of the choice of the difference formula and stepsize h on roundoff errors, truncation error, convergence, and stability are clearly shown using (a) and (b) and summarizing the results in Table 1.8.2. However, these do not cover higher-order difference formulas which are sometimes considered more accurate and allow a large stepsize. Accepting certain facts and formulas as given, we use one more approach to indicate some of the pitfalls of higher-order formulas, emphasize the importance of choosing formulas, and develop a basic criteria for the stability of difference formulas.

Table 1.8.2

x	True value	1.8.3 $h=0.1$	1.8.3 $h=0.5$	1.8.3 $h=1$	$h=0.1$	1.8.5 $h=0.5$	1.8.5 $h=1$	1.8.7 $h=0.5$	1.8.7 $h=1$
0	0	0	0	0	0	0	0	0	0
0.1	0.16	0.16			0.16				
0.2	0.31	0.32			0.32				
0.3	0.45	0.48			0.47				
0.4	0.60	0.63			0.61			0.79	
0.5	0.71	0.77	0.79		0.74	0.79			
0.6	0.81	0.90			0.86				
0.7	0.89	1.01			0.96				
0.8	0.95	1.10			1.04				
0.9	0.99	1.17			1.10				
1.0	1.00	1.22	1.58	1.57	1.14	1.09	1.57	1.09	1.09
1.1	0.99	1.25			1.16				
1.2	0.95	1.26			1.16				
1.3	0.89	1.24			1.14				
1.4	0.81	1.19			1.10				
1.5	0.71	1.12	1.88		1.04	0.71		0.71	
1.6	0.60	1.03			0.96				
1.7	0.45	0.92			0.86				
1.8	0.31	0.79			0.74				
1.9	0.16	0.64			0.61				
2.0	0	0.47	1.20	3.14	0.47	-0.11	-0.74	-0.62	-0.11
2.1	-0.16	0.29			0.32				
2.2	-0.31	0.10			0.16				

			1.8.3			1.8.5			1.8.7	
x	True value	$h = 0.1$	$h = 0.5$	$h = 1$	$h = 0.1$	$h = 0.5$	$h = 1$	$h = 0.5$	$h = 1$
2.3	−0.45	−0.10			0				
2.4	−0.60				−0.16				
2.5	−0.71		−0.65		−0.32	−0.86		−9.31	
2.6	−0.81				−0.47				
2.7	−0.89				−0.61				
2.8	−0.95				−0.74				
2.9	−0.99				−0.86				
3.0	−1.00		−3.25	0.82		−1.07	−1.22	−124.68	−1.07
3.5	−0.71		−5.45			−0.62		−1790.4	
4.0	0		−5.63	−9.29		0.21	1.31	−27,078.22	0.36
4.5	0.71		−2.43						
5.0	1.00		4.26	−14.73			0.6		3.30
5.5	0.71		12.46						
6.0	0		18.02	−2.87			−1.58		35.66
6.5	−0.71		15.85						
7.0	−1.00		2.51	−57.00			0.14		576.2
7.5	−0.71		−20.66						
8.0	0		−45.39	123.99			1.51		9258.8
8.5	0.71		−57.31				−0.85		
9.0	1.00		−41.09	446.34			−1.01		
10.0	0			461.19					
11.0	−1.00			−630.88			1.32		
12.0	0			−2866.7			0.39		

The second derivative in (1.8.2) could be replaced by the following truncated higher-order difference formula (Hildebrand, Chapter 5):

$$y_n'' = \frac{-\frac{1}{12}y_{n+2} + \frac{4}{3}y_{n+1} - \frac{5}{2}y_n + \frac{4}{3}y_{n-1} - \frac{1}{12}y_{n-2}}{h^2}. \tag{1.8.6}$$

Substituting in (1.8.2) and simplifying, we get the fourth-order difference equation

$$y_{n+2} = 16y_{n+1} + (29.64h^2 - 30)y_n + 16y_{n-1} - y_{n-2}. \tag{1.8.7}$$

Again using (1.7.6) and (1.8.5) to get starting values y_0, y_1, y_2, y_3, we obtained results from (1.8.7) with $h = 0.5$ and 1, and these results are shown in Table 1.8.2.

Even with the additional roundoff error due to using only two decimal places, Table 1.8.2 gives a very clear picture of the effects of the choice of the numerical formula and stepsize on roundoff error, truncation error, and stability. Formulas (1.8.3) and (1.8.5) with $h = 0.1$ indicate roundoff error due to smaller stepsize. Formula (1.8.5) with $h = 1$ indicates a stable but very poor approximation due to increased truncation error resulting from the larger stepsize. Formula (1.8.3) with $h = 0.5$ and $h = 1$ indicates a growing, oscillating instability, while (1.8.7) with $h = 0.5$ and $h = 1$ indicates complete instability. Formula (1.8.5) with $h = 0.5$ indicates the best approximation shown. However, as explained in Section 1.7, this may not be the optimum h to give the minimum roundoff and truncation error. This error might be found by trial and error.

One may now ask how the stability of a difference equation can be determined. One method of doing this is illustrated as follows:

The fourth-order difference equation (1.8.7) has the form

$$a_1 y_{n+4} + a_2 y_{n+3} + a_3 y_{n+2} + a_4 y_{n+1} + a_5 y_n = 0.$$

A solution of this equation has the form $y = \beta^n$. Substituting this in the above equation we have

$$a_1 \beta^4 + a_2 \beta^3 + a_3 \beta^2 + a_4 \beta + a_5 = 0$$

with roots β_1, β_2, β_3, and β_4.

Therefore, the general solution, if the roots are distinct, is

$$y_n = c_1 \beta_1^n + c_2 \beta_2^n + c_3 \beta_3^n + c_4 \beta_4^n.$$

If $|\beta_i| < 1$, then the solution is stable.

Since the roots β_i are determined by the coefficients a_i, which are functions of h, it may be possible to make the solution stable by an appropriate choice of h.

Example 3. Many computations are extremely sensitive to the rounding of numbers. The use of very crude approximations (purely for convenience) in many areas of formal education, the use of the slide rule, etc., have helped develop a certain carelessness, indifference, and misunderstanding related to rounding of numbers. A very simple, but obvious, example of how drastic the effects of rounding can be is illustrated in solving the system of equations

$$0.0995x + 0.9949y = 1.0944, \qquad 0.0985x + 0.9951y = 1.0936.$$

The evident solution of this problem is (1, 1). However, if we round all numbers to three decimal places

$$0.100x + 0.995y = 1.094, \qquad 0.099x + 0.995y = 1.094,$$

then the solution is (0, 1.099). One must be very conscious of the effects of rounding at all times.

Another somewhat prevalent, but sometimes erroneous, belief is that measured or observed data, rounded to a certain number of places, can give computed results which are accurate to more places than the data. Averages may be an exception.

A more thorough understanding of roundoff and its effects is obtained by relating it to a study of significant figures, absolute error, and relative error, as presented in the next section.

1.9 SIGNIFICANT FIGURES, RELATIVE ERROR, AND ACCURACY

There is widespread belief that accuracy of a measurement or computed result is indicated by the number of decimal places required to express it. This is erroneous, for the accuracy is indicated by the number of significant figures required to express it.

The difference between the magnitudes of the true value of a number and its approximate value is the absolute error. The relative error is the absolute error divided by the true value of the number. The relative error is the best index, if the scale has a natural zero, of the accuracy, since absolute error is related to the number of decimal places, whereas the relative error is related to the number of significant figures.

A number of interesting facts found in the literature concerning significant figures, errors, and relative errors are now summarized.

1) Hildebrand [73]:

a) If two numbers are rounded to n significant figures, the product of the rounded numbers differs from the true product by less than six units in the place of its nth significant digit.

b) The square of a number rounded to n digits differs from the square of the unrounded number by less than four units in the place of its nth digit.

2) $\overline{N}$ as the approximation to N:

a) If two given numbers are added or subtracted, the maximum error in the sum or difference is just the sum of the maximum errors in the two given numbers:

$$\overline{N}_3 = \overline{N}_1 + \overline{N}_2 = N_1 + \epsilon_1 + N_2 + \epsilon_2$$

or

$$\overline{N}_3 = (N_1 + N_2) + (\epsilon_1 + \epsilon_2) = N_3 + \epsilon_3.$$

b) If two given numbers are multiplied or divided, the resulting number has a maximum relative error given by the sum of the relative errors of the two given numbers:

$$\overline{N}_3 = \overline{N}_1\overline{N}_2 = (N_1 + \epsilon_1)(N_2 + \epsilon_2),$$
$$\overline{N}_3 = N_1N_2 + \epsilon_1N_2 + \epsilon_2N_1 + \epsilon_1\epsilon_2.$$

Neglecting $\epsilon_1\epsilon_2$, we have

$$\overline{N}_3 = N_3 + \epsilon_3,$$
$$\frac{\epsilon_3}{|N_3|} = \frac{\epsilon_1N_2 + \epsilon_2N_1}{|N_1|\,|N_2|} = \frac{\epsilon_1}{|N_1|} + \frac{\epsilon_2}{|N_2|},$$

and also

$$\overline{N}_3 = \frac{\overline{N}_1}{\overline{N}_2} = \frac{N_1 + \epsilon_1}{N_2 + \epsilon_2} = \frac{N_1}{N_2} + \frac{\epsilon_1}{N_2} + \frac{N_1\epsilon_2}{N_2^2} = N_3 + \epsilon_3,$$
$$\frac{\epsilon_3}{|N_3|} = \frac{\epsilon_1}{|N_1|} + \frac{\epsilon_2}{|N_2|}.$$

3) Scarborough [134]:

a) If the first significant figure of a number is k, and the number is correct to n significant figures, then the relative error in this number is less than $1/(k \cdot 10^{n-1})$.

b) If the relative error in an approximate number is less than $1/[(k+1)10^{n-1}]$, the number is correct to n significant figures or at least is in error by less than a unit in the nth significant figure.

c) If the relative error of any number is not greater than $1/(2 \cdot 10^n)$, the number is certainly correct to n significant figures.

Errors of a sum and product are compensating to an extent. This is particularly true in a long sequence of computations. However, time and experience have proved that in a long chain of computations, the loss of significance by subtraction is a chief source of error. This happens when two numbers of nearly equal value are subtracted. For example, if

$$N_1 = 23{,}867 \quad \text{and} \quad N_2 = 23{,}859$$

are correct to five significant figures, $N_1 - N_2 = 8$, which is correct to only one significant figure. It is not unusual in machine computation to lose all significance with very disastrous results.

In evaluating a function, $N = f(u_1, u_2, \ldots, u_n)$, of several variables with committed errors, $\Delta u_1, \Delta u_2$, etc., in the independent variables, an associated error ΔN in the function value is committed. We now establish a formula for computing the relative error $\Delta N/N$:

$$N = f(u_1, u_2, \ldots, u_n),$$
$$N + \Delta N = f(u_1 + \Delta u_1, \ldots, u_n + \Delta u_n).$$

Expanding in a Taylor series, we have

$$f(u_1 + \Delta u_1, u_2 + \Delta u_2, \ldots) = f(u_1, u_2, \ldots) + \Delta u_1 \frac{\partial f}{\partial u_1} + \Delta u_2 \frac{\partial f}{\partial u_2}$$

$$+ \cdots + \Delta u_n \frac{\partial f}{\partial u_n} + \frac{1}{2} \left[(\Delta u_1)^2 \frac{\partial^2 f}{\partial u_1^2} + \cdots + (\Delta u_n)^2 \frac{\partial^2 f}{\partial u_n^2} \right.$$

$$\left. + 2 \Delta u_1 \Delta u_2 \frac{\partial^2 f}{\partial u_1 \, \partial u_2} + \cdots \right].$$

If errors Δu_1, Δu_2, etc., are relatively small, we can neglect their squares, products, and higher powers. Then, subtracting N from $N + \Delta N$, we get

$$\Delta N = \Delta u_1 \frac{\partial f}{\partial u_1} + \Delta u_2 \frac{\partial f}{\partial u_2} + \cdots + \Delta u_n \frac{\partial f}{\partial u_n}.$$

The relative error is then given by

$$E = \frac{\Delta N}{N} = \frac{\partial f}{\partial u_1} \frac{\Delta u_1}{N} + \frac{\partial f}{\partial u_2} \frac{\Delta u_2}{N} + \cdots + \frac{\partial f}{\partial u_n} \frac{\Delta u_n}{N}.$$

1.10   ERROR IN POLYNOMIAL APPROXIMATION

In finding a polynomial $P_n(x)$ of nth degree through $n + 1$ data points, it is important to find how much the true function and the approximating polynomial differ at points other than the data points (where they agree within roundoff).

The theoretical difference between the original function $y(x)$, and the approximating polynomial $P(x)$, is determined in the following manner. The error is given by $E(x) = y(x) - P(x)$. The error $E(x)$ must be zero at the $(n + 1)$ given data points.

First, define $\pi(x) = (x - x_1)(x - x_2) \cdots (x - x_{n+1})$ which also vanishes at the $(n + 1)$ data points. It is easily shown that $\pi^{(n+1)}(x) = (n + 1)!$. Now we construct a linear combination of these functions

$$F(x) = y(x) - P(x) - K\pi(x), \tag{1.10.1}$$

and determine K such that $F(x)$ vanishes, not only at the $(n + 1)$ data points, but also at a different arbitrarily chosen point $\bar{x}$. Since $\pi(x)$ vanishes only at the $(n + 1)$ points, K can be determined. Then, if $F(x)$ vanishes at $(n + 2)$ points, by Rolle's theorem, $F'(x)$ vanishes $(n + 1)$ times, $F''(x)$ vanishes n times, and $F^{(n+1)}(x)$ vanishes at least once, say at the point ξ. Therefore

$$F^{(n+1)}(x) = y^{(n+1)}(x) - P^{(n+1)}(x) - K\pi^{(n+1)}(x). \tag{1.10.2}$$

Now assuming $y(x)$ has an $(n + 1)$-derivative, $P^{(n+1)}(x)$ vanishes identically since $P(x)$ is of nth degree, $\pi^{(n+1)}(x) = (n + 1)!$, and $F^{(n+1)}(\xi) = 0$, we have

$$0 = y^{(n+1)}(\xi) - K(n + 1)!, \tag{1.10.3}$$

or

$$K = \frac{1}{(n + 1)!} y^{(n+1)}(\xi). \tag{1.10.4}$$

Substituting this in Eq. (1.10.1), we have

$$F(x) = y(x) - P(x) - \frac{\pi(x)}{(n+1)!} y^{(n+1)}(\xi).$$ (1.10.5)

Since $F(x)$ vanishes at $\bar{x}$, then

$$F(\bar{x}) = y(\bar{x}) - P(\bar{x}) - \frac{\pi(\bar{x})}{(n+1)!} y^{(n+1)}(\xi) = 0.$$ (1.10.6)

But $\bar{x}$ was arbitrarily chosen, so the bar may be dropped, and we have

$$y(x) - P(x) = \frac{\pi(x)}{(n+1)!} y^{(n+1)}(\xi)$$ (1.10.7)

or

$$E(x) = \frac{\pi(x)}{(n+1)!} y^{(n+1)}(\xi).$$ (1.10.8)

1.11 ITERATION AND CONVERGENCE

A powerful procedure often used in numerical computation is iteration. The most common type is one in which one or more numerical values are improved by repeated substitution into a formula. For example, if $x_{n+1} = f(x_n)$, x_0 substituted into the right member is assumed to give an improved value x_1, x_1 gives an improved value x_2, and so on, until the sequence of improved values *converges* to the true value of x. This is a simple explanation of the procedure, but in practice it may not be as simple. The formula itself may contain certain inherent difficulties, or the *starting value* x_0 may be such that the procedure, instead of converging, *diverges*. A simple but very good illustration of an iteration formula is given by Newton's well-known formula for finding roots.

The Taylor expansion for $f(x)$ about a point x_n is

$$f(x) = f(x_n) + (x - x_n)f'(x_n) + [(x - x_n)^2/2!]f''(x_n) + \cdots$$ (1.11.1)

Assuming x_{n+1} to be a root of $f(x)$ and substituting into Eq. (1.11.1), we have

$$f(x_{n+1}) = f(x_n) + (x_{n+1} - x_n)f'(x_n)$$
$$+ [(x_{n+1} - x_n)^2/2!]f''(x_n) + \cdots$$ (1.11.2)

Truncating the right member after the second term and setting equal to zero, since $f(x_{n+1}) = 0$, we get

$$f(x_n) + (x_{n+1} - x_n)f'(x_n) = 0.$$ (1.11.3)

The truncation error is of the order of $(x_{n+1} - x_n)^2$. Solving Eq. (1.11.3) for x_{n+1}, we have

$$x_{n+1} = x_n - \frac{f(x_n)}{f'(x_n)}.$$ (1.11.4)

This gives us an iteration formula for finding a root of $f(x)$. It is immediately evident that difficulties could be encountered if $f'(x_n)$ approaches zero.

One important application of this formula is the derivation of a formula for finding the rth root of a number. If

$$x = \sqrt[r]{N},$$ (1.11.5)

then

$$x^r = N, \qquad f(x) = x^r - N, \qquad f'(x) = rx^{r-1}.$$

Using Eq. (1.11.4), we obtain

$$x_{n+1} = x_n - \frac{x_n^r - N}{rx_n^{r-1}} = \frac{(r-1)x_n^r + N}{rx_n^{r-1}}.$$

Therefore

$$x_{n+1} = \frac{1}{r}\left[(r-1)x_n + \frac{N}{x_n^{r-1}}\right].$$ (1.11.6)

This formula is a good example of a derived numerical method which is simple, rapidly convergent, and accurate.

1.12 SUMMARY REMARKS

The purpose of this chapter was to establish a foundation in some of the basic concepts and principles of numerical computation. The end result of numerical computation is a number or a set of numbers. The result must be reliable and acceptable.

One may be interested in the actual numerical values of results, or only in the trend established. A number of particular solutions may give insight to a general solution. Consequently, interpretation of results is very important.

The practicing numerical analyst must be a type of diagnostician. He must be aware of the types of errors, difficulties, and pitfalls of numerical computation. In evaluating the reliability and accuracy of results, he must realize that there is a difference between a theoretical error analysis and a practical error analysis. In fact, he must realize that a theoretical error analysis may be prohibitive, if not impossible. For example, many error estimates are given in terms of higher derivatives, which are unavailable in actual practice. Also, roundoff error, truncation error, generated error, and propagated error may be so interlaced in a long sequence of computations that the accumulated error in final results may be impossible to determine.

However, armed with a good basic theoretical knowledge of these errors, difficulties, pitfalls, several good typical check cases, a sufficient number of computed intermediate results, and with a willingness to do hand computations, revise numerical techniques, try different mathematical methods, and finally with a certain amount of insight, intuition, experience, perseverance, and hard work, the practicing numerical analyst may be generally successful in his efforts.

EXERCISES

1. Derive the formula

$$\int_0^2 f(x)\, dx = \tfrac{1}{15}[7f(0) + 16f(1) + 7f(2)] + \tfrac{1}{15}[f'(0) - f'(2)] + [f^{(6)}(\theta)/4725].$$

2. Derive the trapezoidal formula for integration.

3. Determine the weighting coefficients:

$$\int_{-1}^1 f(x) \sin(\pi/2)x\, dx = W_{-1}f(-1) + W_0 f(0) + W_1 f(1).$$

4. Given the following first-order ordinary differential equation, find its discrete solution which approximates its analytic solution:

$$y' = 2\sqrt{y}, \qquad x = 0, \qquad y = 0, \qquad y' = 0.$$

5. Find the approximate value of h for which the finite difference equation (1.8.5) becomes unstable.

6. Using formula (1.8.4) to approximate the second derivative, find the discrete solution of the following:

$$y'' = y, \qquad x = 0, \qquad y = 1, \qquad y' = 1, \qquad y'' = 1.$$

7. What are the major sources of error in numerical computation?

8. Discuss truncation and roundoff error.

9. Derive an error estimate for polynomial approximation.

10. Discuss the best criterion for the indication of the accuracy of computed results.

11. What question characterizes the instability of a numerical procedure?

12. What question characterizes the convergence of a numerical procedure?

13. What is meant by an iterative method?

14. Discuss the problems encountered by a practicing numerical analyst and the approach he should take to numerical computation.

15. Determine the weights and abscissas for the formula

$$\int_{-1}^1 f(x)\, dx = W_{-1}f(x_1) + W_0 f(x_2) + W_1 f(x_3),$$

such that $W_{-1} = W_0 = W_1$.

16. If $\pi(x) = (x - x_1)(x - x_2) \cdots (x - x_{n+1})$, show that $\pi^{(n+1)}(x) = (n + 1)!$.

17. Determine the abscissas for the formula

$$\int_0^1 f(x) \log x\, dx = -W_1 f(x_1) - W_2 f(x_2),$$

such that $W_1 = 0.72$ and $W_2 = 0.28$.

18. Determine the weights for the formula

$$\frac{d^2 y}{dx^2}\bigg]_{x=1} = W_0 f(0) + W_1 f(1) + W_2 f(2).$$

CHAPTER 2

FINITE AND DIVIDED DIFFERENCES

2.1 INTRODUCTION

Much has been written on finite differences and operations with finite differences. A classic example is *A Treatise on the Calculus of Finite Differences*, written by George Boole and first published in 1860 [republished by Stechert-Hafner of New York in 1946]. It is the purpose of this chapter to give a background in the calculus of finite differences and linear operators and then discuss forms of finite and divided differences that will be of use in other material covered in this book.

2.2 CALCULUS OF FINITE DIFFERENCES

Let

$$u_x = \phi(x), \qquad u_{x+h} = \phi(x+h), \text{ etc.} \tag{2.2.1}$$

The fundamental operation of the calculus of finite differences is defined as

$$\frac{\Delta u_x}{\Delta x} = \frac{u_{x+\Delta x} - u_x}{\Delta x}. \tag{2.2.2}$$

Here $\Delta u_x/\Delta x$ is a true fraction, and Δu_x stands for a true magnitude. Hence, Δ might be taken as the fundamental operation of this calculus, always assuming the actual value of Δx as given.

It suffices to establish the rules of the calculus on the assumption that the finite difference of the independent variable is unity. This reduces to equivalence the symbols $\Delta/\Delta x$ and Δ. Therefore, we shall develop the theory of the operation denoted by Δ and defined by the equation

$$\Delta u_x = u_{x+1} - u_x, \tag{2.2.3}$$

but where convenience suggests, we shall use the more general equation of (2.2.2).

If $u_x = ax^n + bx^{n-1} + cx^{n-2} + \cdots$, then

$$\Delta u_x = anx^{n-1} + b_1 x^{n-2} + \cdots,$$
$$\Delta^2 u_x = \Delta(\Delta u_x) = an(n-1)x^{n-2} + c_1 x^{n-3} + \cdots,$$
$$\vdots$$
$$\Delta^n u_x = an(n-1)(n-2)\cdots 2 \cdot 1 = an!. \tag{2.2.4}$$

23

That is, the nth difference of an nth degree polynomial is constant when the values of the independent variable are taken at equal intervals. That constant value is

$$\Delta^n u_x = a_n n! h^n, \qquad (2.2.5)$$

where a_n is the coefficient of the nth-degree term, and h is the interval size. From this

$$\Delta^n x^n = 1 \cdot 2 \cdots n = n!. \qquad (2.2.6)$$

A special function, called the factorial function, is defined as

$$x^{(n)} = x(x - 1)(x - 2)(x - 3) \cdots (x - n + 1). \qquad (2.2.7)$$

The mth difference of this function is

$$\Delta^m x^{(n)} = n(n - 1)(n - 2) \cdots (n - m + 1)x^{(n-m)}. \qquad (2.2.8)$$

We now look at several relations between successive values, successive differences, and successive differential coefficients of the functions. Formula (2.2.3) connects the first difference with two successive functions.

In Taylor's expansion with $h = 1$ we have

$$u_{x+1} - u_x = \frac{du_x}{dx} + \frac{1}{2!}\frac{d^2 u_x}{dx^2} + \frac{1}{3!}\frac{d^3 u_x}{dx^3} + \cdots. \qquad (2.2.9)$$

This connects the first difference in terms of successive differential coefficients.

If we rewrite (2.2.3) in the form

$$u_{x+1} = u_x + \Delta u_x, \qquad (2.2.10)$$

then

$$
\begin{aligned}
u_{x+2} &= u_{x+1} + \Delta u_{x+1} \\
&= u_x + \Delta u_x + \Delta(u_x + \Delta u_x) \\
&= u_x + 2\,\Delta u_x + \Delta^2 u_x, \\
u_{x+3} &= u_x + 3\,\Delta u_x + 3\,\Delta^2 u_x + \Delta^3 u_x, \\
&\vdots \\
u_{x+n} &= u_x + n\,\Delta u_x + \frac{n(n-1)}{2!}\Delta^2 u_x + \cdots. \qquad (2.2.11)
\end{aligned}
$$

This expresses u_{x+n} in terms of u_x and its successive differences.

We now introduce a symbol E to denote the operation of giving the increment unity to x in a function. That is,

$$E u_x = u_{x+1}. \qquad (2.2.12)$$

The symbol E is called a shifting operator. We may rewrite Eq. (2.2.10) in the form

$$E u_x = u_x + \Delta u_x$$

or

$$E u_x = (1 + \Delta)u_x.$$

Therefore the two symbols, Δ and $\mathbf{E}$, are connected by the equation

$$\mathbf{E} = 1 + \Delta. \tag{2.2.13}$$

Letting the differential operator (d/dx) be represented by the symbol $\mathbf{D}$, we may combine (2.2.9) and (2.2.12) to write

$$\mathbf{E}u_x = u_{x+1} = u_x + \mathbf{D}u_x + \frac{1}{2!}\mathbf{D}^2 u_x + \frac{1}{3!}\mathbf{D}^3 u_x + \cdots$$

$$= \left(1 + \mathbf{D} + \frac{1}{2!}\mathbf{D}^2 + \frac{1}{3!}\mathbf{D}^3 + \cdots\right)u_x$$

or

$$\mathbf{E}u_x = e^{\mathbf{D}}u_x. \tag{2.2.14}$$

Thus, $\mathbf{E} = 1 + \Delta = e^{\mathbf{D}}$. We can easily show that these symbols satisfy the distributive law, the commutative law, and exponent law. The symbols combine each with itself, with constant quantities, and with each other, as if each were an individual symbol of quantity.

We express $\mathbf{D}^n = d^n/dx^n$ in terms of successive differences in the following manner. Since $e^{\mathbf{D}} = 1 + \Delta$, we have

$$\mathbf{D} = \log(1 + \Delta),$$
$$\mathbf{D}^n = [\log(1 + \Delta)]^n. \tag{2.2.15}$$

In particular, when $n = 1$,

$$\mathbf{D}u_x = \Delta u_x - \tfrac{1}{2}\Delta^2 u_x + \tfrac{1}{3}\Delta^3 u_x \cdots. \tag{2.2.16}$$

2.3 RELATED DIFFERENCES AND OPERATORS

Formula (2.2.3), written in the general form

$$\Delta f(x) = f(x + h) - f(x), \tag{2.3.1}$$

is called the first *forward difference*. We now define two other differences, which will be of interest later. Using the operator symbol ∇, we have

$$\nabla f(x) = f(x) - f(x - h), \tag{2.3.2}$$

which is called the first *backward difference*. Using the operator symbol δ, we have

$$\delta f(x) = f\left(x + \frac{h}{2}\right) - f\left(x - \frac{h}{2}\right), \tag{2.3.3}$$

called the first *central difference*.

We define two additional operators related to the five already discussed in the following manner:

The symbol μ, when used such that

$$\mu f(x) = \tfrac{1}{2}\left[f\left(x + \frac{h}{2}\right) + f\left(x - \frac{h}{2}\right)\right], \tag{2.3.4}$$

Table 2.3.1

	E	Δ	δ	∇	hD
E	E	$1 + \Delta$	$1 + \tfrac{1}{2}\delta^2 + \delta(1 + \tfrac{1}{4}\delta^2)^{1/2}$	$(1 - \nabla)^{-1}$	e^{hD}
Δ	$E - 1$	Δ	$\delta(1 + \tfrac{1}{4}\delta^2)^{1/2} + \tfrac{1}{2}\delta^2$	$\nabla(1 - \nabla)^{-1}$	$e^{hD} - 1$
δ	$E^{1/2} - E^{-1/2}$	$\Delta(1 + \Delta)^{-1/2}$	δ	$\nabla(1 - \nabla)^{-1/2}$	$2\sinh\tfrac{1}{2}hD$
∇	$1 - E^{-1}$	$\Delta(1 + \Delta)^{-1}$	$\delta(1 + \tfrac{1}{4}\delta^2)^{1/2} - \tfrac{1}{2}\delta^2$	∇	$1 - e^{-hD}$
hD	$\log E$	$\log(1 + \Delta)$	$2\sinh^{-1}\tfrac{1}{2}\delta$	$-\log(1 - \nabla)$	hD
μ	$\tfrac{1}{2}(E^{1/2} + E^{-1/2})$	$(1 + \tfrac{1}{2}\Delta)(1 + \Delta)^{-1/2}$	$(1 + \tfrac{1}{4}\delta^2)^{1/2}$	$(1 - \tfrac{1}{2}\nabla)(1 - \nabla)^{-1/2}$	$\cosh\tfrac{1}{2}hD$

is called an *averaging operator*. The symbol **J**, when used such that

$$\mathbf{J}f(x) = \int_{x}^{x+h} f(t)\, dt,$$ (2.3.5)

is called the *integral operator*.

All seven of the operators, Δ, ∇, δ, **E**, **D**, μ, and **J** satisfy the distributive, commutative, associative, and exponent laws. All seven are also called linear operators, since they meet the conditions specified in the theory of linear operators.

Formulas relating the different operators are conveniently given in Table 2.3.1.

2.4 DIFFERENCING OF DISCRETE DATA

Much of the work in numerical computation is devoted to functions of a single variable defined at a set of discrete equally spaced points. For example, if $x_1 = x_0 + h$, $x_2 = x_0 + 2h, \ldots, x_{n-1} = x_0 + (n-1)h$, then $f(x_0) = f_0$, $f(x_1) = f_1, \ldots, f(x_{n-1}) = f_{n-1}$ are values of the function $f(x)$ at n equally spaced points. We write these equally spaced abscissas and corresponding function values in the following tabular form:

$$\begin{array}{c|c|c|c|c|c|c|} x_0 & x_1 & x_2 & \cdots & x_{n-2} & x_{n-1} \\ \hline f_0 & f_1 & f_2 & \cdots & f_{n-2} & f_{n-1} \end{array}$$ (2.4.1)

One of the basic operations associated with (2.4.1) is differencing. The remainder of this chapter will be devoted to a more detailed discussion of forward differences, backward differences, central differences, and divided differences.

In general, one finds the various types of differences with the notation peculiar to each presented in conjunction with certain numerical formulas. This often proves confusing to the beginner. The above types of differences are presented as a related unit, separate from other numerical formulas, thus showing that each type with its notation is merely a different interpretation of the same quantity.

2.5 FORWARD DIFFERENCES

For uniformly spaced abscissas with spacing h, we define the first forward difference associated with the point x_0 as

$$\Delta f(x_0) = f(x_0 + h) - f(x_0).$$ (2.5.1)

If $x_1 = x_0 + h$, $x_2 = x_0 + 2h$, etc., then Eq. (2.5.1) can be written as

$$\Delta f(x_0) = f(x_1) - f(x_0)$$ (2.5.2)

or simply as

$$\Delta f_0 = f_1 - f_0.$$ (2.5.3)

In general, we may write

$$\Delta f_i = f_{i+1} - f_i, \quad i = 0, 1, 2, \ldots.$$ (2.5.4)

Table 2.5.1

x_0	x_1	x_2	x_3	x_4	x_5
f_0	f_1	f_2	f_3	f_4	f_5
Δf_0	Δf_1	Δf_2	Δf_3	Δf_4	
$\Delta^2 f_0$	$\Delta^2 f_1$	$\Delta^2 f_2$	$\Delta^2 f_3$		
$\Delta^3 f_0$	$\Delta^3 f_1$	$\Delta^3 f_2$			
$\Delta^4 f_0$	$\Delta^4 f_1$				
$\Delta^5 f_0$					

Using the linear operator Δ, we obtain from (2.5.3) the second forward difference associated with x_0:

$$\Delta(\Delta f_0) = \Delta f_1 - \Delta f_0$$
$$= f_2 - f_1 - f_1 + f_0$$

or

$$\Delta^2 f_0 = f_2 - 2f_1 + f_0. \tag{2.5.5}$$

The rth forward difference associated with x_0 is

$$\Delta^r f_0 = \Delta^{r-1} f_1 - \Delta^{r-1} f_0, \tag{2.5.6}$$

or in general, the rth forward difference associated with x_i is

$$\Delta^r f_i = \Delta^{r-1} f_{i+1} - \Delta^{r-1} f_i. \tag{2.5.7}$$

A table of forward differences may be constructed as in Table 2.5.1. It should be noted that the rth forward difference associated with f_i involves all the ordinates $f_i, f_{i+1}, f_{i+2}, \ldots, f_{i+r}$.

2.6 BACKWARD DIFFERENCES

Near the end of a tabulated range, the notation of backward differences is more convenient. We define the first backward difference associated with x_i as

$$\nabla f_i = f_i - f_{i-1}. \tag{2.6.1}$$

Applying the linear operator ∇, we obtain the second backward difference associated with x_i:

$$\nabla(\nabla f_i) = \nabla f_i - \nabla f_{i-1}$$
$$= f_i - f_{i-1} - f_{i-1} + f_{i-2}$$

or

$$\nabla^2 f_i = f_i - 2f_{i-1} + f_{i-2}. \tag{2.6.2}$$

In general, the rth backward difference associated with x_i is

$$\nabla^r f_i = \nabla^{r-1} f_i - \nabla^{r-1} f_{i-1}. \tag{2.6.3}$$

A table of backward differences may be constructed as in Table 2.6.1.

Table 2.6.1

x_{n-5}	x_{n-4}	x_{n-3}	x_{n-2}	x_{n-1}	x_n
f_{n-5}	f_{n-4}	f_{n-3}	f_{n-2}	f_{n-1}	f_n
	∇f_{n-4}	∇f_{n-3}	∇f_{n-2}	∇f_{n-1}	∇f_n
		$\nabla^2 f_{n-3}$	$\nabla^2 f_{n-2}$	$\nabla^2 f_{n-1}$	$\nabla^2 f_n$
			$\nabla^3 f_{n-2}$	$\nabla^3 f_{n-1}$	$\nabla^3 f_n$
				$\nabla^4 f_{n-1}$	$\nabla^4 f_n$
					$\nabla^5 f_n$

2.7 CENTRAL DIFFERENCES

Quite often it is convenient and desirable to define the differences as associated with the midpoint of a range. These differences are called the central differences, and the linear operator symbol used is δ. The first central difference associated with x_i is

$$\delta f_i = f_{i+(1/2)} - f_{i-(1/2)}. \tag{2.7.1}$$

By repeated application of the linear operator δ we obtain the second, third, and fourth central differences:

$$\delta^2 f_i = f_{i+1} - 2f_i + f_{i-1}, \tag{2.7.2}$$

$$\delta^3 f_i = f_{i+(3/2)} - 3f_{i+(1/2)} + 3f_{i-(1/2)} - f_{i-(3/2)}, \tag{2.7.3}$$

$$\delta^4 f_i = f_{i+2} - 4f_{i+1} + 6f_i - 4f_{i-1} + f_{i-2}, \tag{2.7.4}$$

where i may have any value: $-\frac{3}{2}, -1, -\frac{1}{2}, 0, \frac{1}{2}, 1, \frac{3}{2}, \ldots$.

We should note that the coefficients of the ordinates associated with any order central difference can conveniently and easily be obtained from Pascal's triangle of binomial coefficients with alternating signs.

2.8 RELATIONSHIP BETWEEN FORWARD, CENTRAL, AND BACKWARD DIFFERENCES

We may now write general formulas for relating any order of forward, central, and backward differences. We have

$$\Delta f_i = \delta f_{i+1/2} = \nabla f_{i+1}, \tag{2.8.1}$$

$$\Delta^2 f_i = \delta^2 f_{i+1} = \nabla^2 f_{i+2}, \tag{2.8.2}$$

$$\Delta^3 f_i = \delta^3 f_{i+(3/2)} = \nabla^3 f_{i+3}, \tag{2.8.3}$$

$$\vdots$$

$$\Delta^r f_i = \delta^r f_{i+(r/2)} = \nabla^r f_{i+r}, \tag{2.8.4}$$

from the preceding sections.

2.9 DIVIDED DIFFERENCES

Many formulas involve forward, central, and backward differences but are limited to equal spacing of the data. In the general case, when the data are not necessarily equally spaced, the use of *divided differences* is convenient, even though more cumbersome. Relative to the set of data given in (2.4.1), *divided differences* of order 0, 1, 2, ..., k are defined iteratively by the relations

$$f[x_0] = f(x_0) = f_0, \tag{2.9.1}$$

$$f[x_0, x_1] = \frac{f[x_1] - f[x_0]}{x_1 - x_0} = \frac{f_1 - f_0}{x_1 - x_0}, \tag{2.9.2}$$

$$f[x_0, x_1, x_2] = \frac{f[x_1, x_2] - f[x_0, x_1]}{x_2 - x_0}, \tag{2.9.3}$$

$$\vdots$$

$$f[x_0, x_1, \ldots, x_k] = \frac{f[x_1, x_2, \ldots, x_k] - f[x_0, x_1, \ldots, x_{k-1}]}{x_k - x_0}. \tag{2.9.4}$$

We notice that the first $k - 1$ arguments in the first term of the numerator are the same as the last $k - 1$ arguments in the second term, and that the denominator is the difference between the two arguments which are not common to the two terms.

The divided difference is a symmetric function of its arguments:

$$f[x_0, x_1] = f[x_1, x_0], \tag{2.9.5}$$

$$f[x_0, x_1, x_2] = \frac{f_0}{(x_0 - x_1)(x_0 - x_2)} + \frac{f_1}{(x_1 - x_0)(x_1 - x_2)}$$

$$+ \frac{f_2}{(x_2 - x_0)(x_2 - x_1)}. \tag{2.9.6}$$

It follows from the symmetry, that the order of the arguments is irrelevant.

2.10 DIFFERENTIATION OF DIVIDED DIFFERENCES

From Eqs. (2.9.2) and (2.9.5) we may write

$$f[x_0, x] = f[x, x_0] = \frac{f[x_0] - f[x]}{x_0 - x}. \tag{2.10.1}$$

Letting $x_0 = x + \epsilon$, we have

$$f[x + \epsilon, x] = \frac{f[x + \epsilon] - f(x)}{\epsilon},$$

and the limit as ϵ approaches zero gives us

$$f'[x] = f[x, x]. \tag{2.10.2}$$

Therefore,

$$f'[x_0, x] = f[x_0, x, x] \tag{2.10.3}$$

or

$$f'[c, x] = f[c, x, x]. \tag{2.10.4}$$

Then, if $c = x_0, x_1, \ldots, x_k$, we have

$$f'[x_0, x_1, \ldots, x_k, x] = f[x_0, x_1, \ldots, x_k, x, x]. \tag{2.10.5}$$

Hint: Use (3.3.6) with $n = 1, 2, \ldots$; differentiate; use (2.10.2); and solve for $f'[c, x]$. Likewise, if u_1 is a function of x,

$$f'[c, u_1] = \frac{df[c, u_1]}{du_1} \frac{du_1}{dx} = f[c, u_1, u_1] \frac{du_1}{dx} \tag{2.10.6}$$

or

$$f'[c, u_1, u_2, \ldots, u_n] = \sum_{i=1}^{n} f[c, u_1, u_2, \ldots, u_n, u_i] \frac{du_i}{dx}. \tag{2.10.7}$$

It follows that if $u_i = x$, then

$$f'[c, \overbrace{x, x, \ldots, x}^{n \text{ times}}] = nf[c, \overbrace{x, x, \ldots, x}^{n+1 \text{ times}}]. \tag{2.10.8}$$

Also, from Eqs. (2.10.4) and (2.10.8), we have

$$f^{(r)}[c, x] = r! f[c, \overbrace{x, x, \ldots, x}^{r+1 \text{ times}}]. \tag{2.10.9}$$

2.11 RELATIONSHIP BETWEEN FINITE AND DIVIDED DIFFERENCES

Using the notations of Sections 2.5 and 2.9 and assuming the abscissas are equally spaced by h, we may write

$$\Delta f_i - f_{i+1} - f_i = (x_{i+1} - x_i) \frac{f_{i+1} - f_i}{x_{i+1} - x_i} = hf[x_i, x_{i+1}]. \tag{2.11.1}$$

Also,

$$\begin{aligned}
\Delta^2 f_i &= \Delta f_{i+1} - \Delta f_i = hf[x_{i+1}, x_{i+2}] - hf[x_i, x_{i+1}] \\
&= h(x_{i+2} - x_i)f[x_i, x_{i+1}, x_{i+2}] \\
&= 2h^2 f[x_i, x_{i+1}, x_{i+2}].
\end{aligned} \tag{2.11.2}$$

In general, then, we have

$$\Delta^r f_i = r! h^r f[x_i, x_{i+1}, \ldots, x_{i+r}]. \tag{2.11.3}$$

Likewise, we may show that

$$\nabla^r f_i = r! h^r f[x_i, x_{i-1}, \ldots, x_{i-r}] \tag{2.11.4}$$

or

$$\nabla^r f_{i+r} = r! h^r f[x_i, x_{i+1}, \ldots, x_{i+r}]. \tag{2.11.5}$$

Therefore, combining Eq. (2.8.4) and other results which we have, we obtain a general relationship for any order between forward, backward, central, and divided differences and the appropriate ordinates:

$$\Delta^r f_i = \delta^r f_{i+(r/2)} = \nabla^r f_{i+r}$$

$$= r! h^r f[x_i, x_{i+1}, \ldots, x_{i+r}]$$

$$= \sum_{k=0}^{r} (-1)^k \binom{r}{k} f_{i+r-k}, \tag{2.11.6}$$

where $i = \ldots, -\frac{3}{2}, -1, -\frac{1}{2}, 0, \frac{1}{2}, 1, \frac{3}{2}, \ldots$, and $\binom{r}{k} = \dfrac{r!}{(r-k)!k!}$.

2.12 FINITE DIFFERENCES OF POLYNOMIALS

The nth forward difference of an nth degree polynomial is a constant given by (2.2.5) when the values of the independent variable are taken at equal intervals. For example, the forward difference table for

$$y = f(x) = x^3 - 5x^2 + 6x + 1$$

is given in Table 2.12.1.

Table 2.12.1

x	-2	-1	0	1	2	3	4	5	6	7	8
y	-39	-11	1	3	1	1	9	31	73	141	241
Δy	28	12	2	-2	0	8	22	42	68	100	
$\Delta^2 y$	-16	-10	-4	2	8	14	20	26	32		
$\Delta^3 y$	6	6	6	6	6	6	6	6			

2.13 ERRORS IN A TABULAR ENTRY

If an error exists in a tabular entry, the differences which are affected by the error spread fanwise from the incorrect function value and can be used to locate an error. The effect of an error increases with the successive differences. In fact, the coefficients of the error ϵ are the binomial coefficients with alternating signs. The algebraic sum of the errors in any difference row is zero. This is illustrated in Table 2.13.1.

Table 2.13.1

—	—	—	—	ϵ	—	—	—	—	—	—
—	—	—	ϵ	$-\epsilon$	—	—	—	—	—	
—	—	ϵ	-2ϵ	ϵ	—	—	—			
—	ϵ	-3ϵ	3ϵ	$-\epsilon$	—	—				
ϵ	-4ϵ	6ϵ	-4ϵ	ϵ	—					

Table 2.13.2

x	-2	-1	0	1	2	3	4	5	6	7	8
y	-39	-11	1	3	1	1	9	33	73	141	241
Δy	28	12	2	-2	0	8	24	40	68	100	
$\Delta^2 y$	-16	-10	-4	2	8	16	16	28	32		
$\Delta^3 y$	6	6	6	6	8	0	12	4			

Corrections to $\Delta^3 y$: -2 6 -6 2

If an error of 2 had been made in the eighth entry of the function values of Table 2.12.1, then the table would appear as in Table 2.13.2.

EXERCISES

1. Compute a table of squares using a difference table.
2. Compute a table of cubes using a difference table.
3. Derive the symmetric form of $f[x_0, x_1, x_2]$.
4. Show that

$$f[x_0, x_1, x_2, x_3] = \frac{f[x_1, x_2, x_3] - f[x_0, x_1, x_2]}{x_3 - x_0}$$

$$= \frac{f[x_0, x_2, x_3] - f[x_1, x_2, x_3]}{x_0 - x_1}$$
$$\vdots$$

5. Compute the constant third difference, the first three functional values, start a difference table and compute the remaining functional values for $x = -3(1)8$ by means of the difference table for $y = x^3 - 3x^2 + 2x - 1$.

6. Assume that the following are tabulated values of a polynomial. Use a difference table to find and correct the error which exists.

x	y	x	y
0	358	7	1124
1	370	8	1476
2	397	9	1888
3	451	10	2383
4	543	11	2965
5	683	12	3637
6	880		

BASIC INTERPOLATING AND APPROXIMATING POLYNOMIALS

3.1 INTRODUCTION

Often the first experience in numerical computation is in the area of function evaluation or interpolation for missing values in a table. We are given a set of function values at specified abscissa values and asked to compute an estimate of some value not in the table. A straight line may be assumed between successive points, but often quadratic or higher degree polynomials may be assumed. In this case, we may need analytic operations such as differentiation, integration, finding zeros, minimization, etc. We may encounter many of the difficulties of numerical analysis in all these areas. The given function values are approximate or contain "noise". Since polynomials are easy to handle, many problems in numerical analysis are based on polynomial approximation. Often this is simply an application of the principle of analytic substitution, i.e., representing a complex function by a simpler one.

We use the principle of least squares with some "goodness-of-fit" criterion to derive a polynomial to fit the given data. Difficulties are encountered here, however. The polynomial may fit well at the given data points but oscillate undesirably between points. An error estimate could be difficult to obtain or the higher derivatives (see Section 1.10) could grow without bound as the degree increases. The data may contain such a significant amount of noise that we get a poor fit of the true data. Smoothing the data (discussed in a later chapter) may improve the situation. Again, unless a great deal is known about the given data, the "art" of numerical analysis is used as much as the "science" of numerical analysis.

There are many types of formulas involving tabulated values, derivatives, finite differences, and divided differences. One could almost make a career of the study of interpolation. The aim of this chapter, however, is to give a brief theoretical background, develop several of the basic, well-known formulas, and give a comprehensive set of very significant references for the benefit of those desiring to pursue the subject further.

3.2 THE CARDINAL FUNCTION OF INTERPOLATION

Many functions may agree in value at given data points but differ at other points. One of the most significant functions associated with interpolation was developed and introduced by E. T. Whittaker [a].*   Professor Whittaker expressed this function, which he called the cardinal function of interpolation theory, in two forms:

$$C(x) = \sum_{n=-\infty}^{\infty} \frac{f(a + nh) \sin \left[(\pi/h)(x - a - nh) \right]}{(\pi/h)(x - a - nh)} \tag{3.2.1}$$

or

$$C(x) = \frac{h}{\pi} \sin \left[(\pi/h)(x - a) \right] \sum_{n=-\infty}^{\infty} \frac{(-1)^n f(a + nh)}{(x - a - nh)}. \tag{3.2.2}$$

He showed that, in order to construct this function, we do not need to know anything about $f(x)$ except its values $f(a), f(a + h), f(a - h)$, etc. at the tabulated values of the argument. He also showed that these values are not peculiar to $f(x)$, but are common to a whole set of functions, and that we arrive at the same function, (3.2.1), regardless of which function of the set we start with. The function (3.2.1) is, therefore, an invariant function of the set and Whittaker regards it as the simplest function.

In addition to agreeing with $f(x)$ at the given data points, Professor Whittaker then proceeds to prove the following significant facts:

a) The cardinal function is equivalent to the Gauss interpolation formula:

$$f(s) = f_0 + s \, \delta f_{(1/2)} + \frac{s(s - 1)}{2!} \delta^2 f_0 + \frac{(s + 1)s(s - 1)}{3!} \delta^3 f_{(1/2)}$$

$$+ \frac{(s + 1)s(s - 1)(s - 2)}{4!} \delta^4 f_0 + \cdots . \tag{3.2.3}$$

b) $C(x)$ has no singularities in the finite part of the x-plane.

c) $C(x)$ contains no frequencies higher than $1/2h$.

W. L. Ferrar [b] showed that when the cardinal function converges, the Gauss interpolation formula also converges and has the same sum. He further showed that if the Gauss formula is convergent, the cardinal function is either convergent or has a *generalized sum* (in the sense used by de la Vallée Poussin for the Fourier series) equal to the sum of the Gauss series. Ferrar also shows that the cardinal function is a limiting case of Lagrange's interpolation formula (which is an equivalent form of Newton's well-known and fundamental interpolation formula).

Professor Whittaker gives the following illustrative example in his classic paper. Suppose that the given tabular values of the function $f(x)$ are

$$f(0) = 0, \; f(1) = -1, \; f(2) = \tfrac{1}{2}, \; f(3) = -\tfrac{1}{3}, \ldots, \; f(n) = (-1)^n/(n)$$

$$f(-1) = 1, \; f(-2) = -\tfrac{1}{2}, \; f(-3) = \tfrac{1}{3}, \ldots, \; f(-n) = \frac{(-1)^{n+1}}{n}.$$

---

* Letters in brackets are keyed to the references cited in Section 3.12.

The corresponding cardinal function is, by Formula (3.2.2),

$$C(x) = \frac{1}{\pi} \sin \pi x \left[\begin{array}{l} \dfrac{1}{x-1} + \dfrac{1}{2(x-2)} + \dfrac{1}{3(x-3)} + \dfrac{1}{4(x-4)} + \cdots \\[2mm] \dfrac{1}{x+1} - \dfrac{1}{2(x+2)} - \dfrac{1}{3(x+3)} - \dfrac{1}{4(x+4)} + \cdots \end{array} \right]$$

or, summing the series,

$$C(x) = \frac{\sin \pi x}{\pi x} \left[\frac{\Gamma'(1-x)}{\Gamma(1-x)} - \frac{\Gamma'(x+1)}{\Gamma(x+1)} \right]$$

$$= -\frac{\sin \pi x}{\pi x} \frac{d}{dx} \log[\Gamma(1+x)\Gamma(1-x)]$$

$$= \frac{\sin \pi x}{\pi x} \frac{d}{dx} \log \frac{\sin \pi x}{\pi x}$$

$$= \frac{\cos \pi x}{x} - \frac{\sin \pi x}{\pi x^2}.$$

This is the required cardinal function. It is the only analytic function having the given tabular values which has no singularities in the finite part of the x-plane and no oscillations of period less than 2.

So much for a brief theoretical introduction to interpolation theory. A more comprehensive study can be made of this theory through the selected references given in Section 3.12. Attention will now be given to several selected, well-known, fundamental formulas. The development of these formulas will be based on fundamental ideas previously presented in Chapters 1 and 2.

3.3 NEWTON'S FUNDAMENTAL FORMULA

The first formula to be considered is due to Newton and based on divided differences. Even though the notation is more cumbersome, it has the very important advantage of being applicable to unequally spaced data. Also, the other basic formulas can be obtained from it.

From the basic definition (Section 2.9) of divided differences, we have

$$f[x_0, x] = \frac{f(x) - f(x_0)}{x - x_0} \tag{3.3.1}$$

or

$$f(x) = f(x_0) + (x - x_0)f[x_0, x]. \tag{3.3.2}$$

Also

$$f[x_0, x] = f[x_0, x_1] + (x - x_1)f[x_0, x_1, x]. \tag{3.3.3}$$

Therefore, substituting (3.3.3) in (3.3.2), we get

$$f(x) = f(x_0) + (x - x_0)f[x_0, x_1] + (x - x_0)(x - x_1)f[x_0, x_1, x]. \tag{3.3.4}$$

And since

$$f[x_0, \ldots, x_{n-1}, x] = f[x_0, x_1, \ldots, x_n] + (x - x_n)f[x_0, \ldots, x_n, x], \quad (3.3.5)$$

by successive substitution we get

$$f(x) = f[x_0] + (x - x_0)f[x_0, x_1] + (x - x_0)(x - x_1)f[x_0, x_1, x_2]$$
$$+ \cdots + (x - x_0)(x - x_1) \cdots (x - x_{n-1})f[x_0, x_1, \ldots, x_n] \quad (3.3.6)$$
$$+ E(x),$$

where

$$E(x) = (x - x_0)(x - x_1) \cdots (x - x_n)f[x_0, x_1, \ldots, x_n, x]. \quad (3.3.7)$$

If the error term is suppressed, the resultant approximating polynomial, which is of degree n, may be denoted by $y(x) \equiv y_{0,\ldots,n}(x)$. Therefore,

$$y(x) = f[x_0] + (x - x_0)f[x_0, x_1] + (x - x_0)(x - x_1)f[x_0, x_1, x_2]$$
$$+ \cdots + (x - x_0)(x - x_1) \cdots (x - x_{n-1})f[x_0, x_1, \ldots, x_n]. \quad (3.3.8)$$

The error resulting from approximating $f(x)$ by $y(x)$ is then

$$E(x) = f(x) - y(x)$$
$$= (x - x_0)(x - x_1) \cdots (x - x_n)f[x_0, x_1, \ldots, x_n, x]$$
$$= \pi(x)f[x_0, x_1, \ldots, x_n, x] \quad (3.3.9)$$

or, by (1.10.8),

$$E(x) = \frac{\pi(x)}{(n+1)!} f^{(n+1)}(\xi). \quad (3.3.10)$$

3.4 NEWTON'S FORWARD DIFFERENCE FORMULA

From Eq. (2.11.3) we have

$$\Delta^r f_i = r! \, h^r f[x_i, x_{i+1}, \ldots, x_{i+r}]$$

or

$$f[x_i, x_{i+1}, \ldots, x_{i+r}] = \Delta^r f_i / r! \, h^r. \quad (3.4.1)$$

Letting $i = 0$, and substituting into (3.3.6), we obtain Newton's formula in terms of forward differences:

$$f(x) = f_0 + (x - x_0)\frac{\Delta f_0}{1! \, h} + (x - x_0)(x - x_1)\frac{\Delta^2 f_0}{2! \, h^2} + \cdots$$

$$+ (x - x_0)(x - x_1) \cdots (x - x_{n-1})\frac{\Delta^n f_0}{n! \, h^n} + E(x). \quad (3.4.2)$$

Now, assuming equally spaced data, if we introduce the dimensionless variable s, such that

$$s = (x - x_0)/h, \quad x = x_0 + hs, \quad x - x_k = h(s - k), \quad (3.4.3)$$

we obtain, from (3.4.2),

$$f_s = f_0 + s\,\Delta f_0 + \frac{s(s-1)}{2!}\Delta^2 f_0 + \cdots$$

$$+ \frac{s(s-1)(s-2)\cdots(s-n+1)}{n!}\Delta^n f_0 + E_s, \qquad (3.4.4)$$

where

$$E_s = [h^{n+1}/(n+1)!]s(s-1)\cdots(s-n)f^{(n+1)}(\xi). \qquad (3.4.5)$$

The tabular form associated with (3.4.4) is shown in Fig. 3.4.1.

$\longmapsto s \longrightarrow$				
x_0	x_1	x_2	x_3	$x_4 \ldots$
f_0	f_1	f_2	f_3	f_4
Δf_0	Δf_1	Δf_2	Δf_3	
$\Delta^2 f_0$	$\Delta^2 f_1$	$\Delta^2 f_2$		
$\Delta^3 f_0$	$\Delta^3 f_1$			
$\vdots$	$\vdots$	$\vdots$		

Figure 3.4.1

Since

$$\binom{s}{k} = \frac{s(s-1)(s-2)\cdots(s-k+1)}{k!},$$

Newton's forward difference formula may be written

$$f_s = \sum_{k=0}^{n}\binom{s}{k}\Delta^k f_0. \qquad (3.4.6)$$

3.5 NEWTON'S BACKWARD DIFFERENCE FORMULA

From Formula (2.11.5) we have

$$\nabla^r f_{i+r} = r!\,h^r f[x_i, x_{i+1}, \ldots, x_{i+r}]$$

or

$$f[x_i, x_{i+1}, \ldots, x_{i+r}] = \nabla^r f_{i+r}/r!\,h^r. \qquad (3.5.1)$$

Letting $i + r = n$ or $i = n - r$, and reordering the arguments in the left member of (3.5.1), we have

$$f[x_n, x_{n-1}, \ldots, x_{n-r}] = \nabla^r f_n/r!\,h^r. \qquad (3.5.2)$$

If we replace x_0 by x_n, x_1 by x_{n-1}, x_2 by $x_{n-2}, \ldots, x_n$ by x_{n-r} in (3.3.6), we obtain

$$f(x) = f(x_n) + (x - x_n)f[x_n, x_{n-1}] + (x - x_n)(x - x_{n-1})f[x_n, x_{n-1}, x_{n-2}]$$
$$+ \cdots + (x - x_n)(x - x_{n-1})\cdots(x - x_1)f[x_n, x_{n-1}, \ldots, x_1, x_0]$$
$$+ E(x), \qquad (3.5.3)$$

where

$$E(x) = (x - x_n)(x - x_{n-1})\cdots(x - x_0)[f^{(n+1)}(\xi)/(n+1)!]. \qquad (3.5.4)$$

Now, introducing the dimensionless variable s, such that

$$s = (x - x_n)/h, \qquad x = x_n + hs, \tag{3.5.5}$$

and using (3.5.2), we can write Eq. (3.5.3) as

$$f_{n+s} = f_n + s\nabla f_n + \frac{s(s+1)}{2!}\nabla^2 f_n + \cdots$$

$$+ \frac{s(s+1)(s+2)\cdots(s+n-1)}{n!}\nabla^n f_n + E_s, \tag{3.5.6}$$

$$E_s = \frac{h^{n+1}}{(n+1)!}s(s+1)(s+2)\cdots(s+n)f^{(n+1)}(\xi). \tag{3.5.7}$$

The tabular form associated with (3.5.6) is shown in Fig. 3.5.1.

$$\vdash\!\!\!-\!\!\!-\!\!\!- \; s \longrightarrow$$

x_{n-4}	x_{n-3}	x_{n-2}	x_{n-1}	x_n
f_{n-4}	f_{n-3}	f_{n-2}	f_{n-1}	f_n
	∇f_{n-3}	∇f_{n-2}	∇f_{n-1}	∇f_n
		$\nabla^2 f_{n-2}$	$\nabla^2 f_{n-1}$	$\nabla^2 f_n$
			$\nabla^3 f_{n-1}$	$\nabla^3 f_n$
				$\nabla^4 f_n$

Figure 3.5.1

Since

$$\binom{s+k-1}{k} = \frac{s(s+1)(s+2)\cdots(s+k-1)}{k!}$$

$$= (-1)^k \frac{(-s)(-s-1)\cdots(-s-k+1)}{k!} = (-1)^k \binom{-s}{k},$$

we write Newton's backward difference formula in the compact form

$$f_{n+s} = \sum_{k=0}^{n} (-1)^k \binom{-s}{k} \nabla^k f_n. \tag{3.5.8}$$

3.6   LINEAR INTERPOLATION

If Newton's fundamental formula (3.3.6) is truncated after the first two terms in the right member, we obtain the linear approximating polynomial

$$y_{0,1}(x) = f[x_0] + (x - x_0)f[x_0, x_1] \tag{3.6.1}$$

$$= f(x_0) + (x - x_0)\frac{f(x_1) - f(x_0)}{x_1 - x_0}$$

$$= \frac{1}{x_1 - x_0}[(x_1 - x)f_0 - (x_0 - x)f_1]$$

$$= \frac{1}{x_1 - x_0}\begin{vmatrix} f_0 & x_0 - x \\ f_1 & x_1 - x \end{vmatrix} \tag{3.6.2}$$

or
$$y_{0,1} = \frac{1}{x_1 - x_0} \begin{vmatrix} y_0 & x_0 - x \\ y_1 & x_1 - x \end{vmatrix}, \tag{3.6.3}$$

where $y_0 = f(x_0)$ and $y_1 = f(x_1)$ are two independent polynomials of degree zero.

This last form, (3.6.3), is well adapted to machine computation, since its evaluation involves the difference of two cross products followed by a division. The linear function defined by the right-hand member of Eq. (3.6.3) is denoted by $y_{0,1}(x)$ or $y_{0,1}$ for simplicity.

3.7 HIGHER-ORDER INTERPOLATION

The method of Section 3.6 is applied very conveniently to higher-order interpolation. That is, quadratic interpolation can be effected by linear interpolation over two independent linear interpolation polynomials; cubic interpolation can be effected by linear interpolation over two independent quadratic interpolation polynomials, etc. For example,

a) Quadratic or second-order:

$$y_{0,1,2}(x) = \frac{1}{x_2 - x_0} \begin{vmatrix} y_{0,1} & x_0 - x \\ y_{1,2} & x_2 - x \end{vmatrix} = \frac{1}{x_2 - x_1} \begin{vmatrix} y_{0,1} & x_1 - x \\ y_{0,2} & x_2 - x \end{vmatrix},$$

$$y_{0,1,3}(x) = \frac{1}{x_3 - x_0} \begin{vmatrix} y_{0,1} & x_0 - x \\ y_{1,3} & x_3 - x \end{vmatrix} = \frac{1}{x_3 - x_1} \begin{vmatrix} y_{0,1} & x_1 - x \\ y_{0,3} & x_3 - x \end{vmatrix};$$

b) Cubic or third-order

$$y_{0,1,2,3}(x) = \frac{1}{x_3 - x_2} \begin{vmatrix} y_{0,1,2} & x_2 - x \\ y_{0,1,3} & x_3 - x \end{vmatrix}.$$

3.8 AITKEN'S METHOD

The procedure used in Sections 3.6 and 3.7 is not only convenient for machine computation, but can be used to obtain a sequence of interpolates. This fact is used in an iterative interpolation method due to Aitken. If the abscissa nearest the argument of the interpolant $\bar{x}$ is designated by x_0, second nearest by x_1, etc., then the quantities $y_0, y_{0,1}, y_{0,1,2}$, etc. may be expected to give the best estimates which can be obtained by polynomial interpolation of orders zero, one, two, etc.

x_0	y_0					$x_0 - \bar{x}$
x_1	y_1	$y_{0,1}$				$x_1 - \bar{x}$
x_2	y_2	$y_{0,2}$	$y_{0,1,2}$			$x_2 - \bar{x}$
x_3	y_3	$y_{0,3}$	$y_{0,1,3}$	$y_{0,1,2,3}$		$x_3 - \bar{x}$
x_4	y_4	$y_{0,4}$	$y_{0,1,4}$	$y_{0,1,2,4}$	$y_{0,1,2,3,4}$	$x_4 - \bar{x}$
x_5	y_5	$y_{0,5}$	$y_{0,1,5}$	$y_{0,1,2,5}$	$y_{0,1,2,3,5}$	$y_{0,1,2,3,4,5}$ $x_5 - \bar{x}$

Figure 3.8.1

Each estimate makes use of all the information used in the preceding estimate, together with an additional data value. Successive orders can be computed until apparent convergence is reached. Aitken's method is conveniently summarized in Fig. 3.8.1.

To compute Aitken's method, we proceed as follows:

a) Entries in Column 2:

$$y_{0,1} = \frac{1}{x_1 - x_0} \begin{vmatrix} y_0 & x_0 - \bar{x} \\ y_1 & x_1 - \bar{x} \end{vmatrix}, \qquad y_{0,2} = \frac{1}{x_2 - x_0} \begin{vmatrix} y_0 & x_0 - \bar{x} \\ y_2 & x_2 - \bar{x} \end{vmatrix}, \text{ etc.;}$$

b) Entries in Column 3:

$$y_{0,1,2} = \frac{1}{x_2 - x_1} \begin{vmatrix} y_{0,1} & x_1 - \bar{x} \\ y_{0,2} & x_2 - \bar{x} \end{vmatrix}, \qquad y_{0,1,3} = \frac{1}{x_3 - x_1} \begin{vmatrix} y_{0,1} & x_1 - \bar{x} \\ y_{0,3} & x_3 - \bar{x} \end{vmatrix}, \text{ etc.;}$$

c) Entries in Column 4:

$$y_{0,1,2,3} = \frac{1}{x_3 - x_2} \begin{vmatrix} y_{0,1,2} & x_2 - \bar{x} \\ y_{0,1,3} & x_3 - \bar{x} \end{vmatrix},$$

$$y_{0,1,2,4} = \frac{1}{x_4 - x_2} \begin{vmatrix} y_{0,1,2} & x_2 - \bar{x} \\ y_{0,1,4} & x_4 - \bar{x} \end{vmatrix}, \text{ etc.}$$

We compute the entries of succeeding columns in a similar manner. The following example illustrates the method.

Example. Given the tabular values $x_0 = 0$, $y_0 = 0$, $x_1 = 1$, $y_1 = 1$, $x_2 = 2$, $y_2 = 4$, $x_3 = 3$, $y_3 = 9$, find the function value corresponding to $\bar{x} = 1.5$ by Aitken's method of interpolation.

Solution. We tabulate

0	0				−1.5
1	1	1.5			−0.5
2	4	3.0	2.25		0.5
3	9	4.5	2.25	2.25	1.5

where the column entries are computed as follows:

$$y_{0,1} = 1 \begin{vmatrix} 0 & -1.5 \\ 1 & -0.5 \end{vmatrix} = 1.5, \qquad y_{0,2} = \tfrac{1}{2} \begin{vmatrix} 0 & -1.5 \\ 4 & 0.5 \end{vmatrix} = 3.0,$$

$$y_{0,3} = \tfrac{1}{3} \begin{vmatrix} 0 & -1.5 \\ 9 & 1.5 \end{vmatrix} = 4.5, \qquad y_{0,1,2} = 1 \begin{vmatrix} 1.5 & -0.5 \\ 3.0 & 0.5 \end{vmatrix} = 2.25,$$

$$y_{0,1,3} = \tfrac{1}{2} \begin{vmatrix} 1.5 & -0.5 \\ 4.5 & 1.5 \end{vmatrix} = 2.25, \qquad y_{0,1,2,3} = 1 \begin{vmatrix} 2.25 & 0.5 \\ 2.25 & 1.5 \end{vmatrix} = 2.25.$$

3.9 GAUSSIAN FORMULAS

If the ordinates are used in the order $f_0, f_1, f_{-1}, f_2, f_{-2}, \ldots$, the result of replacing $x_0, x_1, x_2, x_3, x_4, \ldots$, by $x_0, x_1, x_{-1}, x_2, x_{-2}, \ldots$, and the divided differences by the appropriate corresponding central differences in Newton's fundamental formula (3.3.6) leads to the form

$$f(x) = f_0 + (x - x_0)\frac{\delta f_{1/2}}{1!h} + (x - x_0)(x - x_1)\frac{\delta^2 f_0}{2!h^2}$$

$$+ (x - x_0)(x - x_1)(x - x_{-1})\frac{\delta^3 f_{1/2}}{3!h^3} \tag{3.9.1}$$

$$+ (x - x_0)(x - x_1)(x - x_{-1})(x - x_2)\frac{\delta^4 f_0}{4!h^4}$$

$$+ \cdots$$

If $s = (x - x_0)/h$, $x = x_0 + hs$, then we write (3.9.1) in the form

$$f_s = f_0 + s\,\delta f_{1/2} + \frac{s(s - 1)}{2!}\delta^2 f_0$$

$$+ \frac{(s + 1)s(s - 1)}{3!}\delta^3 f_{1/2} + \frac{(s + 1)s(s - 1)(s - 2)}{4!}\delta^4 f_0$$

$$+ \cdots$$

$$+ \frac{s(s^2 - 1)\cdots(s^2 - m - 1)(s - m)}{(2m)!}\delta^{2m} f_0 \tag{3.9.2}$$

or

$$+ \frac{s(s^2 - 1)\cdots(s^2 - m^2)}{(2m + 1)!}\delta^{2m+1}f_{1/2}$$

$$+ E_s.$$

If nth differences are retained, then $n = 2m$ when n is even and $n = 2m + 1$ when n is odd. The error term has the form

$$E_s = h^{2m+1}\frac{s(s^2 - 1)\cdots(s^2 - m^2)}{(2m + 1)!}f^{(2m+1)}(\xi) \tag{3.9.3}$$

when $n = 2m$, and has the form

$$E_s = h^{2m+2}\frac{s(s^2 - 1)\cdots(s^2 - m^2)(s - m - 1)}{(2m + 1)!}f^{(2m+2)}(\xi) \tag{3.9.4}$$

when $n = 2m + 1$.

Formula (3.9.2) follows the path shown in Fig. 3.9.1 and is known as Gauss' forward formula. This is the Gauss interpolation formula discussed by Whittaker and Ferrar in Section 3.2. It is written in a more compact form as

$$f_s = f_0 + \binom{s}{1}\delta f_{1/2} + \binom{s}{2}\delta^2 f_0 + \binom{s + 1}{3}\delta^3 f_{1/2} + \binom{s + 1}{4}\delta^4 f_0 + \cdots \tag{3.9.5}$$

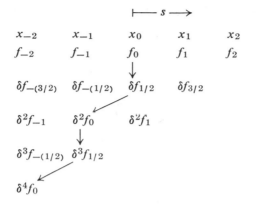

Figure 3.9.1

A formula using the backward zigzag difference path and known as Gauss' backward formula can be developed in a similar manner. It has the form

$$f_s = f_0 + \binom{s}{1} \delta f_{-(1/2)} + \binom{s+1}{2} \delta^2 f_0 + \binom{s+1}{3} \delta^3 f_{-(1/2)}$$

$$+ \binom{s+2}{4} \delta^4 f_0 + \cdots \tag{3.9.6}$$

Neither of these formulas is of very practical use, but they are of theoretical significance and are used to develop more useful formulas. A more extensive treatment of the Gaussian formulas may be found in Hildebrand [73] and Hamming [65].

3.10 LAGRANGE'S INTERPOLATION FORMULA

It is often desirable to have a formula expressed explicitly in terms of the ordinates, rather than finite or divided differences. The basic formula, apparently due to Waring, but associated with the name of Lagrange, is a formula of this type and is considered in this section.

Lagrange's form of the polynomial $y(x) = y_{0,...,n}(x)$ of degree n, which takes on the same values as a given function $f(x)$ for $(n+1)$ points $x_0, x_1, \ldots, x_n$, differs from the Newtonian form in that ordinates are involved instead of divided differences.

Whereas it is possible to derive Lagrange's form from Newton's fundamental formula, its importance justifies alternative methods of approach. Two methods will be outlined briefly, and a third method will be discussed more fully.

a) First method:
   We write $y(x)$ in the form

$$y(x) = A_0 + A_1 x + A_2 x^2 + \cdots + A_n x^n = \sum_{k=0}^{n} A_k x^k, \tag{3.10.1}$$

where the A's are to be determined in such a way that $y(x_i) = f(x_i)$ for $i = 0, 1, \ldots, n$. This gives us $n + 1$ linear equations to solve for the A's:

$$A_0 + A_1 x_0 + A_2 x_0^2 + \cdots + A_n x_0^n = f(x_0),$$
$$\vdots \qquad (3.10.2)$$
$$A_0 + A_1 x_n + A_2 x_n^2 + \cdots + A_n x_n^n = f(x_n).$$

b) Second method:

We write $y(x)$ directly in the form

$$y(x) = l_0(x)f(x_0) + l_1(x)f(x_1) + \cdots + l_n(x)f(x_n) = \sum_{k=0}^{n} l_k(x)f(x_k), \quad (3.10.3)$$

where $l_0(x), \ldots, l_n(x)$ are polynomials of degree n or less, to be determined by the requirement that the result of replacing $y(x)$ by $f(x)$ be an identity, when $f(x)$ is an arbitrary polynomial of degree n or less. It is clear that this is true if the result of replacing $y(x)$ by $f(x)$ is an identity when $f(x) = 1, x, x^2, \ldots, x^n$. The requirements are represented by the $n + 1$ equations

$$l_0(x) + l_1(x) + \cdots + l_n(x) = 1,$$
$$x_0 l_0(x) + x_1 l_1(x) + \cdots + x_n l_n(x) = x,$$
$$\vdots \qquad (3.10.4)$$
$$x_0^n l_0(x) + x_1^n l_1(x) + \cdots + x_n^n l_n(x) = x^n.$$

We can then solve these $n + 1$ equations for the coefficient functions $l_i(x)$, $i = 0, 1, \ldots, n$.

c) Third method:

Rather than pursue either of the two previous methods, we may avoid rather lengthy calculations by taking the following approach.

We notice that the expression

$$y(x) = \sum_{k=0}^{n} l_k(x)f(x_k) \qquad (3.10.5)$$

will indeed take on the value $f(x_i)$ when $x = x_i$, if $l_i(x_j) = 0$ when $j \neq i$. With the convenient notation of the Kronecker delta,

$$\delta_{ij} = \begin{cases} 0 & \text{if } i \neq j, \\ 1 & \text{if } i = j, \end{cases} \qquad (3.10.6)$$

the requirement becomes merely

$$l_i(x_j) = \delta_{ij}, \quad (i = 0, 1, \ldots, n; \, j = 0, 1, \ldots, n). \qquad (3.10.7)$$

Since $l_i(x)$ is a polynomial of degree n which vanishes when $x = x_0, x_1, \ldots, x_{i-1}, x_{i+1}, \ldots, x_n$, then

$$l_i(x) = c_i[(x - x_0)(x - x_1) \cdots (x - x_{i-1})(x - x_{i+1}) \cdots (x - x_n)], \qquad (3.10.8)$$

where c_i is a constant. By the requirement $l_i(x_i) = 1$,

$$c_i = \frac{1}{(x_i - x_0)(x_i - x_1) \cdots (x_i - x_{i-1})(x_i - x_{i+1}) \cdots (x_i - x_n)}$$

$$= \frac{1}{\pi'(x_i)}. \tag{3.10.9}$$

Therefore, the required Lagrangian coefficient functions, $l_i(x)$, are given by

$$l_i(x) = \frac{(x - x_0)(x - x_1) \cdots (x - x_{i-1})(x - x_{i+1}) \cdots (x - x_n)}{(x_i - x_0)(x_i - x_1) \cdots (x_i - x_{i-1})(x_i - x_{i+1}) \cdots (x_i - x_n)} \tag{3.10.10}$$

$$= \frac{\pi(x)}{(x - x_i)\pi'(x_i)} \tag{3.10.11}$$

and

$$y(x) = \sum_{i=0}^{n} l_i(x)f(x_i), \tag{3.10.12}$$

where again

$$E(x) = \pi(x)f[x_0, x_1, \ldots, x_n, x] = \pi(x)\frac{f^{(n+1)}(\xi)}{(n + 1)!}. \tag{3.10.13}$$

Using the form of Eq. (3.10.10) we see that the form of $l_i(x)$ is invariant under any linear change in variables

$$x - a + hs, \qquad x_i = a + hs_i, \tag{3.10.14}$$

where a and h are constants. Then

$$l_i(s) = \frac{(s - s_0)(s - s_1) \cdots (s - s_{i-1})(s - s_{i+1}) \cdots (s - s_n)}{(s_i - s_0)(s_i - s_1) \cdots (s_i - s_{i-1})(s_i - s_{i+1}) \cdots (s_i - s_n)}. \tag{3.10.15}$$

The constants a and h are chosen in such a way that the dimensionless variable s, which measures distance from a in units of h, takes on convenient values at the tabular points. For equally spaced abscissas, h is conveniently identified with the spacing. If $a = x_0$ and $x_0, x_1, x_2, \ldots, x_n$ are equally spaced by h, then

$$l_i(s) = \frac{s(s - 1)(s - 2) \cdots (s - i + 1)(s - i - 1) \cdots (s - n)}{i(i - 1)(i - 2) \cdots (i - i + 1)(i - i - 1) \cdots (i - n)}. \tag{3.10.16}$$

The compact form of (3.10.12) is then written in the form

$$y_s = \sum_{i=0}^{n} l_i(s)f_i. \tag{3.10.17}$$

3.11 OTHER SPECIAL FORMULAS

The preceding formulas discussed in this chapter are the most well-known, fundamental, and frequently-used formulas. We now conclude the chapter with a brief mention of three other special formulas and some references.

Stirling's formula is a special formula for interpolating for values of an interpolant near an interior point. Its derivation is based on the mean of the Gaussian
forward and backward formulas. It involves the so-called mean central differences. A discussion of this formula is found in Hildebrand [73] and Scarborough [134].

Everett's formulas are formulas which involve only central differences of even
order or central differences of odd order. A discussion of these is found in Hildebrand [73].

Bessel's formula is one in which the array of central differences involved is
symmetric about a line midway between the endpoints of an interval of interest.
A discussion of this formula is found in Hildebrand [73] and Scarborough [134].

3.12 SUPPLEMENTARY REFERENCES

Only fundamentals of interpolation have been presented in this chapter. For those who
wish to pursue the study of interpolation theory, many classic and elegant papers have
been written on the subject. A list of some of the most well-known and quoted papers
is given below. A summary of theorems (including some from the listed papers) relating
to interpolation function theory, as given by J. M. Whittaker in 1935, is presented in
Appendix C.

a) E. T. WHITTAKER, "Expansions of the Interpolation Theory," *Proc. Roy. Soc. of
Edin.* **3** (1915), 181–194.

b) W. L. FERRAR, "The Cardinal Function of Interpolation Theory," *Proc. Roy. Soc.
of Edin.* **45** (1925), 269–282.

c) CH.-J. DE LA VALLÉE POUSSIN, "Sur la convergence des formules d'interpolation entre
ordonnées équidistantes," *Bull. de l'Acad. Roy. de Belgique*, Classe des Sciences
(1908), 319–410.

d) T. A. BROWN, "Fourier's Integral," *Proc. Edin. Math. Soc.* **34** (1915–16), 3–10.

e) W. L. FERRAR, "The Cardinal Function of Interpolation Theory," *Proc. Roy. Soc. of
Edin.* **46** (1926), 323–333; **47** (1927), 230–242.

f) MARIA THEIS, "Über eine Interpolationsformel von de la Vallée Poussin," *Mathematische Zeitschrift III* (1919), 93–113.

g) E. C. TITCHMARSH, "Reciprocal Formulae Involving Series and Integrals," *Mathematische Zeitschrift* **25** (1926), 321–347. Also, *Proc. London Math. Soc.* (2), **26**
(1926), 1–11.

h) J. M. WHITTAKER, "On the Cardinal Function of Interpolation Theory," *Proc. Edin.
Math. Soc.* (2), **1** (1927), 41–46.

i) I. BENDIXSON, "Sur une extension à l'infini de la formule d'interpolation de Gauss,"
Acta Math. **9** (1886), 1–34.

j) H. HAHN, "Über das Interpolationsproblem," *Math. Zeitschrift* **1** (1918), 115–142.

k) C. RUNGE, "Über empirische Functionen und die Interpolation zwischen equidis-
tanten Ordinaten," *Zeitschrift f. Math. u. Phys.* **46** (1901), 224–243.

l) F. G. TEIXEIRA, "Sur la convergence des formules d'interpolation de Lagrange, de
Gauss, etc.," *Journal für Math.* **126** (1903), 116–162.

m) T. A. BROWN, "On a Class of Factorial Series," *Proc. London Math. Soc.* (2), **23**
(1924), 149–171.

n) J. F. STEFFENSEN, "Über eine Klasse von ganzen Funktionen und ihre Anwendung auf die Zahlentheorie," *Acta Math.* **37** (1914), 75–112.

o) G. H. HARDY, "On an Integral Equation," *Proc. London Math. Soc.* (2), **7** (1909), 445–472.

EXERCISES

1. Using the first two terms of Newton's formula, (3.3.6), interpolate linearly for $f(2.5)$. Estimate the error using Eq. (3.3.7).

x	0	1	2	3	4	5
$f(x)$	-4	-2	2	14	40	86

2. Using the tabular values in Exercise 1, do a quadratic interpolation for $f(2.5)$. Use the first three terms of Newton's formula (3.3.6) and compute the error estimate.

3. Using the tabular values in Exercise 1, do a cubic interpolation for $f(2.5)$. Use the first four terms of Newton's formula (3.3.6) and compute the error estimate.

4. Using the tabular values in Exercise 1, interpolate for $f(2.5)$. Use Aitken's method.

5. Using the tabular values in Exercise 1, obtain Lagrange's interpolating polynomial (3.10.12). Compute the estimate of $f(2.5)$ and the error.

6. Using the tabular values of Exercise 1 and the first five terms of Newton's forward difference formula (3.4.4), interpolate for $x = 2.5$ and estimate the error.

7. Using the tabular values of Exercise 1 and the first five terms of Newton's backward difference formula (3.5.6), interpolate for $x = 2.5$ and estimate the error.

CHAPTER 4

DIFFERENTIATION AND INTEGRATION

4.1 INTRODUCTION

Once an interpolating polynomial $y(x)$ has been determined so that it approximates $f(x)$ reliably over the given interval, the result of differentiating $y(x)$, or integrating it, will hopefully approximate the corresponding derivative or integral of $f(x)$.

However, if the approximating curve oscillates about the curve of the function approximated, the slopes of the two curves may differ appreciably. Also, roundoff errors of alternating sign in consecutive ordinates could affect the calculation of the derivative strongly.

Integration is essentially a smoothing process. The error associated with a numerical integration may hopefully be small, even though the approximating polynomial is only a moderately good approximation to $f(x)$.

In Section 1.5 on formula derivation, we considered a direct approach for obtaining particular formulas for differentiation or integration. In this chapter we shall consider types of formulas derived by differentiating or integrating a Lagrangian interpolating polynomial, several formulas derived by means of finite difference operations, and several formulas such as Gregory's formula and the Gaussian formulas.

4.2 LAGRANGIAN DIFFERENTIATION FORMULAS

From Eqs. (3.10.12) and (3.10.13) we have the Lagrange interpolation polynomial

$$f(x) = \sum_{k=0}^{n} l_k(x) f_k + E(x), \tag{4.2.1}$$

where

$$E(x) = \pi(x) \frac{f^{(n+1)}(\xi)}{(n+1)!}. \tag{4.2.2}$$

By differentiating Eq. (4.2.1) r times, one obtains the approximation

$$f^{(r)}(x) \approx \sum_{k=0}^{n} l_k^{(r)}(x) f_k + E^{(r)}(x), \tag{4.2.3}$$

where

$$E^{(r)}(x) = \frac{1}{(n+1)!} \frac{d^r}{dx^r} [\pi(x) f^{(n+1)}(\xi)]. \tag{4.2.4}$$

48

The differentiation in (4.2.4) cannot be explicitly accomplished, however, since the dependence of ξ upon x is unknown.

We may obtain a more useful form of the remainder if we replace (4.2.2) by the equivalent first form of (3.10.13), which involves the current variable x itself. The error (4.2.4) can then be expressed in the form

$$E^{(r)}(x) = \frac{d^r}{dx^r} \{\pi(x)f[x_0, \ldots, x_n, x]\}. \tag{4.2.5}$$

We write the rth derivative of a product as

$$\frac{d^r}{dx^r}(uv) = uD^rv + rDuD^{r-1}v + \frac{r(r-1)}{2!}D^2uD^{r-2}v + \cdots + vD^ru$$

$$= \sum_{i=0}^{r} \binom{r}{i} D^iuD^{r-i}v, \tag{4.2.6}$$

where $D \equiv d/dx$ and $\binom{r}{i}$ represents the binomial coefficient

$$\binom{r}{i} = \frac{r(r-1)\cdots(r-i+1)}{i!} = \frac{r!}{(r-i)!i!}. \tag{4.2.7}$$

The error in (4.2.5) now takes the form

$$E^{(r)}(x) = \sum_{i=0}^{r} \binom{r}{i} \pi^{(i)}(x) \frac{d^{r-i}}{dx^{r-i}} f[x_0, \ldots, x_n, x],$$

and making use of (2.10.9), we have

$$E^{(r)}(x) = \sum_{i=0}^{r} \frac{r!}{i!} \pi^{(i)}(x)f[x_0, \ldots, x_n, \overbrace{x, \ldots, x}^{r-i+1 \text{ times}}]. \tag{4.2.8}$$

From Section 2.10 and Eq. (3.10.13) we find that

$$f[x_0, \ldots, x_n, \overbrace{x, \ldots, x}^{r \text{ times}}] = \frac{1}{(n+r)!} f^{(n+r)}(\xi_m), \tag{4.2.9}$$

where, for given n, ξ_m lies somewhere in the interval I limited by the largest and smallest of $x_0, \ldots, x_n$ and x. Hence, (4.2.8) is expressed in the form

$$E^{(r)}(x) = \sum_{i=0}^{r} \frac{r!}{(n+r-i+1)!i!} \pi^{(i)}(x)f^{(n+r-i+1)}(\xi_i), \tag{4.2.10}$$

where each of the $r+1$ numbers $\xi_0, \ldots, \xi_r$ lies in I.

This expression for the error is rather complicated in the general case, and when the rth derivative is calculated by differentiating an interpolation polynomial of the nth degree, the estimation of the error may involve the estimation of derivatives of $f(x)$ of orders $n+1, n+2, \ldots, n+r$, and $n+r+1$ in the interval I.

When $r > n$ the right-hand member of Eq. (4.2.3) vanishes identically, since $l_k(x)$ is a polynomial of degree n. In general, this formula gives significant accuracy only when r is small relative to n.

In the case $r = 1$, Formula (4.2.3) becomes

$$f'(x) = \sum_{k=0}^{n} l'_k(x) f_k. \tag{4.2.11}$$

The associated error, as given by (4.2.10), is of the form

$$E'(x) = \pi'(x) \frac{f^{(n+1)}(\xi_1)}{(n+1)!} + \pi(x) \frac{f^{(n+2)}(\xi_0)}{(n+2)!}, \tag{4.2.12}$$

where both ξ_1 and ξ_0 lie in the interval I. For numerical differentiation at a tabular point, it follows that

$$f'(x_i) = \sum_{k=0}^{n} l'_k(x_i) f_k + \pi'(x_i) \frac{f^{(n+1)}(\xi_1)}{(n+1)!}, \tag{4.2.13}$$

and $\pi(x)$ vanishes [Section 1.10] when $x = x_i$. For three points x_0, x_1, and x_2, we have

$$f(x) = \sum_{k=0}^{2} l_k(x) f_k = l_0(x) f_0 + l_1(x) f_1 + l_2(x) f_2, \tag{4.2.14}$$

$$f'(x) = l'_0(x) f_0 + l'_1(x) f_1 + l'_2(x) f_2. \tag{4.2.15}$$

Differentiating the $l_i(x)$ and $\pi(x)$ and evaluating at the equally spaced points, we have

$$
\begin{array}{lll}
l'_0(x_0) = -\dfrac{3}{2h}, & l'_1(x_0) = \dfrac{2}{h}, & l'_2(x_0) = -\dfrac{1}{2h}, \\[2mm]
l'_0(x_1) = -\dfrac{1}{2h}, & l'_1(x_1) = 0, & l'_2(x_1) = \dfrac{1}{2h}, \\[2mm]
l'_0(x_2) = \dfrac{1}{2h}, & l'_1(x_2) = -\dfrac{2}{h}, & l'_2(x_2) = \dfrac{3}{2h}, \\[2mm]
\pi'(x_0) = 2h^2, & \pi'(x_1) = -h^2, & \pi'(x_2) = 2h^2.
\end{array}
\tag{4.2.16}
$$

Substituting the values from (4.2.16) in (4.2.15) and (4.2.13), we obtain the following set of three-point formulas:

$$f'_0 = \frac{1}{2h}(-3f_0 + 4f_1 - f_2) + \frac{h^2}{3} f^{(3)}(\xi), \tag{4.2.17}$$

$$f'_1 = \frac{1}{2h}(-f_0 + f_2) - \frac{h^2}{6} f^{(3)}(\xi), \tag{4.2.18}$$

$$f'_2 = \frac{1}{2h}(f_0 - 4f_1 + 3f_2) + \frac{h^2}{3} f^{(3)}(\xi), \qquad x_0 < \xi < x_2. \tag{4.2.19}$$

Using five data points and repeating the process, we obtain the following five-point formulas:

$$f_0' = \frac{1}{12h}(-25f_0 + 48f_1 - 36f_2 + 16f_3 - 3f_4) + \frac{h^4}{5}f^{(5)}(\xi), \qquad (4.2.20)$$

$$f_1' = \frac{1}{12h}(-3f_0 - 10f_1 + 18f_2 - 6f_3 + f_4) - \frac{h^4}{20}f^{(5)}(\xi), \qquad (4.2.21)$$

$$f_2' = \frac{1}{12h}(f_0 - 8f_1 + 8f_3 - f_4) + \frac{h^4}{30}f^{(5)}(\xi), \qquad (4.2.22)$$

$$f_3' = \frac{1}{12h}(-f_0 + 6f_1 - 18f_2 + 10f_3 + 3f_4) - \frac{h^4}{20}f^{(5)}(\xi), \qquad (4.2.23)$$

$$f_4' = \frac{1}{12h}(3f_0 - 16f_1 + 36f_2 - 48f_3 + 25f_4) + \frac{h^4}{5}f^{(5)}(\xi), \qquad (4.2.24)$$

where $x_0 < \xi < x_4$. It is observed that the truncation error is least when the derivative is calculated at the central point, and the ordinate at that point is not involved.

4.3 DERIVATIVE FORMULAS FROM FINITE DIFFERENCE OPERATIONS

In Section 2.3 we presented relationships between the various linear operators. Using appropriately chosen relationships, we shall now derive a set of formulas for finding derivatives.

a) *Backward and forward difference formulas.* Making use of the fact that $\mathbf{hD} = -\log(1 - \nabla)$, we write

$$hy_n' = \mathbf{hD}y_n = -\{\log(1 - \nabla)\}y_n$$
$$= (\nabla + \tfrac{1}{2}\nabla^2 + \tfrac{1}{3}\nabla^3 + \cdots)y_n. \qquad (4.3.1)$$

Also, since $\mathbf{hD} = \log(1 + \Delta)$, we write

$$hy_n' = \mathbf{hD}y_n = \{\log(1 + \Delta)\}y_n$$
$$= (\Delta - \tfrac{1}{2}\Delta^2 + \tfrac{1}{3}\Delta^3 - \cdots)y_n. \qquad (4.3.2)$$

By appropriate iteration the above two formulas may be obtained in a more general form for giving the rth derivative at y_n in terms of backward and forward differences. Thus

$$h^r y_n^{(r)} = \left[\nabla^r + \frac{r}{2}\nabla^{r+1} + \frac{r(3r + 5)}{24}\nabla^{r+2} + \cdots\right]y_n, \qquad (4.3.3)$$

$$h^r y_n^{(r)} = \left[\Delta^r - \frac{r}{2}\Delta^{r+1} + \frac{r(3r + 5)}{24}\Delta^{r+2} - \cdots\right]y_n. \qquad (4.3.4)$$

The coefficients in these formulas usually decrease slowly, and it is preferable to use central differences if they are available.   If the first derivative is required at next to the last point of a table, one of the following formulas may be used:

$$hy'_{n-1} = \mathbf{h}DE^{-1}y_n = -(1 - \nabla)\{\log(1 - \nabla)\}y_n$$

$$= (\nabla - \tfrac{1}{2}\nabla^2 - \tfrac{1}{6}\nabla^3 - \cdots)y_n, \tag{4.3.5}$$

$$hy'_{n-1} = \mathbf{h}DEy_{n-2} = (1 + \Delta)\{\log(1 + \Delta)\}y_{n-2}$$

$$= (\Delta + \tfrac{1}{2}\Delta^2 - \tfrac{1}{6}\Delta^3 + \cdots)y_{n-2}. \tag{4.3.6}$$

b) *Central difference formulas.* Using another relationship from Section 2.3, we write

$$h^2 y''_n = \mathbf{h}^2 D^2 y_n = (2 \sinh^{-1} \tfrac{1}{2}\delta)^2 y_n$$

$$= (\delta^2 - \tfrac{1}{12}\delta^4 + \tfrac{1}{90}\delta^6 - \tfrac{1}{560}\delta^8 + \cdots)y_n. \tag{4.3.7}$$

Using relationship (2.11.6), we write this formula in terms of backward and forward differences. Thus we have

$$h^2 y''_n = \delta^2 y_n - \tfrac{1}{12}\delta^4 y_n + \tfrac{1}{90}\delta^6 y_n - \cdots$$

$$= \nabla^2 y_{n+1} - \tfrac{1}{12}\nabla^4 y_{n+2} + \tfrac{1}{90}\nabla^6 y_{n+3} - \cdots \tag{4.3.8}$$

$$= \Delta^2 y_{n-1} - \tfrac{1}{12}\Delta^4 y_{n-2} + \tfrac{1}{90}\Delta^6 y_{n-3} - \cdots \tag{4.3.9}$$

In the case of the first derivative corresponding to the above formula, the series obtained would be in terms of odd-order differences $\delta^{2n+1}y_n$, which involve ordinates that do not appear in the data table. We remedy this by using mean differences of odd order $\mu \delta^{2n+1}y_n$. This is attained by introducing the averaging operator, μ, into the numerator and the corresponding factor $(1 + \tfrac{1}{4}\delta^2)^{1/2}$ into the denominator. We obtain

$$hy'_n = \mathbf{h}Dy_n = (2 \sinh^{-1} \tfrac{1}{2}\delta)y_n$$

$$= (1 + \tfrac{1}{4}\delta^2)^{-1/2}(2 \sinh^{-1} \tfrac{1}{2}\delta)\mu y_n$$

$$= (\mu\delta - \tfrac{1}{6}\mu\delta^3 + \tfrac{1}{30}\mu\delta^5 - \cdots)y_n. \tag{4.3.10}$$

4.4 LAGRANGIAN INTEGRATION FORMULAS

From the Lagrange interpolation polynomial, (4.2.1) and (4.2.2), we obtain by integration

$$\int_a^b f(x)\,dx = \sum_{k=0}^{n} C_k f_k, \tag{4.4.1}$$

where the weighting coefficients are

$$C_k = \int_a^b l_k(x)\,dx. \tag{4.4.2}$$

We integrate (4.2.2) to obtain the associated error; that is,

$$E = \int_a^b \frac{\pi(x)f^{(n+1)}(\xi)}{(n+1)!} \, dx.$$

The right-hand side is of the form

$$\int_a^b \pi(x)\phi(x) \, dx.$$

If $\pi(x)$ does not change sign on the interval $[a, b]$, then we can apply the second mean-value theorem [Appendix A, 9] and get

$$\int_a^b \pi(x)\phi(x) \, dx = \phi(\eta) \int_a^b \pi(x) \, dx$$

for some point η on $[a, b]$. Hence we get

$$E = \frac{f^{(n+1)}(\eta)}{(n+1)!} \int_a^b \pi(x) \, dx \tag{4.4.3}$$

for some point η on $[a, b]$.

     With a change of variable such that

$$x = a + \frac{b-a}{n} s = a + hs, \tag{4.4.4}$$

then

$$f(x) = f(a + hs) = F(s) = \sum_{k=0}^{n} l_k(s)F_k \quad \text{for} \tag{4.4.5}$$

Integrating (4.4.5) between the limits a and b, we obtain

$$\int_a^b f(x) \, dx = h \int_0^n F(s) \, ds - \sum_{k=0}^{n} C_k F(k), \tag{4.4.6}$$

or since $F(k) = f(x_k) = f_k$, we have

$$\int_a^b f(x) \, dx = h \sum_{k=0}^{n} C_k f_k, \tag{4.4.7}$$

where

$$C_k = \int_0^n l_k(s) \, ds, \tag{4.4.8}$$

and the form of $l_k(s)$ is given by Eq. (3.10.16).

     The associated error is given by

$$E = \int_a^b \pi(x) \frac{f^{(n+1)}(\xi)}{(n+1)!} \, dx = h \int_0^n \pi(s) \frac{F^{(n+1)}(\xi)}{(n+1)!} \, ds,$$

or, since $F^{(n+1)}(\xi) = h^{n+1} f^{(n+1)}(\eta)$, with appropriate manipulation we may obtain*

$$E_n = \frac{h^{n+2} f^{(n+1)}(\xi)}{(n+1)!} \int_0^n s(s-1) \cdots (s-n) \, ds \qquad (n \text{ odd}) \qquad (4.4.9)$$

or

$$E_n = \frac{h^{n+3} f^{(n+2)}(\xi)}{(n+2)!} \int_0^n \left(s - \frac{n}{2}\right)(s) \cdots (s-n) \, ds. \qquad (n \text{ even}). \qquad (4.4.10)$$

To illustrate, consider the case $n = 2$:

$$C_0 = \int_0^2 \frac{(s-1)(s-2)}{(-1)(-2)} \, ds = \tfrac{1}{3},$$

$$C_1 = \int_0^2 \frac{s(s-2)}{(1)(-1)} \, ds = \tfrac{4}{3},$$

$$C_2 = \int_0^2 \frac{s(s-1)}{(2)(1)} \, ds = \tfrac{1}{3},$$

$$E_2 = \frac{h^5 f^{(4)}(\xi)}{24} \int_0^2 s(s-1)^2(s-2) \, ds = -\frac{h^5 f^{(4)}(\xi)}{90}.$$

Therefore,

$$\int_{x_0}^{x_2} f(x) \, dx = \frac{h}{3}(f_0 + 4f_1 + f_2) - \frac{h^5 f^{(4)}(\xi)}{90}. \qquad (4.4.11)$$

This, of course, is the celebrated *Simpson's rule*.

Formulas of this type are sometimes called Newton-Cotes integration formulas of closed type. They are derived by approximating $f(x)$ by an nth degree polynomial over $(n + 1)$ points and integrating over the whole interval from 0 to n.

Just as $n = 2$ gives the simplest form of Simpson's rule, $n = 1$ gives the simplest form of the trapezoidal rule,

$$\int_{x_0}^{x_1} f(x) \, dx = \frac{h}{2}(f_0 + f_1) - \frac{h^3}{12} f^{(2)}(\xi), \qquad (4.4.12)$$

and $n = 3$ gives Newton's three-eighths rule,

$$\int_{x_0}^{x_3} f(x) \, dx = \frac{3h}{8}(f_0 + 3f_1 + 3f_2 + f_3) - \frac{3h^5}{80} f^{(4)}(\xi). \qquad (4.4.13)$$

---

* See A. Ralston, *A First Course in Numerical Analysis*, McGraw-Hill, New York, 1965; p. 116.

If an interval (a, b) is divided into n intervals, and the simple trapezoidal rule is applied n times, we get the general or composite trapezoidal rule,

$$\int_a^b f(x)\, dx = \frac{h}{2} (f_0 + 2f_1 + 2f_2 + \cdots + 2f_{n-1} + f_n) - \frac{nh^3}{12} f^{(2)}(\xi). \qquad (4.4.14)$$

If the interval (a, b) is divided into n(even) intervals, and the simple Simpson's rule is applied $n/2$ times, we get the general or composite Simpson's rule,

$$\int_a^b f(x)\, dx = \frac{h}{3} (f_0 + 4f_1 + 2f_2 + \cdots + 2f_{n-2} + 4f_{n-1} + f_n) - \frac{nh^5}{180} f^{(4)}(\xi).$$
$$(4.4.15)$$

If we are given a set of points, $x_0, x_1, \ldots, x_n$, we can renumber the points as $x_{-1}, x_0, \ldots, x_{n-1}$. We can then fit a polynomial of degree $(n - 2)$,

$$f(x) = \sum_{k=0}^{n-2} l_k(x) f_k, \qquad (4.4.16)$$

over the $(n - 2)$ interior points. Then integrating over the whole interval we have

$$\int_{x_{-1}}^{x_{n-1}} f(x)\, dx = h \sum_{k=0}^{n-2} C_k f_k, \qquad (4.4.17)$$

where

$$C_k = \int_{-1}^{n-1} l_k(s)\, ds. \qquad (4.4.18)$$

Now, if we renumber the limits on the left and the subscripts of the ordinates on the right in terms of the original set, we have a formula which expresses

$$\int_{x_0}^{x_n} f(x)\, dx$$

in terms of the interior ordinates $f_1, f_2, \ldots, f_{n-1}$. Formulas of this type are called Newton-Cotes integration formulas of open type. Although formulas of this type are not usually as accurate as closed formulas, they can be used if the end points are unknown or of uncertain value.

4.5 INTEGRATION FORMULAS INVOLVING FINITE DIFFERENCES

Forward differences. In Section 3.4 we derived the forward difference form of Newton's interpolation formula. This is given by (3.4.6) in the form

$$y(s) = \sum_{k=0}^{n} \binom{s}{k} \Delta^k f_0. \qquad (4.5.1)$$

Using this polynomial with the transformation, $x = x_0 + hs$, $dx = h\,ds$, we obtain

$$\int_{x_0}^{x_n} y(x)\,dx = h \int_0^n y(s)\,ds$$

$$= h \int_0^n \left(f_0 + s\,\Delta f_0 + \frac{s(s-1)}{2!}\Delta^2 f_0 + \cdots \right) ds$$

$$= h\left[n f_0 + \frac{n^2}{2}\Delta f_0 + (\tfrac{1}{6}n^3 - \tfrac{1}{4}n^2)\Delta^2 f_0 + \cdots \right]$$

or, in general,

$$= h(a_0 f_0 + a_1\,\Delta f_0 + \cdots + a_k\,\Delta^k f_0 + \cdots), \qquad (4.5.2)$$

where

$$a_k = \int_0^n \binom{s}{k} ds = \frac{1}{k!}\int_0^n \prod_{j=0}^{k-1}(s-j)\,ds. \qquad (4.5.3)$$

The first few coefficients obtained by using (4.5.3) are

$$a_0 = n, \quad a_1 = \tfrac{1}{2}n^2, \qquad a_2 = \tfrac{1}{12}(2n^3 - 3n^2),$$

$$a_3 = \tfrac{1}{24}(n^4 - 4n^3 + 4n^2), \qquad a_4 = \tfrac{1}{720}(6n^5 - 45n^4 + 110n^3 - 90n^2),$$

$$a_5 = \tfrac{1}{1440}(2n^6 - 24n^5 + 105n^4 - 200n^3 + 144n^2). \qquad (4.5.4)$$

To illustrate, consider the case $n = 2$:

$$\int_{x_0}^{x_2} y(x)\,dx = h(a_0 f_0 + a_1\,\Delta f_0 + a_2\,\Delta^2 f_0 + a_3\,\Delta^3 f_0 + \cdots),$$

$$a_0 = n = 2, \qquad a_1 = \tfrac{1}{2}n^2 = 2, \qquad a_2 = \tfrac{1}{12}(2n^3 - 3n^2) = \tfrac{1}{3},$$

$$a_3 = \tfrac{1}{24}(n^4 - 4n^3 + 4n^2) = 0.$$

Therefore

$$\int_{x_0}^{x_2} y(x)\,dx = h(2f_0 + 2\,\Delta f_0 + \tfrac{1}{3}\Delta^2 f_0)$$

$$= (h/3)(f_0 + 4f_1 + f_2). \qquad (4.5.5)$$

Again, we have obtained Simpson's rule.

Central differences. A useful central difference integration formula is obtained if the integral over two intervals is expressed in terms of the central differences at the middle point:

$$\frac{1}{2h}\int_{x_0}^{x_2} f(x)\,dx = \tfrac{1}{2}\{(\mathbf{h}\mathbf{D})^{-1}f_2 - (\mathbf{h}\mathbf{D})^{-1}f_0\}$$

$$= (\mathbf{h}\mathbf{D})^{-1}\mu\,\delta f_1$$

$$= (2\sinh^{-1}\tfrac{1}{2}\delta)^{-1}(1 + \tfrac{1}{4}\delta^2)^{1/2}\,\delta f_1$$

$$= (1 + \tfrac{1}{6}\delta^2 - \tfrac{1}{180}\delta^4 + \cdots)f_1. \qquad (4.5.6)$$

Neglecting fourth- and higher-order differences in Formula (4.5.6), we again obtain Simpson's rule as given in (4.5.5).

Gregory's formula. Central difference formulas are desirable whenever possible, since they are the most rapidly convergent. In some cases, however, the integrand may not be readily computable outside of the range of integration. In such cases Gregory's formula, which uses only available differences, can be used. This formula is composed of the trapezoidal rule, plus correction terms which are computed from available finite differences. One form of this equation is

$$\frac{1}{h} \int_0^{nh} f(x)\,dx = (\tfrac{1}{2}f_0 + f_1 + f_2 + \cdots + f_{n-1} + \tfrac{1}{2}f_n)$$
$$+ A_1(\Delta f_0 - \Delta f_{n-1}) + A_2(\Delta^2 f_0 + \Delta^2 f_{n-2}) \quad (4.5.7)$$
$$+ A_3(\Delta^3 f_0 - \Delta^3 f_{n-3}) + A_4(\Delta^4 f_0 + \Delta^4 f_{n-4})$$
$$+ A_5(\Delta^5 f_0 - \Delta^5 f_{n-5}) + \cdots,$$

where we compute the coefficients A_i by the following recursion formula:

$$C_1 = 1, \qquad C_2 = \tfrac{1}{2},$$
$$C_{i+1} = \frac{C_i}{2} - \frac{C_{i-1}}{3} + \frac{C_{i-2}}{4} - \cdots + (-1)^{i+1}\frac{C_1}{i+1}, \quad (4.5.8)$$
$$A_i = -C_{i+2}.$$

4.6 GAUSSIAN INTEGRATION FORMULAS

In Section 1.5 we developed a special formula, (1.5.14), and mentioned the general form, (1.5.17),

$$\int_a^b K(x)f(x)\,dx = \sum_{i=1}^n w_i f(x_i) \qquad K(x) > 0, \quad (4.6.1)$$

which has $2n$ parameters and can be made exact for $1, x, x^2, \ldots, x^{2n-1}$. We obtain the equations

$$m_0 = w_1 + w_2 + \cdots + w_n,$$
$$m_1 = w_1 x_1 + w_2 x_2 + \cdots + w_n x_n,$$
$$m_2 = w_1 x_1^2 + w_2 x_2^2 + \cdots + w_n x_n^2, \quad (4.6.2)$$
$$\vdots$$
$$m_{2n-1} = w_1 x_1^{2n-1} + w_2 x_2^{2n-1} + \cdots + w_n x_n^{2n-1}.$$

This system of nonlinear equations is solved in the following manner. Define the polynomial

$$\pi(x) = \prod_{i=1}^n (x - x_i) = \sum_{k=0}^n C_k x^k,$$

where $\pi(x_i) = 0$ for $i = 1, 2, \ldots, n$. Multiply the top equation of (4.6.2) by C_0, the second by C_1, etc., and the nth by $C_n = 1$. Add to get

$$\sum_{k=0}^n C_k m_k = \sum_{i=1}^n w_i \pi(x_i) = 0. \quad (4.6.3)$$

Shift each coefficient down one equation and repeat the process to obtain

$$\sum_{k=0}^{n} C_k m_{k+1} = \sum_{i=1}^{n} w_i x_i \pi(x_i) = 0. \tag{4.6.4}$$

Doing this n times, we have

$$\sum_{k=0}^{n} C_k m_{k+j} = 0, \qquad j = 0, 1, 2, \ldots, n - 1. \tag{4.6.5}$$

If the determinant of coefficients of the C_k, $|m_{k+j}|$ is not zero, we can solve for the C_k (using $C_n = 1$). If the determinant is zero, the equations may be inconsistent, and there is no such formula. If the rank is $(n - 1)$, we may add one more equation to (4.6.2), and derive one more equation involving the m_{k+j} and C_k. We repeat this process until we have n linearly independent equations for the C_k.

From the C_k, which are coefficients of the sample polynomial,

$$\pi(x) = x^n + C_{n-1} x^{n-1} + \cdots + C_1 x + C_0, \tag{4.6.6}$$

we can find the zeros of $\pi(x)$. These zeros are taken as the sample points. This now reduces the problem to the case of known sample points, and we can use the first n equations of (4.6.2) to find the w_i.

The name Gaussian quadrature is associated with problems of this type in which all the sample points are unassigned. There are three frequently used forms of Gaussian quadrature. The first is the Gauss-Legendre with integration interval $(-1, 1)$ and weight factor 1. The second is the Gauss-Laguerre with integration interval $(0, \infty)$ and weight factor e^{-x}, and the third is the Gauss-Hermite with integration range $(-\infty, \infty)$ and weight factor e^{-x^2}. In each case the second name is attached because the sample points are the zeros of the corresponding orthogonal polynomial of degree n. In the Legendre (n equals 1 to 16) and Laguerre (n equals 1 to 15) cases, the zeros and weights have been tabulated in the Applied Mathematics Series No. 37, Tables of Functions and Zeros of Functions, published by the National Bureau of Standards (1954).

The sample points are all real, distinct and lie in the interval of integration. The weights arc all positive. The error estimate is proportional to the $2n$th derivative,

$$E = \frac{f^{(2n)}(\xi)}{(2n)!} \int_a^b \pi^2(x)\, dx,$$

where $\pi(x) = (x - x_1)(x - x_2) \cdots (x - x_n)$ and $a < \xi < b$.

Many other special cases have been investigated in which $K(x)$ has singularities at one or both of the ends of the range of integration. One case of interest is the Gauss-Chebyshev equation:

$$\int_{-1}^{1} \frac{f(x)}{\sqrt{1 - x^2}}\, dx = \sum_{i=1}^{n} w_i f(x_i). \tag{4.6.7}$$

The sample points turn out to be

$$x_j = \cos \frac{2j - 1}{2n} \pi, \tag{4.6.8}$$

and the weights, w_i, are all equal. Thus

$$w_i = \frac{\pi}{n}. \tag{4.6.9}$$

Recursion formulas for generating the Legendre polynomials, $P_n(x)$, Laguerre polynomials, $L_n(x)$, Hermite polynomials, $H_n(x)$, and the Chebyshev polynomials, $T_n(x)$, are found in Chapter 5. To obtain a better understanding of the above discussion, we now consider an example of each special type mentioned.

Example 1 (Gauss-Legendre). Find the weighting coefficients and unknown sample points in the following formula for $n = 3$:

$$\int_{-1}^{1} f(x)\, dx = \sum_{k=1}^{n} w_k f(x_k) + E, \tag{4.6.10}$$

where x_i is the ith zero of $P_n(x)$ and

$$w_i = \frac{2}{nP_{n-1}(x_i)P_n'(x_i)}, \tag{4.6.11}$$

$$E = \frac{2^{2n+1}(n!)^4}{(2n + 1)[(2n)!]^3} f^{(2n)}(\xi), \qquad -1 < \xi < 1. \tag{4.6.12}$$

Solution. From Eq. (5.7.1) we have $P_2(x) = \frac{1}{2}(3x^2 - 1)$ and $P_3(x) = \frac{5}{2}x(x^2 - \frac{3}{5})$. Also $P_3'(x) = \frac{15}{2}x^2 - \frac{3}{2}$. The roots of $P_3(x)$ are

$$x_1 = -\sqrt{15}/5, \qquad x_2 = 0, \qquad x_3 = \sqrt{15}/5.$$

Therefore, from (4.6.11)

$$w_1 = \tfrac{5}{9}, \qquad w_2 = \tfrac{8}{9}, \qquad w_3 = \tfrac{5}{9},$$

and we have

$$\int_{-1}^{1} f(x)\, dx = \tfrac{1}{9}[5f(-\sqrt{15}/5) + 8f(0) + 5f(\sqrt{15}/5)] + \frac{f^{(4)}(\xi)}{15750}.$$

Example 2 (Gauss-Laguerre). Find the weighting coefficients and unknown sample points in the following formula for $n = 2$:

$$\int_{0}^{\infty} e^{-x} f(x)\, dx = \sum_{k=1}^{n} w_k f(x_k) + E, \tag{4.6.13}$$

where x_i is the ith zero of $L_n(x)$ and

$$w_i = -\frac{[(n - 1)!]^2}{L_n'(x_i)L_{n-1}(x_i)}, \tag{4.6.14}$$

$$E = \frac{(n!)^2}{(2n)!} f^{(2n)}(\xi), \qquad 0 < \xi < \infty. \tag{4.6.15}$$

Solution. From (5.8.2) we have $L_1(x) = 1 - x$ and $L_2(x) = x^2 - 4x + 2$. Also $L_2'(x) = 2x - 4$. The roots of $L_2(x)$ are

$$x_1 = 2 - \sqrt{2}, \qquad x_2 = 2 + \sqrt{2}.$$

Therefore, from (4.6.14)

$$w_1 = (2 + \sqrt{2})/4, \qquad W_2 = (2 - \sqrt{2})/4,$$

and we have

$$\int_0^\infty e^{-x} f(x)\, dx = \tfrac{1}{4}[(2 + \sqrt{2})f(2 - \sqrt{2}) + (2 - \sqrt{2})f(2 + \sqrt{2})] + \frac{f^{(4)}(\xi)}{6}.$$

A more general form of this formula is

$$\int_0^\infty e^{-\alpha x} f(x)\, dx = \frac{1}{4\alpha}\left[(2 + \sqrt{2})f\left(\frac{2 - \sqrt{2}}{\alpha}\right) + (2 - \sqrt{2})f\left(\frac{2 + \sqrt{2}}{\alpha}\right)\right]$$
$$+ \frac{f^{(4)}(\xi)}{6\alpha^5}.$$

Example 3 (Gauss-Hermite). Find the weighting coefficients and unknown sample points in the following formula for $n = 3$:

$$\int_{-\infty}^\infty e^{-x^2} f(x)\, dx = \sum_{k=1}^n w_k f(x_k) + E, \tag{4.6.16}$$

where x_i is the ith root of $H_n(x)$ and

$$w_i = \frac{2^n(n - 1)!\sqrt{\pi}}{H_n'(x_i)H_{n-1}(x_i)}, \tag{4.6.17}$$

$$E = \frac{n!\sqrt{\pi}}{2^n(2n)!} f^{(2n)}(\xi), \qquad -\infty < \xi < \infty. \tag{4.6.18}$$

Solution. From (5.9.2) we have

$$H_2(x) = 4x^2 - 2 \qquad \text{and} \qquad H_3(x) = 8x^3 - 12x.$$

Also $H_3'(x) = 24x^2 - 12$. The roots of $H_3(x)$ are

$$x_1 = -\sqrt{6}/2, \qquad x_2 = 0, \qquad x_3 = \sqrt{6}/2.$$

Therefore, from (4.6.17)

$$w_1 = \sqrt{\pi}/6, \qquad w_2 = 2\sqrt{\pi}/3, \qquad w_3 = \sqrt{\pi}/6,$$

and we have

$$\int_{-\infty}^\infty e^{-x^2} f(x)\, dx = \frac{\sqrt{\pi}}{6}\left[f\left(-\frac{\sqrt{6}}{2}\right) + 4f(0) + f\left(\frac{\sqrt{6}}{2}\right)\right] + \frac{\sqrt{\pi} f^{(6)}(\xi)}{960}.$$

A more general form of this formula is

$$\int_{-\infty}^{\infty} e^{-\alpha^2 x^2} f(x)\, dx = \frac{\sqrt{\pi}}{6\alpha}\left[f\left(-\frac{\sqrt{6}}{2\alpha}\right) + 4f(0) + f\left(\frac{\sqrt{6}}{2\alpha}\right) \right] + \frac{\sqrt{\pi} f^{(6)}(\xi)}{960\alpha^7}.$$

Example 4 (Gauss-Chebyshev). From (5.12.5) and (5.12.6) we can obtain $T_n(x)$ and $T_{n+1}(x)$. Then, relative to weighting function $1/\sqrt{1 - x^2}$, we have

$$\int_{-1}^{1} \frac{f(x)}{\sqrt{1 - x^2}}\, dx = \sum_{k=1}^{n} w_k f(x_k) + E, \tag{4.6.19}$$

where x_i is the ith root of $T_n(x)$ and

$$w_i = -\frac{\pi}{T_n'(x_i) T_{n+1}(x_i)}, \tag{4.6.20}$$

$$E = \frac{2\pi}{2^{2n}(2n)!}\, f^{(2n)}(\xi), \qquad |\xi| < 1. \tag{4.6.21}$$

As will be shown in Chapter 5,

$$x_i = \cos\left[\frac{(2i - 1)\pi}{2n}\right], \qquad i = 1, 2, \ldots, n.$$

Also,

$$T_n'(x_i) = \frac{(-1)^{i+1} n}{\sin \alpha_i}, \qquad T_{n+1}(x_i) = (-1)^i \sin \alpha_i,$$

where $\alpha_i = [(2i - 1)/n]\pi$. Hence $w_i = \pi/n$, and we have

$$\int_{-1}^{1} \frac{f(x)}{\sqrt{1 - x^2}}\, dx = \frac{\pi}{n} \sum_{k=1}^{n} f\left(\cos\frac{2k - 1}{2n}\pi\right) + \frac{2\pi}{2^{2n}(2n)!}\, f^{(2n)}(\xi), \tag{4.6.22}$$

where $-1 < \xi < 1$.

4.7 OTHER METHODS OF NUMERICAL INTEGRATION

There are several other integration formulas or methods of numerical integration which are not discussed here but are worthy of mention. These are the Radau quadrature formula and Lobatto quadrature formula for assigned abscissas, Richardson extrapolation, and Romberg integration. A procedure in which two approximate results are used to get a third and, hopefully, better one is called a Richardson-type extrapolation. Two methods of this type using the trapezoidal rule are Gregory's method and Romberg's method. A brief discussion of Gregory's formula was given in Section 4.5. A detailed discussion of the Romberg integration is found in *A First Course in Numerical Analysis* by A. Ralston (McGraw-Hill, 1965). One advantage of the Romberg integration, in contrast to the Gregory formula, is that the coefficients of the correction terms do not change signs. However, it has the disadvantage that higher order derivatives must be computed.

EXERCISES

1. Differentiate a four-point Lagrangian interpolation polynomial and obtain a set of four-point differentiation formulas.

2. Derive Formula (4.3.2), truncate it after the second term, and express it in terms of appropriate ordinates.

3. Show a more complete derivation of Formula (4.3.7).

4. Using Formula (4.4.7) show that the sum of the weighting coefficients must be equal to the length of the integration interval.

5. Using Formula (4.4.7) derive the formulas for $n = 4$ and $n = 5$.

6. Apply Formula (4.4.13) to integrate e^{-x} from $x = 0$ to $x = 1$.

7. Using Formula (4.5.2) derive Weddle's rule for a set of seven points.

8. Compute the first four coefficients in Gregory's formula, (4.5.7).

9. Compute the weighting coefficients and unknown sample points in Formula (4.6.10) for $n = 2$.

10. Compute the weighting coefficients and unknown sample points in Formula (4.6.13) for $n = 3$.

CHAPTER 5

CURVE FITTING AND DATA SMOOTHING

5.1 INTRODUCTION

In Chapter 3 we used polynomials and the criterion of exact matching of the polynomial to the sample points. The criterion of exact matching is open to criticism. We may use it knowing that our samples contain noise (roundoff, measurement, etc.). If the noise level is low, then the procedure of exact matching is a reasonable one. When the noise level is high, as can happen in some computations and almost always happens when the data come from physical measurements, then it is foolish to attempt to determine a polynomial of high degree which fits such data exactly and probably represents a curve which oscillates violently about the curve representing the true function. Instead of determining a polynomial approximation $y(x)$ of degree n to a certain function $f(x)$, by requiring that the values of $y(x)$ at a set of $n + 1$ points agree with known exact or approximate values of $f(x)$ at those points, it is often preferable to require that $y(x)$ and $f(x)$ agree as well as possible (in some sense) over a domain of greater extent. This domain may be taken as a continuous interval, when $f(x)$ is specified analytically, or as a set of $N + 1$ points, where $N > n$.

5.2 PRINCIPLE OF LEAST SQUARES

When the given data are exact or of equal reliability, it is frequently assumed that the "best approximation" is that one for which the aggregate of the squared error over the whole domain is least. This is known as Legendre's principle of least squares. In general, if $w(x_i)$ is a measure of the relative precision of the value assigned to $f(x)$ when $x = x_i$, the criterion is modified by multiplying the squared error at x_i by the weight $w(x_i)$ before the sum is calculated.

Assume that exact values of $f(x)$ are known over a certain domain, which consists of a discrete set of points $x_0, x_1, \ldots, x_n$ or of a continuous interval (a, b), and that the approximation is to be of the form

$$f(x) \sim \sum_{k=0}^{n} a_k \phi_k(x) \equiv y(x), \qquad (5.2.1)$$

where $\phi_0(x), \ldots, \phi_n(x)$ are $n + 1$ appropriately chosen functions. In particular, for a polynomial approximation, $\phi_0 = 1, \phi_1 = x, \phi_2 = x^2, \ldots, \phi_n = x^n$. Other choices, as we will see later, could lead to polynomials. It is also assumed that the weighting function $w(x)$ is nonnegative in the domain. That is,

$$w(x) \geqq 0. \qquad (5.2.2)$$

63

If we define the residual $r(x)$ by

$$r(x) = f(x) - \sum_{k=0}^{n} a_k \phi_k(x) = f(x) - y(x), \qquad (5.2.3)$$

the best approximation, in the least squares sense, is defined to be that for which the a's are determined so that the sum of $w(x)r^2(x)$ over the domain is as small as possible. Let us denote the sum by

$$\{wr^2\} = w(x_0)r^2(x_0) + w(x_1)r^2(x_1) + \cdots + w(x_n)r^2(x_n).$$

The requirement that

$$\{wr^2\} \equiv \left\{ w\left[f - \sum_{k=0}^{n} a_k \phi_k \right]^2 \right\} = \min \qquad (5.2.4)$$

imposes the conditions

$$\frac{\partial}{\partial a_j} \left\{ w\left[f - \sum_{k=0}^{n} a_k \phi_k \right]^2 \right\} = 0, \qquad j = 0, 1, \ldots, n, \qquad (5.2.5)$$

or

$$\left\{ w\phi_j \left[f - \sum_{k=0}^{n} a_k \phi_k \right] \right\} = \{w\phi_j(f - y)\} = 0, \qquad (5.2.6)$$

or

$$\sum_{k=0}^{n} a_k \{w\phi_j \phi_k\} = \{w\phi_j f\}, \qquad j = 0, 1, \ldots, n, \qquad (5.2.7)$$

and hence leads to $n + 1$ simultaneous linear equations in the $n + 1$ unknown parameters $a_0, a_1, \ldots, a_n$. These equations are called the normal equations.

As a result of these conditions, when the coefficients $a_0, a_1, \ldots, a_n$ satisfy (5.2.7), the corresponding sum-squared residual reduces to

$$\{wr^2\}_{\min} = \{wrf\} \equiv \{wf(f - y)\} \equiv \{wf^2\} - \sum_{k=0}^{n} a_k \{w\phi_k f\}. \qquad (5.2.8)$$

We use the smallness of this quantity as a criterion for the *goodness-of-fit* of the approximation over the domain.

If the domain consists of $n + 1$ points, the polynomial $y(x)$ of degree n agrees exactly with $f(x)$ at the $n + 1$ points and $\{wr^2\}$ is zero. If the domain consists of $N + 1$ points, where $N > n$, exact fit over the $N + 1$ points is usually impossible, and the procedure gives the best approximate fit.

In Eq. (5.2.7) the coefficients of the unknowns in the left-hand members of the normal equations are independent of the $f(x)$ to be approximated. They can be precalculated once the ϕ's and $w(x)$ have been chosen. Also, since $\{w\phi_i\phi_j\} \equiv \{w\phi_j\phi_i\}$, the array of coefficients of the a's is symmetrical with respect to the principal diagonal.

These equations are simplified if we choose the ϕ's in such a way that

$$\{w\phi_i\phi_j\} = 0, \qquad i \neq j. \qquad (5.2.9)$$

The set of ϕ's having this property over the domain is called an orthogonal set relative to the weighting function $w(x)$. For such a set of functions, the set of normal equations, (5.2.7), takes the uncoupled form

$$a_j\{w\phi_{jj}^2\} = \{w\phi_j f\}, \qquad j = 0, 1, \ldots, n. \tag{5.2.10}$$

Since $w(x)$ is nonnegative, the coefficient a_j cannot vanish, and

$$a_j = \frac{\{w\phi_j f\}}{\{w\phi_{jj}^2\}}, \qquad j = 0, 1, \ldots, n. \tag{5.2.11}$$

The corresponding value of $\{wr^2\}$ is then expressed as

$$\{wr^2\}_{\min} = \{wf^2\} - \sum_{k=0}^{n} a_k^2 \{w\phi_k^2\}. \tag{5.2.12}$$

If the ϕ's have been normalized in such a way that $\{w\phi_j^2\} = 1$, then Eqs. (5.2.11) and (5.2.12) can be further simplified.

Another goodness-of-fit parameter frequently used in science and statistics is the root-mean-square (RMS) error, which is defined as

$$\text{RMS} = \sqrt{\{wr^2\}/\{w\}}. \tag{5.2.13}$$

When $w(x) \equiv 1$, the quantity $\{1\}$ is the length of the interval in the continuous case and the number $(N + 1)$ of sample points in the discrete case. In the discrete case, where the true $f(x)$ is not known, we use the given empirical data for $f(x)$.

For a more extensive study of the least squares principle, consult references [65], [73], [76], [87], [105], [112], [133], and [134].

Example. Given:

x	0	1	2	3	4
y	1	2	1	0	4

Find the least-squares line fitting the data.

Solution. From (5.2.7) we have $N + 1 = 5, n = 1, \phi_0 = 1, \phi_1 - x$, and $w(x) = 1$. Therefore

$$\sum_{k=0}^{1} a_k\{w\phi_j \phi_k\} = \{w\phi_j f\}, \qquad j = 0, 1,$$

$$a_0\{\phi_j \phi_0\} + a_1\{\phi_j \phi_1\} = \{\phi_j f\},$$

$$\begin{cases} a_0\{\phi_0 \phi_0\} + a_1\{\phi_0 \phi_1\} = \{\phi_0 f\}, \\ a_0\{\phi_1 \phi_0\} + a_1\{\phi_1 \phi_1\} = \{\phi_1 f\}, \end{cases}$$

$$\{\phi_0 \phi_0\} = \phi_0^2(x_1) + \phi_0^2(x_2) + \phi_0^2(x_3) + \phi_0^2(x_4) + \phi_0^2(x_5) = 5,$$

$$\{\phi_0 \phi_1\} = \{\phi_1 \phi_0\} = \phi_0(x_1)\phi_1(x_1) + \phi_0(x_2)\phi_1(x_2) + \cdots + \phi_0(x_5)\phi_1(x_5) = 10,$$

$$\{\phi_1 \phi_1\} = \phi_1^2(x_1) + \phi_1^2(x_2) + \cdots + \phi_1^2(x_5) = 30,$$

$$\{\phi_0 f\} = \phi_0(x_1)f_1 + \phi_0(x_2)f_2 + \cdots + \phi_0(x_5)f_5 = 8,$$

$$\{\phi_1 f\} = \phi_1(x_1)f_1 + \phi_1(x_2)f_2 + \cdots + \phi_1(x_5)f_5 = 20.$$

Therefore, the normal equations are

$$\begin{cases} 5a_0 + 10a_1 = 8, \\ 10a_0 + 30a_1 = 20, \end{cases}$$

and yield the solution $a_0 = \frac{4}{5}$ and $a_1 = \frac{2}{5}$. Hence,

$$y(x) = \tfrac{2}{5}(2 + x).$$

5.3 POLYNOMIAL CURVE FITTING

We commonly use the least-squares approach when N observations $(x_i\ y_i)$, $(i = 1, 2, \ldots, N)$ are made, and we wish to approximate the data by a poly-nomial of degree $M < N$,

$$y(x) = a_0 + a_1x + a_2x^2 + \cdots + a_Mx^M. \tag{5.3.1}$$

The calculated curve $y(x)$, in the least-squares sense, gives a smoothed set of values $y(x_i)$ which are, in general, different from the observed y_i. We note that (5.3.1) is the equation of (5.2.1) with $\phi_0 = 1, \phi_1 = x, \phi_2 = x^2$, etc. This is some-times called the direct solution.

The direct method of least squares presents a rather serious problem, however. The normal equations tend to be unstable; i.e., the determinant of coefficients tends to be very small. This is shown by Hamming [65]. A comprehensive discussion of this problem is given by Forsythe [47]. When the determinant is small, the coefficients may be very inaccurate, but the sum of the squares of the errors may be very small.

The way out of this difficulty is to avoid the normal equations and compute some form of equivalent information. This leads to the study of orthogonal functions and, in particular, orthogonal polynomials.

5.4 ORTHOGONAL FUNCTIONS

As in classical mathematics, we define two functions, $f_1(x)$ and $f_2(x)$, as orthogonal over the interval $a \leq x \leq b$ if

$$\int_a^b f_1(x)f_2(x)\, dx = 0. \tag{5.4.1}$$

A set of functions, $f_1, f_2, f_3, \ldots, f_n$ is said to be mutually orthogonal if

$$\int_a^b f_i(x)f_j(x)\, dx = 0, \qquad i \neq j, \tag{5.4.2}$$

$$\int_a^b f_i^2(x)\, dx = N_i > 0, \qquad i = j,$$

and the $f_i(x)$ are real, continuous, and not identically zero.
    If we define

$$g_i = f_i/\sqrt{N_i}, \tag{5.4.3}$$

then

$$\int_a^b g_i(x)g_j(x)\,dx = \begin{cases} 0, & i \neq j, \\ 1, & i = j. \end{cases} \tag{5.4.4}$$

The functions $g_i(x)$ are called "orthonormal" functions, and the process of changing the f_i to the g_i is called normalization.

If the functions are known only at discrete points x_k, then the integrals are replaced by sums, and the orthogonality condition becomes

$$\sum_k f_i(x_k)f_j(x_k) = \begin{cases} 0, & i \neq j, \\ N_i, & i = j. \end{cases} \tag{5.4.5}$$

If the data have varying weights, then a weighting function $\rho(x) \geq 0$ can be included in the integral

$$\int_a^b \rho(x)f_i(x)f_j(x)\,dx,$$

and the functions are said to be orthogonal, relative to the weighting function $\rho(x)$ over (a, b).

5.5 ORTHOGONAL POLYNOMIALS

Let us now consider the case where a least-squares approximation is to be determined over the interval (a, b). We use a set of polynomials $\phi_0(x), \phi_1(x), \ldots, \phi_n(x)$ such that each member of the set is orthogonal to all others in the set over (a, b), relative to a weighting function $w(x)$ which is nonnegative over that interval.

Let the approximating function be of the form

$$y(x) = a_0\phi_0(x) + a_1\phi_1(x) + \cdots + a_i\phi_i(x) + \cdots + a_n\phi_n(x). \tag{5.5.1}$$

The coefficients a_i are then determined by the requirement

$$\int_a^b w(x)[f(x) - y(x)]^2\,dx = \min, \tag{5.5.2}$$

in the form

$$a_i = \int_a^b wf\phi_i\,dx \Big/ \int_a^b w\phi_i^2\,dx = \int_a^b wf\phi_i\,dx \Big/ N_i. \tag{5.5.3}$$

A rather comprehensive development of the theory for determining the $\phi_i(x)$, N_i, and a_i in the above equations can be found in Forsythe [47], Hamming [65], Hildebrand [73], Householder [76], Milne [105], and Stiefel [143]. Since this theory is amply covered in the literature for supplementary reading, we shall concentrate on a more comprehensive coverage of certain special functions and formulas of significance for high-speed digit computing.

The first method which we shall consider is based on the very extensive work of Forsythe [47] and Forsythe and Ascher [48]. The method proved very successful in computer programs at a number of computation centers.

5.6 FORSYTHE METHOD

The method recommended by Forsythe is free from some of the usual restrictions of many curve-fitting routines and is very flexible in its use. Restrictions of equal spacing and unit weights are removed. The weighting function may be used as a set of empirical data, or computed as a function of the independent variable. Ill-conditioned normal equations are avoided. Double precision or floating vector arithmetic can be used for greater accuracy, but with computer storage at a premium, the next best approach is to normalize the independent variable for large values or wide ranges. Two normalizing formulas are suggested. The method can be used for exact curve fitting, or for the smoothing of large sets of empirical data.

The Forsythe method may be summarized with the following basic mathematical equations and recursion formulas.

a) Given:

$$(x_i, y_i) \qquad i = 1, 2, \ldots, N,$$
$$N = \text{number of data points},$$
$$w_i^2 = \text{weight assigned each } (x_i, y_i),$$
$$M \leq N - 1 = \text{degree of fitted polynomial}.$$

b) Generated orthogonal polynomials:

$$P_{-i}(x) = 0,$$
$$P_0(x) = 1,$$
$$P_1(x) = (x - u_1)P_0(x),$$
$$P_2(x) = (x - u_2)P_1(x) - v_1P_0(x),$$
$$\vdots$$

$$P_m(x) = (x - u_m)P_{m-1}(x) - v_{m-1}P_{m-2}(x), \tag{5.6.1}$$

where

$$u_m = \frac{\{\sum_{i=1}^{N} x_i[P_{m-1}(x_i)]^2 w_i^2\}}{D_{m-1}}, \tag{5.6.2}$$

$$v_{m-1} = \frac{\{\sum_{i=1}^{N} x_i P_{m-1}(x_i) P_{m-2}(x_i) w_i^2\}}{D_{m-2}}, \tag{5.6.3}$$

$$D_m = \sum_{i=1}^{N} [P_m(x_i)]^2 w_i^2. \tag{5.6.4}$$

c) Fitted polynomial in terms of $P_m(x)$:

$$\bar{y}(x) = \sum_{m=0}^{M} a_m P_m(x), \tag{5.6.5}$$

where

$$a_m = \frac{\{\sum_{i=1}^{N} y_i P_m(x_i) w_i^2\}}{D_m}. \tag{5.6.6}$$

d) Coefficients of the fitted polynomial in powers of the independent variable: If

$$\bar{y}(x) = \sum_{k=0}^{M} C_k^M x^k, \tag{5.6.7}$$

then

$$C_k^M = \sum_{m=k}^{M} a_m b_k^m, \tag{5.6.8}$$

where

$$b_k^m = \begin{cases} 0, & k < 0 \\ 0, & k > m \\ 1, & k = m \\ b_{k-1}^{m-1} - u_m b_k^{m-1} - v_{m-1} b_k^{m-2}, & 0 \leq k < m. \end{cases} \tag{5.6.9}$$

e) The range of the independent variable may be normalized for the range

$$0 \leq x_i' \leq 1 \tag{5.6.10}$$

by applying the transformation

$$x_i' = \frac{x_i - x_1}{x_N - x_1}. \tag{5.6.11}$$

f) The range of the independent variable may be normalized for the range

$$-1 \leq x_i' \leq 1 \tag{5.6.12}$$

by applying the transformation

$$x_i' = \frac{2x_i - x_N - x_1}{x_N - x_1}. \tag{5.6.13}$$

g) When (e) or (f) is used, the coefficients computed in (d) are associated with the normalized values of the independent variable. These are converted to the set of coefficients associated with the unnormalized independent variable by use of the following recursion formula:

$$C_j = \sum_{n=0}^{M-j} (-1)^n (2^j)^P C_{j+n}' \binom{j+n}{n} h^n k^{j+n}, \tag{5.6.14}$$

where

$$M = \text{degree of the polynomial,}$$

$$k = \frac{1}{x_N - x_1},$$

$$\binom{m}{n} = \frac{m(m-1)\cdots(m-n+1)}{n(n-1)\cdots 2 \cdot 1},$$

$$\binom{m}{1} = m, \qquad \binom{m}{0} = 1, \qquad \binom{n}{n} = 1,$$

$$P = 0, \ h = x_1 \text{ for (e),}$$

$$P = 1, \ h = x_1 + x_N \text{ for (f).}$$

h) Goodness of fit parameter $= \Sigma(\bar{y}_i - y_i)^2$,   (5.6.15)

$$\text{RMS} = \sqrt{\Sigma(\bar{y}_i - y_i)^2/N},$$ (5.6.16)

where the y_i are given values and the $\bar{y}_i$ are the corresponding smoothed values.

Example. Fit a second-degree polynomial to the given data using Forsythe's method.

x	0	1	2	3
y	-2	0	0	-2

Solution.

$$N = 4, \ w_i = 1, \ M = 2, \ P_{-i} = 0, \ P_0(x) = 1,$$

$$P_1(x) = (x - u_1)P_0(x),$$

$$D_0 = \sum_{i=1}^{4} [P_0(x_i)]^2 = 4,$$

$$u_1 = \frac{[\sum_{i=1}^{4} x_i[P_0(x_i)]^2 w_i^2]}{D_0} = \frac{6}{4} = \frac{3}{2},$$

$$P_1(x) = x - \tfrac{3}{2},$$

$$P_2(x) = (x - u_2)P_1(x) - v_1 P_0(x),$$

$$D_1 = \sum_{i=1}^{4} [P_1(x_i)]^2 = 5,$$

$$u_2 = \frac{\{\sum_{i=1}^{4} x_i P_1^2(x_i)\}}{D_1} = \frac{3}{2},$$

$$v_1 = \frac{[\sum_{i=1}^{4} x_i P_1(x_i) P_0(x_i)]}{D_0} = \frac{5}{4},$$

$$P_2(x) = x^2 - 3x + 1,$$

$$y(x) = \sum_{m=0}^{2} a_m P_m(x),$$

$$D_2 = \sum_{i=1}^{4} [P_2(x_i)]^2 = 4,$$

$$a_m = \frac{\{\sum_{i=1}^{4} f_i P_m(x_i)\}}{D_m},$$

$$a_0 = \frac{\{\sum_{i=1}^{4} f_i P_0(x_i)\}}{D_0} = -1,$$

$$a_1 = \frac{\{\sum_{i=1}^{4} f_i P_1(x_i)\}}{D_1} = 0,$$

$$a_2 = \frac{\{\sum_{i=1}^{4} f_i P_2(x_i)\}}{D_2} = -1,$$

and

$$y(x) = a_0 P_0(x) + a_1 P_1(x) + a_2 P_2(x)$$
$$= (-1)(1) + (0)(x - \tfrac{3}{2}) + (-1)(x^2 - 3x + 1),$$
$$y(x) = -x^2 + 3x - 2.$$

5.7 LEGENDRE POLYNOMIAL APPROXIMATION

The Legendre polynomials, a classical set of orthogonal polynomials which have been studied extensively, are defined as follows:

$$P_0(x) = 1, \qquad P_1(x) = x,$$
$$P_2(x) = \tfrac{1}{2}(3x^2 - 1), \tag{5.7.1}$$
$$\vdots$$
$$P_{n+1}(x) = \frac{2n + 1}{n + 1} x P_n(x) - \frac{n}{n + 1} P_{n-1}(x),$$

where

$$\int_{-1}^{1} P_m(x) P_n(x)\, dx = \begin{cases} 0, & m \neq n, \\ \dfrac{2}{2n + 1}, & m = n. \end{cases} \tag{5.7.2}$$

The nth-degree least-squares polynomial approximation to $f(x)$ over $(-1, 1)$, relative to a constant weighting function, is defined by

$$y(x) = \sum_{k=0}^{n} a_k P_k(x), \qquad -1 < x < 1, \tag{5.7.3}$$

where

$$a_k = \frac{2k + 1}{2} \int_{-1}^{1} f(x) P_k(x)\, dx. \tag{5.7.4}$$

The least-squares approximation to $f(x)$ over $(-1, 1)$, relative to the weighting function $1/[u(x)]^2$, where $u(x)$ is a specified function, is

$$y(x) = u(x) \sum_{k=0}^{n} b_k P_k(x), \qquad -1 < x < 1, \tag{5.7.5}$$

where

$$b_k = \frac{2k + 1}{2} \int_{-1}^{1} \frac{f(x)}{u(x)} P_k(x)\, dx. \tag{5.7.6}$$

5.8 LAGUERRE POLYNOMIAL APPROXIMATION

Both the Forsythe method and the Legendre approximation give a least-squares approximation over an interval of finite length. For a least-squares polynomial approximation over a semi-infinite interval, it is convenient to transform the interval into the interval $(0, \infty)$. A frequently used approximation uses the weighting function

$$w(x) = e^{-ax}, \tag{5.8.1}$$

where a is a positive constant taken large enough to ensure the existence (when possible) of the integral of the squared error over the semi-infinite interval.

The classical set of orthogonal polynomials used in this approximation are the Laguerre polynomials, defined as follows:

$$L_0(x) = 1, \qquad L_1(x) = 1 - x,$$
$$L_2(x) = 2 - 4x + x^2,$$
$$\vdots$$
$$L_{n+1}(x) = (1 + 2n - x)L_n(x) - n^2 L_{n-1}(x), \tag{5.8.2}$$

where

$$\int_0^\infty e^{-ax} L_m(ax)L_n(ax)\, dx = \begin{cases} 0, & m \neq n, \\ \dfrac{1}{a}(n!)^2, & m = n. \end{cases} \tag{5.8.3}$$

The nth degree least-squares polynomial approximation to $f(x)$ in $(0, \infty)$, relative to the weighting function $w(x) = e^{-ax}$, is

$$y(x) = \sum_{k=0}^n b_n L_n(ax), \qquad 0 < x < \infty, \tag{5.8.4}$$

where

$$b_n = \frac{a}{(n!)^2} \int_0^\infty e^{-ax} f(x)L_n(ax)\, dx. \tag{5.8.5}$$

5.9 HERMITE POLYNOMIAL APPROXIMATION

Over the doubly infinite interval $(-\infty < x < \infty)$, a frequently used weighting function is of the form

$$w(x) = e^{-a^2 x^2}. \tag{5.9.1}$$

The classical set of orthogonal polynomials used for this approximation are the Hermite polynomials, defined as follows:

$$H_0(x) = 1, \qquad H_1(x) = 2x,$$
$$H_2(x) = 4x^2 - 2,$$
$$\vdots$$
$$H_{n+1}(x) = 2xH_n(x) - 2nH_{n-1}(x), \tag{5.9.2}$$

where

$$\int_{-\infty}^\infty e^{-a^2 x^2} H_m(ax)H_n(ax)\, dx = \begin{cases} 0, & m \neq n, \\ \dfrac{2^n n!}{a}\sqrt{\pi}, & m = n. \end{cases} \tag{5.9.3}$$

The nth-degree least-squares polynomial approximation to $f(x)$ over $(-\infty, \infty)$, relative to the weighting function $w(x) = e^{-a^2x^2}$, is

$$y(x) = \sum_{k=0}^{n} b_n H_n(ax), \qquad -\infty < x < \infty, \tag{5.9.4}$$

where

$$b_n = (a/2^n n! \sqrt{\pi}) \int_{-\infty}^{\infty} e^{-a^2x^2} f(x) H_n(ax)\, dx. \tag{5.9.5}$$

5.10 OTHER TYPES OF APPROXIMATIONS

Polynomials are usually the most convenient functions for the approximation of a continuous function when the desired interval of approximation is finite. If $f(x)$ is periodic and is to be approximated over one or more complete periods, it is more desirable to make use of periodic functions such as the composite set of all sines and cosines. We present the fundamental Fourier approximation here; an extension of the subject will be presented in a later chapter entitled "Harmonic Analysis." We will then consider optimum polynomial approximation under the Chebyshev approximation. Finally, we will consider exponential approximation by Prony's method, and approximation by rational functions.

Another type of approximation, which will not be discussed here, is the linearized spline interpolation. This type of interpolation is a piecewise polynomial method, very adaptable to numerical computation. A lengthy detailed discussion of this method is found in a paper entitled "Smooth Surface Interpolation" by G. Birkhoff and H. Garabedian appearing in the *Journal of Mathematics and Physics*, Vol. 39 (1960).

5.11 FOURIER APPROXIMATION

The functions 1, $\sin kx$, $\cos kx$ are orthogonal with respect to integration over the interval $(0, 2\pi)$. That is,

$$\int_0^{2\pi} \sin mx \cos nx\, dx = 0,$$

$$\int_0^{2\pi} \sin mx \sin nx\, dx = \begin{cases} 0, & m \neq n, \\ \pi, & m = n, \end{cases} \tag{5.11.1}$$

$$\int_0^{2\pi} \cos mx \cos nx\, dx = \begin{cases} 0, & m \neq n, \\ \pi, & m = n \neq 0, \\ 2\pi, & m = n = 0. \end{cases}$$

On this basis $f(x)$ can be expanded as a Fourier series

$$f(x) = \frac{a_0}{2} + \sum_{m=1}^{\infty} (a_m \cos mx + b_m \sin mx), \tag{5.11.2}$$

where
$$a_m = \frac{1}{\pi} \int_0^{2\pi} f(x) \cos mx \, dx, \tag{5.11.3}$$

$$b_m = \frac{1}{\pi} \int_0^{2\pi} f(x) \sin mx \, dx.$$

If we have a discrete set of $2N$ equally spaced points, instead of a continuous function for $f(x)$, and if we use summation in place of integration, the set of functions

$$1, \cos x', \cos 2x', \ldots, \cos (N-1)x', \cos Nx', \sin x', \sin 2x', \ldots, \sin (N-1)x', \tag{5.11.4}$$

is orthogonal over the discrete set of points

$$x' = 0, \frac{\pi}{N}, \frac{2\pi}{N}, \ldots, \frac{(2N-1)\pi}{N}. \tag{5.11.5}$$

If the equally spaced points are x_0, $x_0 + h$, $x_0 + 2h$, etc., the transformation

$$x' = (\pi/N)y, \tag{5.11.6}$$

where
$$y = (x - x_0)/h, \tag{5.11.7}$$

gives us unit spacing with the functions of Eq. (5.11.4) in the form

$$1, \cos \frac{\pi}{N} y, \cos \frac{2\pi}{N} y, \ldots, \cos \frac{(N-1)\pi}{N} y, \cos \pi y,$$

$$\sin \frac{\pi}{N} y, \sin \frac{2\pi}{N} y, \ldots, \sin \frac{(N-1)\pi}{N} y, \tag{5.11.8}$$

and (5.11.5) becomes
$$y = 0, 1, 2, 3, \ldots, (2N-1). \tag{5.11.9}$$

Corresponding to Eq. (5.11.1) we have the relations, $m \leq N$, $n \leq N$,

$$\sum_{y=0}^{2N-1} \sin \frac{\pi}{N} my \cos \frac{\pi}{N} ny = 0,$$

$$\sum_{y=0}^{2N-1} \sin \frac{\pi}{N} my \sin \frac{\pi}{N} ny = \begin{cases} 0, & m \neq n, \\ N, & m = n \neq 0, \end{cases} \tag{5.11.10}$$

$$\sum_{y=0}^{2N-1} \cos \frac{\pi}{N} my \cos \frac{\pi}{N} ny = \begin{cases} 0, & m \neq n, \\ N, & m = n \neq 0, N, \ldots, \\ 2N, & m = n = 0, N, \ldots. \end{cases}$$

Assuming that we write an arbitrary function $f(y)$ in the form

$$f(y) = \frac{a_0}{2} + \sum_{m=1}^{N-1} \left(a_m \cos \frac{\pi}{N} my + b_m \sin \frac{\pi}{N} my \right) + \frac{a_N}{2} \cos \pi y, \tag{5.11.11}$$

the coefficients of the expansion are determined by using the orthogonality relations. We get

$$\sum_{y=0}^{2N-1} f(y) \cos \frac{\pi}{N} my = N a_m, \qquad 1 \leq m \leq N - 1, \qquad (5.11.12)$$

$$\sum_{y=0}^{2N-1} f(y) \sin \frac{\pi}{N} my = N b_m, \qquad 1 \leq m \leq N - 1, \qquad (5.11.13)$$

$$\sum_{y=0}^{2N-1} f(y) = N a_0, \qquad (5.11.14)$$

$$\sum_{y=0}^{2N-1} f(y) \cos \pi y = N a_N. \qquad (5.11.15)$$

We write these compactly in the form

$$a_m = \frac{1}{N} \sum_{y=0}^{2N-1} f(y) \cos \frac{\pi}{N} my, \qquad m = 0, 1, \ldots, N, \qquad (5.11.16)$$

$$b_m = \frac{1}{N} \sum_{y=0}^{2N-1} f(y) \sin \frac{\pi}{N} my, \qquad m = 1, 2, \ldots, N - 1, \qquad (5.11.17)$$

Using only terms up to $m = M \leq N - 1$ in the expansion (5.11.11), we get the sum of the first M harmonics. That is,

$$f_M(y) = \frac{a_0}{2} + \sum_{m=1}^{M} \left(a_m \cos \frac{\pi}{N} my + b_m \sin \frac{\pi}{N} my \right). \qquad (5.11.18)$$

This gives an approximation to $f(y)$ whose least-square error is given by

$$E = \sum_{y} j^2 - N \left[\frac{a_0}{2} + \sum_{m=1}^{M} (a_m^2 + b_m^2) \right]. \qquad (5.11.19)$$

By observing how (5.11.19) decreases as M increases, we estimate the necessity of taking additional terms in the expansion.

If we have an odd number $2N + 1$ of discrete equally spaced points, then the analogous formulas are

$$f(y) = \frac{a_0}{2} + \sum_{m=1}^{N} \left(a_m \cos \frac{2\pi m}{2N + 1} y + b_m \sin \frac{2\pi m}{2N + 1} y \right),$$

$$y = 0, 1, 2, \ldots, 2N, \qquad (5.11.20)$$

where

$$a_m = \frac{2}{2N + 1} \sum_{y=0}^{2N} f(y) \cos \frac{2\pi m}{2N + 1} y, \qquad m = 0, 1, \ldots, N, \quad (5.11.21)$$

$$b_m = \frac{2}{2N + 1} \sum_{y=0}^{2N} f(y) \sin \frac{2\pi m}{2N + 1} y, \qquad m = 1, 2, \ldots, N, \quad (5.11.22)$$

and y is given by Eq. (5.11.7).

A very comprehensive coverage of the Fourier approximation is found in Carslaw [16], Hamming [65], Hildebrand [73], Whittaker and Robinson [157], and Willers [164].

Example. Find the Fourier expansion of $f(x)$ for the following data:

x	-2	1	4	7	10
$y = (x - x_0)/h$	0	1	2	3	4
$f(x) = f(y)$	0	4	6	6	4

Solution. For the given data $2N + 1 = 5$ and $N = 2$.

$$f(y) = \frac{a_0}{2} + \sum_{m=1}^{2} \left(a_m \cos \frac{2\pi m}{5} y + b_m \sin \frac{2\pi m}{5} y \right), \qquad y = 0, 1, 2, 3, 4,$$

$$a_m = \frac{2}{5} \sum_{y=0}^{4} f(y) \cos \frac{2\pi m}{5} y, \qquad m = 0, 1, 2,$$

$$b_m = \frac{2}{5} \sum_{y=0}^{4} f(y) \sin \frac{2\pi m}{5} y, \qquad m = 1, 2,$$

Using the above formulas we obtain

$$a_0 = 8, \qquad a_1 = -2.89443, \qquad a_2 = -1.10557,$$
$$b_1 = 0, \qquad b_2 = 0.$$

Therefore

$$f(y) = 4 - 2.89443 \cos \frac{2\pi}{5} y - 1.10557 \cos \frac{4\pi}{5} y$$

or, since $y = (x - x_0)/h = (x + 2)/3$, we have

$$f(x) = 4 - 2.89443 \cos \frac{2\pi(x + 2)}{15} - 1.10557 \cos \frac{4\pi(x + 2)}{15}.$$

5.12 CHEBYSHEV APPROXIMATION

Orthogonal polynomials have the properties that their zeros interlace each other, they are easy to obtain in power-series form, and they satisfy a three-term recurrence formula.

The Fourier series has the properties that alternating maxima and minima of individual terms are equal in size, and that the sine and cosine are orthogonal over both the continuous range and an equally spaced set of discrete data points.

The Chebyshev polynomials have the properties of both the Fourier series and orthogonal polynomials. These polynomials are defined by

$$T_n(x) = \cos (n \text{ arc cos } x). \qquad (5.12.1)$$

Letting $\theta = \arccos x$, we have

$$T_n(x) = \cos n\theta. \tag{5.12.2}$$

By de Moivre's theorem,

$$(\cos n\theta + i \sin n\theta) = (\cos \theta + i \sin \theta)^n.$$

Expanding the right member by the binomial theorem, and then equating the real parts, we obtain

$$\cos n\theta = (\cos \theta)^n - \frac{n(n-1)}{2!}(\cos \theta)^{n-2}(\sin \theta)^2$$
$$+ \frac{n(n-1)(n-2)(n-3)}{4!}(\cos \theta)^{n-4}(\sin \theta)^4 \tag{5.12.3}$$
$$- \frac{n(n-1)(n-2)(n-3)(n-4)(n-5)}{6!}(\cos \theta)^{n-6}(\sin \theta)^6 + \cdots.$$

But from $\theta = \arccos x$, we have $\cos \theta = x$ and $\sin^2 \theta = 1 - x^2$. Substituting in Eq. (5.12.3), we have

$$T_n(x) = \cos n\theta = x^n - \frac{n(n-1)}{2!}x^{n-2}(1-x^2)$$
$$+ \frac{n(n-1)(n-2)(n-3)}{4!}x^{n-4}(1-x^2)^2 \tag{5.12.4}$$
$$- \frac{n(n-1)(n-2)(n-3)(n-4)(n-5)}{6!}x^{n-6}(1-x^2)^3 + \cdots.$$

Hence $T_n(x)$ is a polynomial of degree n in x. The polynomials may be computed from (5.12.4). Thus

$$T_0(x) = 1,$$
$$T_1(x) = x,$$
$$T_2(x) = 2x^2 - 1, \tag{5.12.5}$$
$$T_3(x) = 4x^3 - 3x,$$
$$T_4(x) = 8x^4 - 8x^2 + 1.$$

However, the easiest method of computing the polynomials is by use of the recursion formula

$$T_{n+1}(x) = 2xT_n(x) - T_{n-1}(x). \tag{5.12.6}$$

The Fourier expressions for orthogonality may be written as

$$\int_0^\pi \cos m\theta \cos n\theta \, d\theta = \begin{cases} 0, & m \neq n, \\ \frac{\pi}{2}, & m = n, \\ \pi, & m = n = 0. \end{cases} \tag{5.12.7}$$

From Eq. (5.12.2) this becomes

$$\int_{-1}^{1} T_m(x)T_n(x)(dx/\sqrt{1-x^2}) = \begin{cases} 0, & m \neq n, \\ \frac{\pi}{2}, & m = n, \\ \pi, & m = n = 0. \end{cases} \qquad (5.12.8)$$

Hence the Chebyshev polynomials are orthogonal over the interval $(-1, 1)$ with respect to the weighting function

$$w(x) = 1/\sqrt{1-x^2}. \qquad (5.12.9)$$

Correspondingly, in the discrete domain for N equally spaced data points, we have the relations

$$\sum_{j=0}^{N-1} \cos m\theta_j \cos n\theta_j = \begin{cases} 0, & m \neq n \\ N/2, & m = n \\ N, & m = n = 0 \end{cases} = \sum_{j=0}^{N-1} T_m(x_j)T_n(x_j). \qquad (5.12.10)$$

Chebyshev showed that of all polynomials of degree n, having a leading coefficient equal to 1, the polynomial

$$\frac{T_n(x)}{2^{n-1}}$$

has the smallest least-upper bound for its absolute value in the interval

$$(-1 \leq x \leq 1).$$

Since the upper bound of $|T_n(x)|$ is 1, then this upper bound is $1/2^{n-1}$.

This property is known as the Chebyshev criterion. "Chebyshev approximation" is associated with those approximations which try to keep the maximum error to a minimum. This is known as the *minimax* principle. Normal least-squares approximation keeps the average square error down, but allows isolated extreme errors. Chebyshev keeps extreme errors down but allows a larger average square error.

The nth-degree least-squares polynomial approximation to $f(x)$ in $(-1, 1)$, relative to the weighting function

$$w(x) = 1/\sqrt{1-x^2},$$

is defined by

$$y(x) = \sum_{k=0}^{n} a_k T_k(x), \qquad -1 < x < 1, \qquad (5.12.11)$$

where

$$a_0 = \frac{1}{\pi} \int_{-1}^{1} \frac{f(x)}{\sqrt{1-x^2}} dx \qquad (5.12.12)$$

$$a_k = \frac{2}{\pi} \int_{-1}^{1} \frac{f(x)T_k(x)}{\sqrt{1-x^2}} dx, \qquad k \neq 0. \qquad (5.12.13)$$

It has the property that, of all polynomials of degree n or less, the integrated weighted squared error

$$\int_{-1}^{1} (1/\sqrt{1 - x^2})[f(x) - y_n(x)]^2 \, dx \qquad (5.12.14)$$

is least when $y_n(x)$ is associated with the right-hand member of Eq. (5.12.11).

In practice the above formulas are seldom used to evaluate a_k, but they do yield the following upper bounds:

$$|a_0| \leq 2M, |a_k| \leq \frac{2M}{\pi} \int_0^{\pi} |\cos k\theta| \, d\theta = 4M/\pi, \qquad k > 0, \quad (5.12.15)$$

where M is the maximum value of $|f(x)|$ in $(-1, 1)$.

A more useful method of evaluating the coefficients is based on relations of Formula (5.12.10). The functions $T_0(x)$, $T_1(x)$, ... are orthogonal under integration over $(-1, 1)$, relative to

$$w(x) = 1/\sqrt{1 - x^2}.$$

The functions $T_0(x)$, $T_1(x)$, ..., $T_n(x)$ are orthogonal under summation over the zeros of $T_{n+1}(x)$, relative to $w(x) = 1$. The nth-degree Chebyshev polynomial approximation to $f(x)$ is defined by

$$f(x) = \sum_{k=0}^{n}{}' a_k T_k(x), \qquad (5.12.16)$$

where $\sum'$ indicates a finite sum whose first term is to be halved and

$$a_k = \frac{2}{n+1} \sum_{j=0}^{n} f(x_j) T_k(x_j), \qquad (5.12.17)$$

$$x_j = -\cos\left(\frac{2j + 1}{2n + 2}\pi\right), \qquad j = 0, 1, \ldots, n. \qquad (5.12.18)$$

A complete discussion of the properties and numerical computation of the Chebyshev approximation is found in reference [109].

Example. Find the second-degree Chebyshev approximation for the following tabulated data:

	x_j	$T_0(x_j)$	$T_1(x_j)$	$T_2(x_j)$	$f(x_j)$
$x_0 = -\cos \pi/6 =$	$-\sqrt{3}/2$	1	$-\sqrt{3}/2$	$\frac{1}{2}$	$(-10\sqrt{3} - 3)/4$
$x_1 = -\cos \pi/2 =$	0	1	0	-1	0
$x_2 = -\cos 5\pi/6 =$	$\sqrt{3}/2$	1	$\sqrt{3}/2$	$\frac{1}{2}$	$(10\sqrt{3} - 3)/4$

Solution. We calculate

$$a_0 = \tfrac{2}{3} \sum_{j=0}^{2} f(x_j) T_0(x_j) = -1,$$

$$a_1 = \tfrac{2}{3} \sum_{j=0}^{2} f(x_j) T_1(x_j) = 5,$$

$$a_2 = \tfrac{2}{3} \sum_{j=0}^{2} f(x_j) T_2(x_j) = -\tfrac{1}{2},$$

$$f(x) = \sum_{k=0}^{2} {}' a_k T_k(x)$$

$$= \frac{a_0}{2} + a_1 T_1(x) + a_2 T_2(x)$$

$$= -\tfrac{1}{2} + 5x - \tfrac{1}{2}(2x^2 - 1)$$

$$= 5x - x^2.$$

We should note that the $T_i(x)$ above satisfy the orthogonality condition (5.12.10) and that the x_j are the zeros of $T_3(x)$.

5.13 EXPONENTIAL APPROXIMATION

Given the form of $f(x)$ as

$$f(x) = A_1 e^{a_1 x} + A_2 e^{a_2 x} + \cdots + A_n e^{a_n x}, \tag{5.13.1}$$

if the exponents $a_1, a_2, \ldots, a_n$ are known, then the problem is simply one of solving n linear equations for the n unknowns, $A_1, A_2, \ldots, A_n$. One may use the method of formula derivation discussed in Chapter 1.

When the exponents are unknown, the problem is much more involved, and Prony's method may be used when the data are equally spaced. If $f(x)$ is given by (5.13.1) for some set of values $x = x_k (k = 1, 2, \ldots, 2n)$, which are equally spaced, let $x_k = k$ for simplicity.

Prony noted that each of the

$$e^{a_k x}, \qquad k = 1, 2, \ldots, n, \tag{5.13.2}$$

satisfies an nth-order difference equation with constant coefficients whose characteristic roots are

$$r_k = e^{a_k}; \tag{5.13.3}$$

$f(x)$ also satisfies this difference equation. We assume this difference equation to be

$$C_n f(k) + C_{n-1} f(k + 1) + \cdots + C_1 f(k + n - 1) + f(k + n) = 0,$$
$$k = 1, 2, \ldots, n, \tag{5.13.4}$$

when n is the number of unknown C's.

If we have exactly as many equations as unknowns $C_m (m = 1, 2, \ldots, n)$, and the coefficient determinant is not zero, we can solve for the C_m values. From the C_m, we find the characteristic equation

$$r^n + C_1 r^{n-1} + \cdots + C_n = 0. \tag{5.13.5}$$

1) If r_k is real and positive:

$$r_k = e^{a_k} = e^{\log_e r_k}$$

and

$$r_k^x = e^{x \log_e r_k}. \tag{5.13.6}$$

2) If r_k is real and negative, let

$$r_k = -\rho_k, \rho_k > 0;$$

then $r_k^x = (-\rho_k)^x$ is real only when x takes on the integral values for which the data are prescribed, or values which differ from those values by integral multiples of the unit spacing. Then, since $(-1)^x = \cos \pi x$, for any such value

$$r_k^x = \rho_k^x \cos \pi x = e^{x \log_e \rho_k} \cos \pi x. \tag{5.13.7}$$

3) If r_k is complex:

$$r_k = a + bi, \qquad \bar{r}_k = a - bi = r_{k+1},$$
$$\rho_k = \sqrt{a^2 + b^2}, \qquad \theta_k = \arctan b/a,$$
$$r_k^x = (a + bi)^x = [\rho_k(\cos \theta_k + i \sin \theta_k]^x = \rho_k^x(\cos \theta_k x + i \sin \theta_k x), \tag{5.13.8}$$
$$r_{k+1}^x = (a - bi)^x = \rho_k^x(\cos \theta_k x - i \sin \theta_k x). \tag{5.13.9}$$

Therefore

$$A_k r_k^x + A_{k+1} r_{k+1}^x = \rho_k^x[(A_k + A_{k+1}) \cos \theta_k x + (A_k - A_{k+1})i \sin \theta_k x]. \tag{5.13.10}$$

Since A_k and A_{k+1} must be complex conjugates, let

$$A_k = \frac{C_k + iC_{k+1}}{2},$$

$$A_{k+1} = \frac{C_k - iC_{k+1}}{2},$$

$$A_k r_k^x + A_{k+1} r_{k+1}^x = \rho_k^x(C_k \cos \theta_k x + C_{k+1} \sin \theta_k x),$$

or

$$A_k r_k^x + A_{k+1} r_{k+1}^x = \rho_k^x C_k \cos \theta_k x + \rho_k^x C_{k+1} \sin \theta_k x$$
$$= C_k e^{x \log_e \rho_k} \cos \theta_k x + C_{k+1} e^{x \log_e \rho_k} \sin \theta_k x. \tag{5.13.11}$$

After all the exponents have been determined from the r_k, we can rewrite $f(x)$ as a combination of Eqs. (5.13.6), (5.13.7), and (5.13.11) with unknown coefficients $B_1, B_2, \ldots, B_n$. The problem now becomes one of solving n linear equations for the n unknown coefficients $B_1, B_2, \ldots, B_n$.

Example. Fit the function $y = A_1 e^{a_1 x} + A_2 e^{a_2 x}$ to the following data:

x	0	1	2	3
y	3	2.367879	2.135335	2.049787

$$n = 2, \quad k = 2,$$
$$C_2 f(1) + C_1 f(2) + f(3) = 0,$$
$$C_2 f(2) + C_1 f(3) + f(4) = 0,$$
$$3C_2 + 2.367879C_1 + 2.135335 = 0,$$
$$2.367879C_2 + 2.135335C_1 + 2.049787 = 0.$$

Solution. Solving this system we obtain

$$C_1 = -1.367879, \quad C_2 = 0.367879.$$

Therefore we have

$$r^2 - 1.367879r + 0.367879 = 0.$$

The roots of this equation are $r_1 = 1$ and $r_2 = 0.367879$, from which $a_1 = \log 1 = 0$ and $a_2 = \log 0.367879 = -1$. Therefore, $y = A_1 + A_2 e^{-x}$. From this we have

$$A_1 + A_2 = 3,$$
$$A_1 + 0.367879 A_2 = 2.367879.$$

The solution of this system is $A_1 = 2$ and $A_2 = 1$. Therefore, $y = 2 + e^{-x}$.

5.14 RATIONAL FUNCTIONS

A given function which behaves as the quotient of two polynomials is called a rational function. Rational functions are used to approximate certain functions that cannot be approximated very well by polynomials. For example, rational functions may approximate functions having infinite y-values for finite x-values.

Rational functions are easy and rapid to evaluate on a computer. They may provide the most easily computed approximation for some complicated functions. We shall give only the simplest approach.

Let us define reciprocal differences as follows:

$$r_0[0] = f(x_0) = f_0, \quad r_0[1] = f_1,$$
$$r_1[0] = \frac{x_1 - x_0}{r_0[1] - r_0[0]}, \tag{5.14.1}$$
$$\vdots$$
$$r_{k+1}[m] = \frac{x_{m+k+1} - x_m}{r_k[m + 1] - r_k[m]} + r_{k-1}[m + 1],$$

where

$$k = 0, 1, 2, \ldots; \quad r_{-1} = 0.$$

We construct a reciprocal-difference table in the convenient form

$$
\begin{array}{llllll}
x_0 & r_0[0] \\
& & r_1[0] \\
x_1 & r_0[1] & & r_2[0] \\
& & r_1[1] & & r_3[0] \\
x_2 & r_0[2] & & r_2[1] & & r_4[0] \\
& & r_1[2] & & r_3[1] & & r_5[0] \\
x_3 & r_0[3] & & r_2[2] & & r_4[1] \\
& & r_1[3] & & r_3[2] \\
x_4 & r_0[4] & & r_2[3] \\
& & r_1[4] \\
x_5 & r_0[5]
\end{array}
\qquad (5.14.2)
$$

From this table we determine the coefficients a_i in

$$
f(x) = a_0 + \cfrac{x - x_0}{a_1 + \cfrac{x - x_1}{a_2 + \cfrac{x - x_2}{a_3 + \cdots}}}
\qquad (5.14.3)
$$

in the following manner:

$$
a_0 = r_0[0], \; a_1 = r_1[0], \; a_2 = r_2[0] - r_0[0],
$$
$$
a_3 = r_3[0] - r_1[0], \; a_4 = r_4[0] - r_2[0], \text{ etc.} \qquad (5.14.4)
$$

Example.

$$
\begin{array}{llllll}
0 & 1 \\
& & -2 \\
1 & \frac{1}{2} & & -1 \\
& & -\frac{10}{3} & & 0 \\
2 & \frac{1}{5} & & -\frac{1}{10} & & 0 \\
& & -\frac{50}{5} & & 10 \\
3 & \frac{1}{10} & & -\frac{1}{25} & & 0 \\
& & -\frac{170}{7} & & 140 \\
4 & \frac{1}{17} & & -\frac{1}{46} & & 0 \\
& & -\frac{442}{9} & & 324 \\
5 & \frac{1}{26} & & -\frac{1}{73} \\
& & -\frac{962}{11} \\
6 & \frac{1}{37}
\end{array}
$$

$$
y(x) = 1 + \cfrac{x - 0}{-2 + \cfrac{x - 1}{-2 + \cfrac{x - 2}{2 + \cfrac{x - 3}{1 +}}}}
$$

$$
= \frac{1}{1 + x^2} .
$$

5.15 SMOOTHING OF DATA

The method of least squares with orthogonal polynomials may be applied to the problem of smoothing data, when these data are observations of equally spaced values of some unknown function $f(x)$. We assume that the interval between the equally spaced values is small enough so that $f(x)$ can be represented over several consecutive values with sufficient accuracy by a polynomial of degree m. Then by least squares we fit a polynomial of degree m to $n + 1$ consecutive values obtained by observation, where $n > m$, and use the calculated values in place of the observed values.

It is convenient to take the degree m to be odd and the number $n + 1$ of points also odd. It is also convenient to select the midpoint of the range as the one whose value will be calculated from the approximating polynomial. For example, if $m = 3$ and $n + 1 = 5$ points, the midpoint is then x_2. If y_0, y_1, y_2, y_3, y_4 are five consecutive observed values, and the method of least squares is applied with orthogonal polynomials, we obtain the following third-degree five-point formula to give the smoothed value, $\bar{y}_2$, of y_2:

$$\bar{y}_2 = \tfrac{1}{35}[-3y_0 + 12y_1 + 17y_2 + 12y_3 - 3y_4]. \tag{5.15.1}$$

A formula of this type may be applied several times to a set of data, but should not be repeated too many times or the trend of the original data may be affected drastically.

Following is a list of several smoothing formulas obtained by the method of least squares.

a) Third-degree seven-point formula:

$$\bar{y}_3 = \tfrac{1}{21}[-2y_0 + 3y_1 + 6y_2 + 7y_3 + 6y_4 + 3y_5 - 2y_6]. \tag{5.15.2}$$

b) Third-degree nine-point formula:

$$\bar{y}_4 = \tfrac{1}{231}[-21y_0 + 14y_1 + 39y_2 + 54y_3 + 59y_4 + 54y_5 + 39y_6 + 14y_7 - 21y_8]. \tag{5.15.3}$$

c) Fifth-degree seven-point formula:

$$\bar{y}_3 = \tfrac{1}{231}[5y_0 - 30y_1 + 75y_2 + 131y_3 + 75y_4 - 30y_5 + 5y_6]. \tag{5.15.4}$$

d) Fifth-degree nine-point formula:

$$\bar{y}_4 = \tfrac{1}{429}[15y_0 - 55y_1 + 30y_2 + 135y_3 + 179y_4 + 135y_5 + 30y_6 - 55y_7 + 15y_8]. \tag{5.15.5}$$

EXERCISES

1. Using $w(x) = 1$, $\phi_0 = 1$, $\phi_1 = x$, $\phi_2 = x^2$, set up the normal equations (5.2.7) and find the best second-degree polynomial fit to the data:

x	-1	0	1	2
y	-10	-4	-2	2

Also find the RMS value.

2. Using $w(x) = 1$, $\phi_0 = 1$, $\phi_1 = x$, $\phi_2 = x^2$, and $\phi_3 = x^3$, set up the normal equations (5.2.7) and find the best third-degree polynomial fit to the data given in Problem 1. Also find the RMS value.

3. Using the method of Section 5.6, find the best third-degree polynomial fit and the RMS value for the following data ($w(x) = 1$):

x	-1	0	1	2	3
y	-10	-4	-2	2	14

4. Given $f(x) = x(5 - x)$ at the discrete values of $x = 0, 1, 2, 3, 4, 5$. Find the Fourier expansion of $f(x)$ using the discrete formulas of Section 5.11.

5. Normalize the independent variable of

x	0	1	2	3	4
y	0	3	4	3	0

for the range $-1 \le x' \le 1$. Use Eq. (5.6.13). Then fit the second-degree polynomial to the data using (5.2.11), where $w(x) = 1$, $\phi_0 = 1$, $\phi_1 = x$, $\phi_2 = 2x^2 - 1$. Also obtain the unnormalized polynomial.

6. Fit the function $y = A_1 e^{a_1 x} + A_2 e^{a_2 x}$ to the data

x	0	1	2	3
y	-1	-7.4	-21.9	-60.2

Round the C_i's, a_i's, and A_i's to the nearest whole number as computed.

7. Construct a reciprocal-difference table and fit the rational function to the data

x	0	1	2	3	4	5
y	2	$\frac{3}{2}$	$\frac{4}{5}$	$\frac{1}{2}$	$\frac{6}{17}$	$\frac{7}{26}$

8. Calculate smoothed values for the following data:

x	0	1	2	3	4	5	6	7	8	9
y	3	10	12	16	16	20	34	48	54	90

Use the third-degree five-point formula, (5.15.1), and plot the observed values and the smoothed values.

9. Find the third-degree Chebyshev polynomial approximation to the following data:

x	-0.92	-0.38	0.38	0.92
$f(x)$	-9.33	-5.48	-3.09	-2.25

CHAPTER 6

NONLINEAR ALGEBRAIC EQUATIONS

6.1 INTRODUCTION

Finding zeros of arbitrary nonlinear functions is a difficult problem, and there is no general method that will find the solution of all functions. We may appear to overemphasize polynomial equations, but this is mainly reflecting the literature. Much has been written on methods of finding real linear and real quadratic factors of a polynomial with real coefficients.

There is some justification for this. The important problem of finding eigenvalues of a matrix is often reduced to finding the roots of a polynomial. The question of stability of linear systems often leads to this problem. In the method of analytic substitution, a complicated function is often replaced by an approximating polynomial. For purposes of computing, a polynomial form of a function is frequently used.

It is not the aim of this chapter to attempt a comprehensive coverage of all methods. That has been most adequately done in whole books on the subject, such as the one by Ostrowski [119].

We will consider some of the problems associated with the solution of nonlinear equations, some basic algebraic methods, a comparison of methods, matrix methods, and several methods that have recently appeared in the literature.

6.2 TYPES OF PROBLEMS ASSOCIATED WITH SOLUTION

Given an equation or system of equations, we may be concerned with one or more of the following problems:

  a) determine the number of roots in a given region;

  b) determine the approximate value of all the roots of interest in a given region;

  c) given an approximation to a root, improve the approximation.

Many methods assume that a zero is isolated before we start. Often the problem itself will give some information. Numerous mathematical theorems have been written on the subject, but it is an art to isolate the various zeros.

A polynomial is designated as stable if small changes in the coefficients produce small changes in all the zeros. Wilkinson says equations of the form $Z^n + 1 = 0$ are stable. He says polynomials with linear distribution of the roots are more stable if the mean of the roots is nearly zero. Polynomials whose roots form arithmetic or geometric progressions may be stable under certain conditions and unstable under other conditions. J. H. Wilkinson's works [164] and [165] are excellent sources of an extensive discussion of the stability and accuracy of the roots of polynomials.

Most methods for improving an approximation on high-speed computers are iterative. The approximation is operated on in a certain way to produce a new and hopefully better approximation. The new approximation is operated on in the same or a methodically different way to produce a new approximation, etc.

The result of an iterative method is a sequence of estimates

$$z_1, z_2, z_3, \ldots, z_{i-1}, z_i, \ldots.$$

There are several problems associated with an iterative procedure. Assuming that the arithmetic operations are exact (no roundoff), does the sequence converge to the true value? What are the limitations due to roundoff or noise? When does one cut off the iterative process? A number of criteria have been used to stop the iteration:

a) If the c_i of $P(z)$ are known and the approximation to roots desired within a given $\epsilon > 0$ of the exact root, then

$$|P(z)| < \epsilon \cdot \sum_{i=1}^{n} |c_i| \, |z|^i. \qquad (6.2.1)$$

b) For a given ϵ,

$$|z_i - z_{i-1}| < \epsilon. \qquad (6.2.2)$$

However, this might never be fulfilled if ϵ were a small tolerance.

c) For a given ϵ,

$$\left| \frac{z_i - z_{i-1}}{z_i} \right| < \epsilon \qquad (6.2.3)$$

can be dangerous for roots that are small compared to the largest root.

d) For a given ϵ and k,

$$|z_i - z_{i-1}| < \max \, (\epsilon |z_i|, \, k|\text{largest root}|). \qquad (6.2.4)$$

e) Stop after a specified number of iterations.

There are two theorems which might be stated in relation to an iterative procedure of this type.

Theorem 1. The iteration

$$x_{i+1} = f(x_i) \qquad (6.2.5)$$

is of order n in a neighborhood of a root x if

$$f'(x) = f''(x) = \cdots = f^{(n-1)}(x) = 0 \qquad \text{and} \qquad f^{(n)}(x) \neq 0. \qquad (6.2.6)$$

Theorem 2. When $f(z)$ is analytic in a neighborhood of a root x, the convergence of the iteration can be shown if

$$|f'(z)| < 1 \qquad (6.2.7)$$

for all z in the neighborhood of x.

6.3 METHOD OF BISECTION

If $f(z) = 0$, assume f is a real-valued function of a real variable z, with an odd number of roots in the interval $I: a < z < b$. If f is continuous, the sign of $f(a)$ is opposite to that of $f(b)$.

The bisection procedure produces a sequence of intervals, $I_0, I_1, I_2, \ldots,$ each of which is half its predecessor, and each of which contains at least one root of f by virtue of the fact that f has different signs at the end points of each. The midpoints of the intervals then furnish a sequence of estimates which converges to a zero of f. Thus I_1 is obtained from I_0 by bisecting I_0 and choosing that half at the end points of which f has different signs, I_2 from I_1 in a similar manner, etc.

The error, $e = z_n - z$, at the nth stage is no greater than

$$(\text{length } I_0)2^{-(n+1)}, \qquad (6.3.1)$$

provided the noise level in the computation of f at $z_0, z_1, z_2, \ldots, z_{n-1}$ is not so high as to alter the sign of f. Computational noise can be a problem if f is flat in the vicinity of the root. This can occur in the case of a multiple root. The bisection method does not extend to the complex plane or to systems of equations.

Example. Find the real root of $x^3 - 3.7x^2 + 6.25x - 4.069$ between $x = 0.98$ and $x = 1.52$ by the bisection method.

Solution.

$$I_0 \quad \begin{array}{ll} x = 0.98, & f(x) = - \\ x = 1.52, & f(x) = + \end{array} \qquad \text{bisect:} \quad x = 1.25,$$

$$I_1 \quad \begin{array}{ll} x = 1.25, & f(x) = - \\ x = 1.52, & f(x) = + \end{array} \qquad \text{bisect:} \quad x = 1.385,$$

$$I_2 \quad \begin{array}{ll} x = 1.25, & f(x) = - \\ x = 1.385, & f(x) = + \end{array} \qquad \text{bisect:} \quad x = 1.3175,$$

$$I_3 \quad \begin{array}{ll} x = 1.25, & f(x) = - \\ x = 1.3175, & f(x) = + \end{array} \qquad \text{bisect:} \quad x = 1.28375,$$

$$I_4 \quad \begin{array}{ll} x = 1.28375, & f(x) = - \\ x = 1.3175, & f(x) = + \end{array} \qquad \text{bisect:} \quad x = 1.300675.$$

Note: Exact value of the root is 1.3.

6.4 FALSE POSITION; LINEAR INTERPOLATION

One might feel that convergence could be speeded up if the above procedure were modified to use linear interpolation rather than bisection. This is not always the case. Clearly bisection is better for the function shown in Fig. 6.4.1:

$$\frac{x_n - x_{n+1}}{x_n} = \frac{a}{b}, \tag{6.4.1}$$

$$x_{n+1} = \left(1 - \frac{a}{b}\right) x_n, \tag{6.4.2}$$

where a/b can be made as small as desired. That is,

$$x_{n+1} = c x_n, \tag{6.4.3}$$

where c can be made as near to 1 as desired. For bisection,

$$x_{n+1} = \tfrac{1}{2} x_n. \tag{6.4.4}$$

Although, on the average, interpolation may require fewer steps than bisection, one knows beforehand exactly how many steps will be required by the latter.

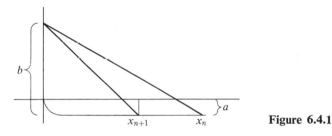

Figure 6.4.1

6.5 PARABOLIC INTERPOLATION

If linear interpolation is better than bisection, then parabolic interpolation using three points may be better than linear interpolation.

Having three points on a curve, we pass a parabola through them and solve the resulting quadratic equation. The zero of this quadratic which falls in the interval gives a fourth point. Then there are at least two possibilities; we can take the two points closest to the estimate of the zero that was just found, or we can be careful to keep two points which also have a change of sign, thus ensuring convergence.

David E. Muller [111], on the other hand, takes as his three new points, the last two points and that root of the quadratic which is closer to the last estimate. Muller's method is very popular for finding zeros of polynomials. There are some cases for which it does not converge.

Example. Find the real root of $x^3 - 3.7x^2 + 6.25x - 4.069$ between $x = 1$ and $x = 1.5$ by the parabolic method.

Solution. Bisecting the given interval we have $x = 1.25$ and the three points $(1, -0.519)$, $(1.25, -0.0846)$, and $(1.5, 0.356)$. Fitting a parabola through these three points we obtain

$$a + b + c = -0.519,$$
$$1.5625a + 1.25b + c = -0.0846,$$
$$2.25a + 1.5b + c = 0.356,$$

and

$$y = -0.00708x^2 + 1.75354x - 2.26546.$$

The two roots of this quadratic are $x_1 = 1.29879$ and $x_2 = 246.3763$. Discarding x_2, x_1 is a very close approximation to the true root 1.3. However, if we now use the points given by $x = 1.25$, 1.29879, and 1.5, and repeat the above process, we obtain a still closer approximation to the root.

6.6 NEWTON-RAPHSON METHOD

From a geometric point of view, the method of false position asks where a chord of the function curve intersects the abscissa axis. Newton's method, on the other hand, asks where a tangent to the function curve intersects the abscissa axis. Using the Taylor series expansion about x_n, and assuming x_{n+1} is a root, we have

$$f(x_{n+1}) = f(x_n) + (x_{n+1} - x_n)f'(x_n) + \cdots = 0. \tag{6.6.1}$$

If we are given x_n, truncate after the second term of the right member, and solve for x_{n+1}, we have the formula for obtaining the next term in the sequence:

$$x_{n+1} = x_n - \frac{f(x_n)}{f'(x_n)}. \tag{6.6.2}$$

It is evident that difficulty arises with this formula when the derivative $f'(x_n)$ does not exist, is equal to zero, or is nearly zero. Newton's method is always convergent if the initial guess is sufficiently close to a root. S. Gorn, *Annals of Math.*, Vol. 59 (1954), has shown that a bad guess may cause divergence.

Example. Find the real root of $f(x) - x^3 - 3.7x^2 + 6.25x - 4.069$ by the Newton iteration, using $x_0 = 1.5$.

Solution.

$$f'(x) = 3x^2 - 7.4x + 6.25,$$

$$x_1 = x_0 - \frac{f(x_0)}{f'(x_0)} = 1.5 - \frac{0.356}{1.90} = 1.3126,$$

$$x_2 = 1.3126 - \frac{0.0215}{1.7055} = 1.2986,$$

$$x_3 = 1.2986 - \frac{-0.0024}{1.6996} = 1.3002.$$

6.7 ITERATED SYNTHETIC DIVISION

Let us assume a polynomial

$$f(x) = x^n + a_1 x^{n-1} + a_2 x^{n-2} + \cdots + a_{n-1} x + a_n, \quad (6.7.1)$$

where the coefficients are real or complex. The roots can be complex in either case. Then we write Eq. (6.7.1) as

$$f(x) = (x - z)(x^{n-1} + b_1 x^{n-2} + \cdots + b_{n-2} x + b_{n-1}) + R, \quad (6.7.2)$$

where $R = f(z)$ when $x = z$. Also,

$$x^{n-1} + b_1 x^{n-2} + \cdots + b_{n-2} x + b_{n-1}$$
$$= (x - z)(x^{n-2} + c_1 x^{n-3} + \cdots + c_{n-3} x + c_{n-2}) + R', \quad (6.7.3)$$

so

$$f(x) = (x - z)^2 (x^{n-2} + c_1 x^{n-3} + \cdots + c_{n-2}) + (x - z)R' + R. \quad (6.7.4)$$

Thus $R' = f'(z)$, and, in general, $R^{(k)} = f^{(k)}(z)/k!$. Equating the coefficients, we have

$$\begin{aligned} b_0 &= 1, \\ b_k &= a_k + z b_{k-1}, \quad k = 1(1)n, \\ b_n &= f(z) = R = a_n + z b_{n-1}, \end{aligned} \quad (6.7.5)$$

and

$$\begin{aligned} c_0 &= 1, \\ c_k &= b_k + z c_{k-1}, \quad k = 1(1)n - 1, \\ c_{n-1} &= f'(z) = R'. \end{aligned} \quad (6.7.6)$$

For actual calculation, it is convenient to arrange the entries in the form

$$\begin{array}{ccc|c} 1 & 1 & 1 \\ a_1 & b_1 & c_1 \\ a_2 & b_2 & c_2 \\ \vdots & \vdots & \vdots \\ & b_{n-2} & c_{n-2} \\ a_{n-1} & b_{n-1} & R' \\ a_n & R \end{array}, \quad (6.7.7)$$

so that each element is obtained by adding to its left-hand neighbor, z times its upward neighbor. (Here z is the approximation to x.) If we use the Newton-Raphson procedure to approximate x, starting with an initial approximation z_1, the next approximation is

$$z_{i+1} = z_i - \frac{R}{R'}, \quad (6.7.8)$$

and we repeat the process with z_{i+1}. This method avoids much of the labor involved in evaluating $f(z)$ and $f'(z)$. The process is continued for a given root until $R = 0$. The entire procedure is then repeated to find a root of the reduced polynomial whose coefficients are the b's.

Example. Find the real root of $x^3 - 3.7x^2 + 6.25x - 4.069$, after two iterations with $z_0 = 1.25$. Also write the reduced polynomial.

Solution.

$$
\begin{array}{ccc}
1 & 1 & 1 \\
-3.7 & -2.45 & -1.20 \\
6.25 & 3.1875 & 1.6875 \\
-4.069 & -0.08463 &
\end{array}
$$

$$z_1 = 1.25 - \frac{-0.08463}{1.6875} = 1.30015;$$

$$
\begin{array}{ccc}
1 & 1 & 1 \\
-3.7 & -2.39985 & -0.09970 \\
6.25 & 3.12984 & 3.00022 \\
-4.069 & 0.00026 &
\end{array}
$$

$$z_2 = 1.30015 - \frac{0.00026}{3.00022} = 1.30006.$$

The reduced polynomial is $x^2 - 2.39985x + 3.12984$.

6.8 LIN'S METHOD

This method is based on the fact that, by virtue of Eq. (6.7.5), the condition $f(z) = 0$ is equivalent to $a_n + zb_{n-1} = 0$. That is, if the àssumed value of z is a root, then

$$z_{i+1} = -\frac{a_n}{b_{n-1}}, \tag{6.8.1}$$

and hence

$$z_{i+1} - z_i = -\frac{a_n + z_i b_{n-1}}{b_{n-1}}$$

or

$$z_{i+1} = z_i - \frac{R}{b_{n-1}}. \tag{6.8.2}$$

Note that it is not necessary in this method to compute the c's. Also, note that

$$z_{k+1} = -\frac{a_n z_k}{f(z_k) - a_n}. \tag{6.8.3}$$

Thus Lin's method is equivalent to the method of successive substitution which results from writing $f(z) = 0$ in the form

$$z = -\frac{a_n z}{f(z) - a_n} \equiv F(z). \tag{6.8.4}$$

Also, note that

$$b_{n-1} = \frac{R - a_n}{z} = \frac{f(z) - f(0)}{z},$$

and so Lin's method amounts to false position based on the fixed point $[0, f(0)]$.

6.9 SYNTHETIC DIVISION WITH QUADRATIC FACTORS

Since a real initial estimate invariably leads to real estimates whether we use Lin's method or the Newton-Raphson method, it is clear that to obtain complex roots, one must initiate the iteration with a complex estimate. Complex arithmetic must then be used. When the coefficients are real, complex roots occur in conjugate pairs, and it is usually better to exploit this fact by seeking quadratic real factors, rather than linear complex ones.

By synthetic division with quadratic factors,

$$
\begin{aligned}
f(x) &= x^n + a_1 x^{n-1} + \cdots + a_{n-1} x + a_n \\
&= (x^2 + px + q)(x^{n-2} + b_1 x^{n-3} + \cdots + b_{n-2}) + Rx + S, \quad (6.9.1)
\end{aligned}
$$

so $x^2 + px + q$ is a factor only if $R = 0$ and $S = 0$. Equating coefficients of like powers, we have

$$
\begin{aligned}
a_1 &= b_1 + p, \\
a_2 &= b_2 + pb_1 + q, \\
a_3 &= b_3 + pb_2 + qb_1, \\
&\;\;\vdots \\
a_{n-2} &= b_{n-2} + pb_{n-3} + qb_{n-4}, \\
a_{n-1} &= R + pb_{n-2} + qb_{n-3}, \\
a_n &= S + qb_{n-2},
\end{aligned}
\qquad (6.9.2)
$$

or

$$
\begin{aligned}
b_{-1} &= 0, \qquad b_0 = 1, \\
b_k &= a_k - pb_{k-1} - qb_{k-2}, \quad k = 1(1)n,
\end{aligned}
\qquad (6.9.3)
$$

with

$$
\begin{aligned}
R &= b_{n-1} = a_{n-1} - pb_{n-2} - qb_{n-3}, \\
S &= b_n + pb_{n-1} = a_n - qb_{n-2}.
\end{aligned}
\qquad (6.9.4)
$$

6.10 LIN'S METHOD FOR QUADRATIC FACTORS

In order for $x^2 + px + q$ to be a factor of $f(x)$ we must have

$$R = 0, \qquad S = 0,$$

that is,

$$p = \frac{a_{n-1} - qb_{n-3}}{b_{n-2}}, \qquad q = \frac{a_n}{b_{n-2}}. \qquad (6.10.1)$$

Thus, by successive substitutions, we obtain

$$p_{k+1} - p_k = \frac{a_{n-1} - p_k b_{n-2} - q_k b_{n-3}}{b_{n-2}}, \quad q_{k+1} - q_k = \frac{a_n - q_k b_{n-2}}{b_{n-2}} \quad (6.10.2)$$

or

$$p_{k+1} = p_k + \frac{R}{b_{n-2}}, \quad q_{k+1} = q_k + \frac{S}{b_{n-2}}. \quad (6.10.3)$$

The calculation can be arranged in columns as follows:

$$
\begin{array}{c|c}
1 & 1 \\
a_1 & b_1 \\
\vdots & \vdots \\
a_{n-2} & b_{n-2} \\
a_{n-1} & R \\
a_n & S
\end{array}
$$

Each entry in the b column, except the last, is obtained by subtracting from its left-hand neighbor p times its first upward neighbor and q times its second upward neighbor. In calculating b_0 and b_1 the missing entries are taken to be zero. The last element S is calculated in the same way except that its first upward neighbor is imagined to be replaced by zero. The process is continued for one set of iterated p's and q's until $R = 0$ and $S = 0$. The entire procedure is repeated for the reduced polynomial, if another quadratic factor is sought.

6.11 BAIRSTOW'S METHOD

The equations

$$R(p, q) = 0, \quad S(p, q) = 0, \quad (6.11.1)$$

are written as a Taylor expansion for two variables in the form

$$R(p, q) = R(p_k, q_k) + (p - p_k)R_p(p_k, q_k) + (q - q_k)R_q(p_k, q_k) + \cdots,$$
$$(6.11.2)$$
$$S(p, q) = S(p_k, q_k) + (p - p_k)S_p(p_k, q_k) + (q - q_k)S_q(p_k, q_k) + \cdots.$$

Assuming (p_{k+1}, q_{k+1}) to be a root and truncating after the third term on the right, we have

$$(p_{k+1} - p_k)R_p(p_k, q_k) + (q_{k+1} - q_k)R_q(p_k, q_k) + R(p_k, q_k) = 0,$$
$$(6.11.3)$$
$$(p_{k+1} - p_k)S_p(p_k, q_k) + (q_{k+1} - q_k)S_q(p_k, q_k) + S(p_k, q_k) = 0.$$

From Eq. (6.9.4), $R = b_{n-1}$ and $S = b_n + pb_{n-1}$. Differentiating these expressions we get

$$R_p = \frac{\partial b_{n-1}}{\partial p}, \quad R_q = \frac{\partial b_{n-1}}{\partial q}, \quad S_p = \frac{\partial b_n}{\partial p} + p\frac{\partial b_{n-1}}{\partial p} + b_{n-1},$$

and
$$S_q = \frac{\partial b_n}{\partial q} + p \frac{\partial b_{n-1}}{\partial q}.$$

Substituting the expressions for R, S, R_p, R_q, S_p, and S_q, as well as $p_{k+1} - p_k = \Delta p$ and $q_{k+1} - q_k = \Delta q$, in (6.11.3), we get

$$\frac{\partial b_{n-1}}{\partial p} \Delta p + \frac{\partial b_{n-1}}{\partial q} \Delta q + b_{n-1} = 0, \tag{6.11.4}$$

$$\left(\frac{\partial b_n}{\partial p} + p \frac{\partial b_{n-1}}{\partial p} + b_{n-1} \right) \Delta p + \left(\frac{\partial b_n}{\partial q} + p \frac{\partial b_{n-1}}{\partial q} \right) \Delta q + b_n + p b_{n-1} = 0.$$

If we multiply the first equation by p and subtract from the second equation, we can write the equations in (6.11.4) as

$$\frac{\partial b_{n-1}}{\partial p} \Delta p + \frac{\partial b_{n-1}}{\partial q} \Delta q + b_{n-1} = 0, \tag{6.11.5}$$

$$\left(\frac{\partial b_n}{\partial p} + b_{n-1} \right) \Delta p + \frac{\partial b_n}{\partial q} \Delta q + b_n = 0.$$

Recalling that

$$b_k = a_k - p b_{k-1} - q b_{k-2}, \qquad k = 1(1)n, \qquad b_{-1} = 0, \qquad b_0 = 1, \tag{6.11.6}$$

we have

$$-\frac{\partial b_k}{\partial p} = b_{k-2} + p \frac{\partial b_{k-1}}{\partial p} + q \frac{\partial b_{k-2}}{\partial p}, \qquad k = 1(1)n, \qquad \frac{\partial b_{-1}}{\partial p} = \frac{\partial b_0}{\partial p} = 0, \tag{6.11.7}$$

and

$$-\frac{\partial b_k}{\partial q} = b_{k-2} + p \frac{\partial b_{k-1}}{\partial q} + q \frac{\partial b_{k-2}}{\partial q}, \qquad k = 1(1)n, \qquad \frac{\partial b_{-1}}{\partial q} = \frac{\partial b_0}{\partial q} = 0. \tag{6.11.8}$$

If we introduce the new recursion formula,

$$c_k = b_k - p c_{k-1} - q c_{k-2}, \qquad k = 1(1)n - 1, \qquad c_{-1} = 0, \qquad c_0 = 1, \tag{6.11.9}$$

we can write the above as

$$\frac{\partial b_k}{\partial p} = -c_{k-1}, \qquad \frac{\partial b_k}{\partial q} = -c_{k-2}, \tag{6.11.10}$$

where $k = 1(1)n$ and the c's are obtained from the b's just as the b's are obtained from the a's. The basic equations of the Bairstow iteration then take the form

$$c_{n-2} \Delta p + c_{n-3} \Delta q = b_{n-1},$$
$$\bar{c}_{n-1} \Delta p + c_{n-2} \Delta q = b_n, \tag{6.11.11}$$

where $\bar{c}_{n-1} = c_{n-1} - b_{n-1} = 0 - p c_{n-2} - q c_{n-3}$.

The principal calculation can be arranged as in (6.11.12). Here each element in the b column (including b_n), and each element of the c column, except the last one ($\bar{c}_{n-1}$), is calculated as in the Lin iteration (as the result of subtracting from the element to its left, p times the last calculated element above it and q times the next-to-last element above it). The element $\bar{c}_{n-1}$ is calculated in the same way except that we imagine that the element to its left has been replaced by zero.

In addition it is necessary to solve the linear equations, (6.11.9), for Δp and Δq to be added to p and q. The process is continued with these improved values of p and q until R and S are equal to zero:

$$
\begin{array}{cc|cc}
 & & 0 & 0 \\
1 & & 1 & 1 \\
a_1 & & b_1 & c_1 \\
\vdots & & \vdots & \vdots \\
a_{n-3} & & b_{n-3} & c_{n-3} \\
a_{n-2} & & b_{n-2} & c_{n-2} \\
a_{n-1} & & b_{n-1} & \bar{c}_{n-1} \\
a_n & & b_n &
\end{array}
\qquad (6.11.12)
$$

Example. Find the quadratic factor of $x^3 - 3.7x^2 + 6.25x - 4.069$ after two iterations. Use $p_0 = -2.5$ and $q_0 = 3$.

Solution.

$$
\begin{array}{r|rr}
1 & 1 & 1 \\
-3.7 & -1.2 & 1.3 \\
6.25 & 0.25 & 0.25 \\
-4.069 & 0.156 &
\end{array}
$$

$$
1.3\,\Delta p + \Delta q = 0.25,
$$
$$
0.25\,\Delta p + 1.3\,\Delta q = 0.156.
$$

Solving this system we obtain $\Delta p = 0.11736$ and $\Delta q = 0.09743$. Therefore, $p_1 = -2.38264$ and $q_1 = 3.09743$.

$$
\begin{array}{r|rr}
1 & 1 & 1 \\
-3.7 & -1.31736 & 1.06528 \\
6.25 & 0.01378 & -0.55925 \\
-4.069 & 0.04826 &
\end{array}
$$

$$
1.06528\,\Delta p + \Delta q = 0.01378,
$$
$$
-0.55925\,\Delta p + 1.06528\,\Delta q = 0.04826.
$$

Solving this system we obtain $\Delta p = -0.01982$ and $\Delta q = 0.03489$. Therefore, $p_2 = -2.40246$ and $q_2 = 3.13232$, and the quadratic factor is

$$
x^2 - 2.40246x + 3.13232.
$$

6.12 MODIFIED NEWTON-RAPHSON METHOD

In using synthetic division, we must take care to minimize the accumulation of errors introduced each time because of limited accuracy in roots. This accumulation influences coefficients of the reduced polynomials. It is generally best to find the smaller roots first.

The following way of formulating the Newton-Raphson procedure is said to sometimes yield more accuracy than synthetic division [149, p. 263]. Since we can write a polynomial

$$P_n(z) = \sum_{j=0}^{n} a_{n-j} z^j \tag{6.12.1}$$

in terms of its roots $x_1, \ldots, x_n$ as

$$P_n(z) = a_0(z - x_1) \cdots (z - x_n), \tag{6.12.2}$$

we therefore have

$$\frac{P_n'(z_k)}{P_n(z_k)} = \sum_{i=1}^{n} \frac{1}{z_k - x_i}. \tag{6.12.3}$$

After j roots have been found, the reduced polynomial is $P_{n-j}(z)$, and

$$\frac{P_{n-j}'(z_k)}{P_{n-j}(z_k)} = \sum_{i=1}^{n} \frac{1}{z_k - x_i} - \sum_{i=1}^{j} \frac{1}{z_k - x_i}. \tag{6.12.4}$$

Therefore we can write the Newton-Raphson procedure for the reduced polynomial as

$$z_{k+1} = z_k - 1 \left/ \left[\sum_{i=1}^{n} \frac{1}{z_k - x_i} - \sum_{i=1}^{j} \frac{1}{z_k - x_i} \right] \right. . \tag{6.12.5}$$

6.13 GRAEFFE'S METHOD

When getting first estimates of all roots, Graeffe's method finds approximate values for all roots at the same time. From

$$P_n(z) = \sum_{j=0}^{n} a_{n-j} z^j = a_0 \prod_{i=1}^{n} (z - x_i), \tag{6.13.1}$$

we have the following relations between the roots x_i and the coefficients a_i:

$$\frac{a_1}{a_0} = -\sum_{i=1}^{n} x_i, \quad \frac{a_2}{a_0} = \sum_{i,j=1}^{n} x_i x_j, \quad \ldots, \quad \frac{a_n}{a_0} = (-1)^n x_1 x_2 \cdots x_n. \tag{6.13.2}$$

So, if the x_i are real and well separated, then

$$x_1 > x_2 > x_3 > \cdots > x_n,$$

$$x_1 \approx -\frac{a_1}{a_0}, \quad x_2 \approx -\frac{a_2}{a_1}, \quad \ldots, \quad x_n \approx -\frac{a_n}{a_{n-1}}. \tag{6.13.3}$$

Graeffe's method allows a new polynomial to be constructed whose roots are in simple relation to the original polynomial and are well separated. It makes use of the fact that the roots of

$$P_n^*(z) = \sum_{j=0}^{n} a_{n-j}(-z)^j = \sum_{j=0}^{n} (-1)^j a_{n-j} z^j \qquad (6.13.4)$$

are $-x_1, -x_2, \ldots, -x_n$. Then

$$P_n'(z^2) = (-1)^n P_n(z) P_n^*(z) = a_0^2 \prod_{i=1}^{n} (z + x_i)(z - x_i) = \sum_{j=0}^{n} a_{n-j}'(z^2)^j \qquad (6.13.5)$$

has the roots $x_1^2, x_2^2, \ldots, x_n^2$.

The coefficients of the new polynomial are computed from those of the old by

$$a_j' = (-1)^j \left[a_j^2 + 2 \sum_{k=1}^{\min(j,n-j)} (-1)^k a_{j+k} a_{j-k} \right]. \qquad (6.13.6)$$

For convenience one drops the $(-1)^j$, that is, computes the polynomial with roots $-x_i^2$ instead. By repeated application of this method, polynomials

$$P_n^{(k)}(z) = \sum_{j=0}^{n} a_{n-j}^{(k)} z^j \qquad (6.13.7)$$

can be obtained with roots $-x_i^{2^k}$. The process is terminated when

$$a_j^{(k)} \approx [a_j^{(k-1)}]^2$$

and the approximate relations given before are used to compute the roots

$$\log x_i \approx \frac{1}{2^k} \log \frac{a_i^{(k)}}{a_{i-1}^{(k)}}. \qquad (6.13.8)$$

The roots are determined only up to the sign by the given logarithmic relation. The sign must be determined by substitution or some other method. The Graeffe method can be modified [73] to take care of complex or multiple roots.

6.14 SYSTEMS OF NONLINEAR EQUATIONS

We consider a system of N equations in N unknowns. For the sake of notation we shall discuss the case $N = 2$, which can be extended to arbitrary N. Given the equations

$$f(x, y) = 0, \qquad g(x, y) = 0, \qquad (6.14.1)$$

let us assume they are written in the form

$$x = F(x, y), \qquad y = G(x, y). \qquad (6.14.2)$$

Then, by the method of successive substitutions, we formulate the iterative procedure in the form

$$\begin{matrix} x_{k+1} = F(x_k, y_k) \\ y_{k+1} = G(x_k, y_k) \end{matrix} , \tag{6.14.3}$$

or in the form

$$\begin{matrix} x_{k+1} = F(x_k, y_k) \\ y_{k+1} = G(x_{k+1}, y_k) \end{matrix} . \tag{6.14.4}$$

When one considers that F and G may have many possible equivalent but different forms, and that the possibilities increase as N increases, it is evident that this problem is an art that requires insight, skill, and frequently luck. Again it is important that the initial guesses be reasonably good. It can be shown [119] with some effort that the process converges if

$$|F_x| + |G_x| < 1 \quad \text{and} \quad |F_y| + |G_y| < 1 \tag{6.14.5}$$

in a neighborhood of the root, x, y, which contains all points of the sequence $\{(x_i, y_i)\}$.

6.15 NEWTON-RAPHSON METHOD FOR SYSTEM OF EQUATIONS

The Newton-Raphson procedure reduces the problem of finding the solution of a system of N nonlinear equations to the problem of determining a sequence $\{x_k\}$, each term of which requires the solution of a system of N linear equations. The procedure may be summarized as follows:

The matrix of the system of linear equations is the Jacobian matrix.

$$J_k = \begin{bmatrix} f_x(x_k, y_k) & f_y(x_k, y_k) \\ g_x(x_k, y_k) & g_y(x_k, y_k) \end{bmatrix} . \tag{6.15.1}$$

The Newton-Raphson procedure in matrix form is

$$J_k \Delta_k = -F_k, \tag{6.15.2}$$

where

$$\begin{matrix} \Delta_k = \begin{bmatrix} x_{k+1} - x_k \\ y_{k+1} - y_k \end{bmatrix} \\ \\ F_k = \begin{bmatrix} f(x_k, y_k) \\ g(x_k, y_k) \end{bmatrix} \end{matrix} , \tag{6.15.3}$$

and

$$X_{k+1} = X_k + \Delta_k = X_k - J_k^{-1} F_k, \tag{6.15.4}$$

where

$$X_k = \begin{bmatrix} x_k \\ y_k \end{bmatrix} .$$

A discussion of convergence of this procedure is found in Hildebrand [73].

6.16 MINIMIZING METHODS

The problem, $f(x, y) = 0$, $g(x, y) = 0$, is replaced by finding the minimum of one function, $F(x, y)$, which is so defined that it takes the minimum at a solution of the system. Such a function may be defined as

$$F(z) = f^2(x, y) + g^2(x, y), \tag{10.16.1}$$

or as

$$F(z) = |f(x, y)| + |g(x, y)|. \tag{10.16.2}$$

In numerical work the first form is frequently preferable (according to Todd [149]), since the second form often leads to a very narrow minimum, so that it may be very difficult to find an initial guess which will lead to a solution.

On the other hand, James A. Ward [156] uses the second form where $f(x, y)$ and $g(x, y)$ are understood to be the real and imaginary parts of an analytic function $f(z)$. Ward's problem is to find the zeros of $f(z)$. He defines the surface w by

$$w = |f(x, y)| + |g(x, y)|,$$

and proves that $w(x, y)$ is a minimum if and only if $w = 0$. The application of this "downhill" method to a solution requires a starting value $x_0 + iy_0$. The $w(x_0, y_0)$ is computed and if $w(x_0, y_0) > 0$, new values of x and y, $x_1 = x_0 + h_1$, $y_1 = y_0 + k_1$ are chosen. The h_1 and k_1 are subject to the restriction that $w(x_1, y_1) < w(x_0, y_0)$. Therefore the problem consists primarily in determining suitable values of h_i and k_i.

G. C. Caldwell [15] indicates a method for determination of these increments. Newman's method for minimizing unimodal functions of N variables is also a possibility (see H. A. Spang III, *SIAM Review*, October 1962).

6.17 RICH-SHAW METHOD

A method for finding all the zeros of $f(z)$ is discussed by Rich and Shaw [128]. The problem is that of finding all the zeros of integral order of a function

$$f(z) = u(x, y) + iv(x, y),$$

which lie in the interior of a convex polygon P. Also we must determine the orders, negative as well as positive, of these zeros. Since the zeros of f lie on the intersection of a $u = 0$ contour and a $v = 0$ contour, this problem is a special case of the problem of finding all solutions inside P of a system of two equations,

$$u(x, y) = 0,$$
$$v(x, y) = 0,$$

in x and y.

The method actually considers two problems. The first is to determine first estimates of all solutions inside P. The method assumes that the zero contours of u or v neither close nor originate inside P. Granted this much structure, the method requires only a one-dimensional search of P and its interior. The second problem considered is to improve an estimate.

Another feature of the method is that it computes the number of zeros minus the number of poles inside P while stepping around P to locate the end points of u contours. Adding the orders of the zeros actually found and comparing with this difference we have an overall consistency test.

6.18 MATRIX METHODS

Suppose one wishes to find the roots of the polynomial

$$f(z) = z^n + a_n z^{n-1} + a_{n-1} z^{n-2} + \cdots + a_3 z^2 + a_2 z + a_1.$$

$$(6.18.1)$$

The so-called companion matrix of this polynomial may be formed. We write one form of this companion matrix as

$$\begin{bmatrix} -a_n & -a_{n-1} & \cdots & -a_2 & -a_1 \\ 1 & 0 & \cdots & 0 & 0 \\ 0 & 1 & \cdots & 0 & 0 \\ \vdots & & & & \\ 0 & 0 & \cdots & 1 & 0 \end{bmatrix}. \qquad (6.18.2)$$

The latent roots or eigenvalues of this matrix are the roots of the original polynomial. We find the eigenvalues of this matrix by one of the methods described in Chapter 9. This applies to polynomials with real or complex coefficients.

6.19 COMPARISON OF SEVERAL METHODS

In the methods of "false position" and bisection, the error in z_{k+1} and z_k are in constant ratio and is called a first-order process. In the Newton-Raphson method the error in z_{k+1} is proportional to the square of the error in z_k as the iteration converges and is called a second-order process.

The Graeffe method possesses the theoretical advantages that the iteration leads to all zeros of $f(z)$ at the same time, and that there is no question of the existence of ultimate convergence, if appropriate attention is paid to roundoff errors. It is often laborious. A serious disadvantage follows from the fact that a gross error at any stage invalidates all subsequent calculations (in other methods it would only slow convergence).

A simpler method, due to Lin (*J. Math. and Phys.*, Vol. 20, 1941; Vol. 22, 1943), takes care of cases when two or more pairs of complex roots are present. However, it has disadvantages in that convergence is not certain, even though starting values are good approximations to true values, and that the rate of convergence, when present, is often slow.

Bairstow's method is a second-order process. A comparison of results shows that even though the Bairstow iteration may converge more slowly than the Lin iteration in the early stages, its ultimate rate is far superior. This is due to the fact that it is second-order process while Lin's method is first order. Bairstow is somewhat more sensitive to starting values than Lin; that is, if the Lin iteration is asymptotically stable, it may converge with starting values which are cruder approximations than are required for the convergence of the Bairstow method.

EXERCISES

1. Given $f(x) = x^r - N$, use the Newton-Raphson iteration formula to derive a formula for finding the rth root of N.

2. Use the iteration formula derived in Exercise 1 to find the $\sqrt{5}$ to four decimal places.

3. A real root of $f(x) = x^3 - x - 1$ lies between $x = 1$ and $x = 2$. Use the bisection method to find the root to four decimal places.

4. A real root of $f(x) = x^3 - 2x - 5$ lies between $x = 2$ and $x = 3$. Use the Newton-Raphson iteration method to find the root to four decimal places.

5. Using the method of iterated synthetic division (Section 6.7), find the approximate value of the root of $f(x) = x^3 - 2x - 5$ to four decimal places after two iterations starting with $z_0 = 2$.

6. Using Bairstow's method (Section 6.11), find the approximate value of the quadratic factor of $f(x) = x^3 - 2x - 5$ to three decimal places after two iterations starting with $p_0 = 2$ and $q_0 = 2.5$.

7. Using the method of bisection, find the real root of $f(x) = x^4 - 8x^3 + 23x^2 + 16x - 50$ which lies between $x = -2$ and $x = -1$.

8. Find the real root of the function given in Exercise 7. Use Newton's iteration and $x_0 = 1.5$.

9. Find two roots of the function given in Exercise 7. Use Bairstow's iteration with $p_0 = -7.5$ and $q_0 = 24$.

10. Find two pairs of complex conjugate roots for $f(x) = x^4 - 8x^3 + 39x^2 - 62x + 50$.

11. Find four real roots for $f(x) = x^4 - 16x^3 + 72x^2 - 96x + 24$.

12. Find two real and two complex roots for $f(x) = x^4 - 4x^3 + 7x^2 - 16x + 12$.

CHAPTER 7

MATRIX ALGEBRA AND OPERATIONS

7.1 INTRODUCTION

Although matrices have been investigated by mathematicians for a century, their extensive application in engineering, physical sciences, social sciences, medical sciences, education, and statistics has taken place only since 1925. Use of matrices in aeronautical engineering for solving problems associated with small oscillations, flutter, and elasticity did not receive much attention until 1935. One of the first books on the subject was written by three aeronautical engineers, Frazer, Duncan, and Collar (*Elementary Matrices and Some Applications to Dynamics and Differential Equations*, Cambridge University Press, 1938).

We obtain the numerical solution of some integral equations, partial differential equations, or ordinary differential equations with two-point boundary conditions by solving approximate linear algebraic systems. Many nonlinear problems may be solved by a sequence of linear systems providing progressively improved approximations. Many problems in dynamics and control-systems engineering lead to linear systems. The studying and solving of linear systems is most conveniently and simply done with the compact symbolism of vectors and matrices.

It is not the aim of this chapter to present an extensive and thorough coverage of matrix theory and matrix analysis. That has been well done in books on the subject, such as those given in Section 7.15 on supplementary references. The purpose here is to present an introduction to vector and matrix notation, basic definitions and matrix operations, and a number of selected topics, in order to form a fundamental background for much of the material to be covered in later chapters.

7.2 MATRIX AND VECTOR NOTATION

A collection of elements arranged in rows and columns is said to form an array. An array consisting of m rows and n columns is denoted by

$$A = \begin{bmatrix} a_{11} & a_{12} & \cdots & a_{1n} \\ a_{21} & a_{22} & \cdots & a_{2n} \\ \vdots & & & \vdots \\ a_{m1} & a_{m2} & \cdots & a_{mn} \end{bmatrix} = [a_{ij}], \qquad (7.2.1)$$

and is called a rectangular matrix of order $(m \times n)$. When $m = n$, we have the important case in which A is called a square matrix of order n. The sum of the diagonal elements is called the trace of A.

Interchanging corresponding rows and columns of Eq. (7.2.1), we obtain the transpose of A, and this is denoted as

$$A^t = [a_{ij}]^t = [a_{ji}]. \tag{7.2.2}$$

If A is an array consisting of only 1 row and n columns, denoted by

$$A = [a_{11} \ a_{12} \ a_{13} \ \cdots \ a_{1n}], \tag{7.2.3}$$

then A is called a row matrix or row vector. Likewise, if A has n rows and only one column, denoted by

$$A = \begin{bmatrix} a_{11} \\ a_{21} \\ \vdots \\ a_{n1} \end{bmatrix} = [a_{11} \ a_{21} \ \cdots \ a_{n1}]^t, \tag{7.2.4}$$

then A is called a column matrix or a column vector.

7.3 SPECIAL TYPES OF MATRICES

A matrix with all of its elements equal to zero,

$$0 = [0], \tag{7.3.1}$$

is called the null matrix or zero matrix.

A square matrix whose diagonal elements, a_{ii}, are all ones, and whose remaining elements are zero, is called the identity matrix or unit matrix. It is denoted by I and has the property that $IA = AI = A$.

A square matrix whose diagonal elements are $\alpha_1, \alpha_2, \ldots, \alpha_n$, and whose remaining elements are zero, is called a diagonal matrix. That is,

$$D = \begin{bmatrix} \alpha_1 & 0 & \cdots & 0 \\ 0 & \alpha_2 & \cdots & 0 \\ \vdots & & & \vdots \\ 0 & & \cdots & \alpha_n \end{bmatrix}. \tag{7.3.2}$$

The determinant value of a diagonal matrix is equal to the product of the diagonal elements.

A square matrix whose off-diagonal elements are such that $a_{ij} = a_{ji}$ is called a symmetric matrix. That is, $A^t = A$.

A matrix which has nonzero elements on its principal diagonal, superdiagonal, and subdiagonal, with zero everywhere else, is called a tridiagonal matrix. That is,

$$A = \begin{bmatrix} \alpha_1 & \beta_1 & 0 & \cdots & & 0 \\ \gamma_1 & \alpha_2 & \beta_2 & & & \vdots \\ 0 & \gamma_2 & \alpha_3 & & & \\ \vdots & & & & \beta_{n-1} \\ 0 & \cdots & & \cdots & \gamma_{n-1} & \alpha_n \end{bmatrix}. \tag{7.3.3}$$

If $\beta_i = \gamma_i$, A is also symmetric.

A matrix which has nonzero elements on and above the principal diagonal, and zeros everywhere else, is called an upper-triangular matrix. If it has nonzero elements on and below the principal diagonal, it is called a lower-triangular matrix.

A matrix A to which an $(n + 1)$-column has been added is called an augmented matrix. That is,

$$[A : b] = \begin{bmatrix} a_{11} & \cdots & a_{1n} & \vdots & b_1 \\ \vdots & & \vdots & \vdots & \vdots \\ a_{n1} & \cdots & a_{nn} & \vdots & b_n \end{bmatrix}. \tag{7.3.4}$$

7.4 ADDITION AND MULTIPLICATION OF MATRICES

The sum or difference of two matrices of the same order is the matrix, each of whose elements is the sum or difference of the corresponding elements of the two given matrices, that is,

$$[a_{ij}] \pm [b_{ij}] = [a_{ij} \pm b_{ij}] = [c_{ij}]. \tag{7.4.1}$$

Multiplication of a matrix A by a scalar k is defined by the relation

$$k[a_{ij}] = [a_{ij}]k = [ka_{ij}]. \tag{7.4.2}$$

The product of two matrices A and B in the order AB is defined only if A has the same number of columns as B has rows. If this condition is satisfied, then by definition

$$[a_{ij}][b_{ij}] = [c_{ij}], \tag{7.4.3}$$

where

$$c_{ij} = \sum_{k=1}^{l} a_{ik} b_{kj}, \tag{7.4.4}$$

and the orders of A, B, and C are $(m \times l)$, $(l \times n)$, and $(m \times n)$, respectively.

In this case we say that B is premultiplied by A, or A is postmultiplied by B. If we write BA, then the reverse is true. In general, $AB \neq BA$. The proof of this is left as an exercise.

If $x = [x_1, x_2, \ldots, x_n]$ is a row vector, and $y = [y_1, y_2, \ldots, y_n]'$ is a column vector, then the inner product or scalar product of x and y is defined as

$$\{x, y\} = \sum_{i=1}^{n} x_i y_i. \tag{7.4.5}$$

When $\{x, y\} = 0$, the two vectors are said to be orthogonal. In the case where $y = x$, then

$$\{x, x\} = \sum_{i=1}^{n} x_i^2$$

is called the square of the magnitude (length) of the vector x. In general, if we have a set of vectors $x^1, x^2, \ldots, x^m$ such that

$$\{x^i, x^j\} = \begin{cases} 0, & i \neq j, \\ 1, & i = j, \end{cases} \tag{7.4.6}$$

the set of vectors is said to be an orthonormal set.

7.5 DETERMINANT VALUE, SINGULAR MATRICES, AND RANK

Let A denote a square matrix and $|A|$ the determinant formed from the elements of A. If $|A| \neq 0$, then the matrix A is called a nonsingular matrix.

Let C be a matrix of order $(m \times n)$. We may form a number of square subarrays or submatrices by deleting certain rows and/or columns and compressing the remaining elements into compact form. The rank of the given matrix is defined as the order of the largest such subarray whose determinant value is not zero.

7.6 INVERSION OF MATRICES

The matrix A^{-1}, having the property that

$$A^{-1}A = AA^{-1} = I, \tag{7.6.1}$$

is defined as the inverse of A. The inverse of a matrix exists only if the matrix is nonsingular.

From the theory of determinants, if the ith row and jth column are deleted from a matrix, and the remaining elements compressed, the determinant of this subarray is called the minor of the element a_{ij}. This minor with the appropriate sign determined by $(-1)^{i+j}$ is called the cofactor of the element a_{ij} and is denoted by A_{ij}. Thus we may write the cofactor matrix of the matrix A as

$$C_A = \begin{bmatrix} A_{11} & A_{12} & \cdots & A_{1n} \\ A_{21} & A_{22} & \cdots & A_{2n} \\ \vdots & & & \vdots \\ A_{n1} & A_{n2} & \cdots & A_{nn} \end{bmatrix} = [A_{ij}]. \tag{7.6.2}$$

The transpose of the cofactor matrix,

$$C_A^t = [A_{ij}]^t = [A_{ji}], \tag{7.6.3}$$

is called the adjoint of the matrix A. The inverse of A is then defined by

$$A^{-1} = \frac{[A_{ij}]^t}{|A|} = \frac{[A_{ji}]}{|A|}. \tag{7.6.4}$$

This method of finding the inverse is useful when A is of low order and the calculations are done by hand, or when A is composed of polynomial elements. A more appropriate method for large matrices is discussed in Chapter 8.

It has been mentioned that a singular matrix does not have an inverse. Another vaguely-defined term often used with matrices is "ill conditioned." Many attempts have been made to define this term, but usually it means we have troubles. It can be the result of very large elements, very small elements, or a wide range of elements. The term is associated with matrices whose determinant value is very small. An example of this is the Hilbert matrix, whose determinant is defined by

$$H_n = \left| \frac{1}{i + j - 1} \right| = \frac{[1!2!3! \cdots (n-1)!]^3}{n!(n+1)! \cdots (2n-1)!} \qquad (i, j = 1, 2, 3, \ldots, n). \tag{7.6.5}$$

The determinant value of H_n approaches zero very rapidly as n increases. For example, $H_2 = (8.3)10^{-2}$, $H_6 = (5.4)10^{-18}$, $H_7 = (4.8)10^{-25}$, and $H_9 = (9.7)10^{-43}$. Another definition of the term is that small changes in the elements of a matrix produce large changes in the results obtained from operations with the matrix.

A method of generating a set of matrices with exact integer elements and known inverses (for use in testing digital computer programs) is given in Appendix D.

7.7 THE EIGENVALUE PROBLEM

In this section we only define the basic eigenvalue problem. Methods of solving the problem will be discussed in detail in Chapter 9.

Given a square matrix A, we require those values of λ for which the set of linear equations

$$Ax = \lambda x \qquad (7.7.1)$$

has a nontrivial solution x. The values of λ_i are called the characteristic roots or eigenvalues and the corresponding vectors x^i are called the characteristic vectors or eigenvectors of the matrix A.

The eigenvalues of $Ax = \lambda x$ are given by those values of λ for which

$$|A - \lambda I| = 0. \qquad (7.2.2)$$

From this determinant we obtain a polynomial in λ of degree n (A is of order n). This polynomial is called the characteristic equation of A. We may write this as

$$a_0 + a_1\lambda + a_2\lambda^2 + \cdots + a_{n-1}\lambda^{n-1} + (-1)^n\lambda^n = 0. \qquad (7.7.3)$$

In general, this equation will have n solutions, $\lambda_1, \lambda_2, \ldots, \lambda_n$, and these values are the eigenvalues of A. If A is a real, symmetric matrix, the eigenvalues are all real.

If all the roots of Eq. (7.7.3) are distinct, though in general they may be real or complex, then the following apply:

a) For each i, the equation $[A - \lambda_i I]x^{(i)} - 0$ has only one independent solution, determined apart from an arbitrary multiplier. It is usual to choose this multiplier so as to give the vector $x^{(i)}$ some desirable numerical property. Such a vector is called a normalized eigenvector. The most common forms of normalization are as follows: (1) the sum of the squares of the components of $x^{(i)}$ is equal to one; (2) the largest component of $x^{(i)}$ is equal to one.

b) The set of vectors $x^{(i)}$ forms an independent set of vectors so we can express an arbitrary vector as a linear combination of the x^i.

If the characteristic equation has repeated roots, or closely spaced roots, then the problem of finding the eigenvectors may be difficult.

If A^t is the transpose of A, $[A - \lambda_i I]x^{(i)} = 0$ and $[A^t - \lambda_i I]y^{(i)} = 0$ will have the same λ_i, but $x^{(i)}$ and $y^{(i)}$ will be different except when A is symmetric.

The two sets of vectors, $x^{(i)}$ and $y^{(i)}$, are called biorthogonal. That is,

$$\{x^{(i)}, y^{(j)}\} = 0, \qquad i \neq j. \tag{7.7.4}$$

Example. Find the eigenvalues and eigenvectors of

$$A = \begin{bmatrix} 2 & 3 & 5 \\ 3 & 4 & 6 \\ 5 & 6 & 7 \end{bmatrix}. \tag{7.7.5}$$

Solution.

$$|A - \lambda I| = \begin{vmatrix} 2 - \lambda & 3 & 5 \\ 3 & 4 - \lambda & 6 \\ 5 & 6 & 7 - \lambda \end{vmatrix} \tag{7.7.6}$$

$$= 1 + 20\lambda + 13\lambda^2 - \lambda^3 = 0. \tag{7.7.7}$$

Solving the above characteristic polynomial for its roots, we obtain

$$\lambda_1 = 14.39427, \qquad \lambda_2 = -1.34250, \qquad \lambda_3 = -0.05177. \tag{7.7.8}$$

Solving the homogeneous linear equations, $[A - \lambda_i I]x^{(i)} = 0$ for $i = 1, 2, 3$, we obtain

$$x^{(1)} = \begin{bmatrix} 0.60108 \\ 0.73148 \\ 1 \end{bmatrix}, \quad x^{(2)} = \begin{bmatrix} -0.98362 \\ -0.57073 \\ 1 \end{bmatrix}, \quad \text{and} \quad x^{(3)} = \begin{bmatrix} 3.28833 \\ -3.91557 \\ 1 \end{bmatrix}. \tag{7.7.9}$$

7.8 HERMITIAN MATRICES, POSITIVE DEFINITE MATRICES

Given a matrix A with complex elements and $\overline{A}$ its complex conjugate. If

$$\overline{A} = A^t, \tag{7.8.1}$$

then the matrix is called Hermitian. We can show that the eigenvalues of a Hermitian matrix are real.

If a matrix A is Hermitian, it is said to be positive definite, if and only if each of the n principal (leading) minors is positive. The eigenvalues of a positive definite matrix are real and positive. For matrices in general, $x^t A x$ must be greater than zero for all $x \neq 0$.

7.9 ORTHOGONAL MATRICES, UNITARY MATRICES

A real matrix is orthogonal if the sum of the squares of the elements of each column is equal to one, and the sum of the products of corresponding elements of two different columns is equal to zero. This is denoted by

$$A^t A = I. \tag{7.9.1}$$

A matrix with complex elements is called a unitary matrix if the sum of the squares of the moduli of the elements of each column is equal to one, and the sum of the products of the elements of one column with numbers conjugate to corresponding elements of another column is equal to zero.

From these two definitions we have the following:

a) Orthogonal matrices are special cases of unitary matrices.
b) The identity matrix is orthogonal.
c) If A is orthogonal, then $A^{-1} = A^t$.
d) If A is orthogonal, then A^t is orthogonal.
e) The product of two orthogonal matrices is an orthogonal matrix.
f) If A is orthogonal, then $|A| = 1$ or -1.

7.10 THE JORDAN CANONICAL FORM

Since it is rather complicated to prove that a matrix may be reduced to the Jordan canonical form by a similarity transformation, we shall limit ourselves to a description of this form.

If $L_k(\lambda)$ is a $k \times k$ matrix, such that

$$L_k(\lambda) = \begin{bmatrix} \lambda & 0 & 0 & \cdots & 0 \\ 1 & \lambda & 0 & & \vdots \\ 0 & 1 & \lambda & & \\ \vdots & & & \ddots & 0 \\ 0 & \cdots & & 1 & \lambda \end{bmatrix}, \tag{7.10.1}$$

then $L_k(\lambda)$ is called a canonical box. It has lambdas on the principal diagonal, ones on the subdiagonal, and zeros everywhere else.

Given a matrix A, there exists a matrix T, such that

$$T^{-1}AT = \begin{bmatrix} L_{k1}(\lambda_1) & & & 0 \\ & L_{k2}(\lambda_2) & & \\ & & \ddots & \\ 0 & & & L_{kr}(\lambda_r) \end{bmatrix}, \tag{7.10.2}$$

with $k1 + k2 + \cdots + kr = n$. The λ_i are the eigenvalues of A, not necessarily all distinct. This is called the Jordan canonical form.

7.11 SIMILARITY TRANSFORMATIONS

The matrix B is similar to the matrix A if a nonsingular matrix C exists, such that

$$B = C^{-1}AC. \tag{7.11.1}$$

If C has the eigenvectors of A as its columns, C is called a modal matrix. The matrix B is then diagonal with the eigenvalues of A in corresponding columns. In this case, we write Eq. (7.11.1) as

$$D = X^{-1}AX. \tag{7.11.2}$$

In the special case where A is symmetric, the columns of the modal matrix X are mutually orthogonal and we have $X^{-1} = X^t$. Then Eq. (7.11.2) becomes

$$D = X^tAX, \tag{7.11.3}$$

and this is called an orthogonal similarity transformation. This type of transformation is used in Chapter 9 in the Jacobi method of finding eigenvalues and eigenvectors.

In fact, the diagonal elements of D in this type of similarity transformation are the eigenvalues of A, and the corresponding columns of the matrix X are the eigenvectors.

In addition, based on previous definitions, the sum of the eigenvalues is equal to the trace of A, and the product of the eigenvalues is equal to the determinant value of A.

7.12 VECTOR NORMS AND MATRIX NORMS

A quantity associated with vectors and matrices that is sometimes useful, particularly in theoretical considerations, is the norm. If $x = [x_1, x_2, \ldots, x_n]$ is a vector, there are three commonly used norms associated with it. These are defined as follows:

$$\text{a)} \qquad \|x\| = \max_i |x_i|, \tag{7.12.1}$$

$$\text{b)} \qquad \|x\| = \sum_{i=1}^n |x_i|, \tag{7.12.2}$$

$$\text{c)} \qquad \|x\| = \left\{ \sum_{i=1}^n |x_i|^2 \right\}^{1/2}. \tag{7.12.3}$$

The last of these is the length of the vector in Euclidean space.

The three norms associated with the matrix A correspond to the three vector norms above. They are

$$\text{d)} \qquad \|A\| = \max_i \sum_{j=1}^n |a_{ij}|, \tag{7.12.4}$$

which is the largest row sum of absolute values;

$$\text{e)} \qquad \|A\| = \max_j \sum_{i=1}^n |a_{ij}|, \tag{7.12.5}$$

which is the largest column sum of absolute values; and

$$\text{f)} \qquad \|A\| = \max_i \mu_i^{1/2}, \tag{7.12.6}$$

where the μ_i are the eigenvalues of $A^t A$, which is symmetric and positive definite. If $A^t A = B$, another norm associated with A is defined as

$$\text{g)} \qquad \|A\| = \left\{ \sum_{i,j} a_{ij}^2 \right\}^{1/2} = \left\{ \sum_i b_{ii} \right\}^{1/2} = \left\{ \sum_i \mu_i \right\}^{1/2}. \tag{7.12.7}$$

The quantity

$$\sum_i b_{ii} = \sum_i \mu_i \tag{7.12.8}$$

is the trace of the matrix B.

7.13 TRIANGULAR MATRICES

Matrices of the form

$$
L = \begin{bmatrix}
l_{11} & 0 & \cdots & 0 \\
l_{21} & l_{22} & \cdots & 0 \\
\vdots & & & \vdots \\
l_{n1} & l_{n2} & \cdots & l_{nn}
\end{bmatrix},
\tag{7.13.1}
$$

$$
U = \begin{bmatrix}
u_{11} & u_{12} & \cdots & u_{1n} \\
0 & u_{22} & \cdots & u_{2n} \\
\vdots & & & \vdots \\
0 & 0 & \cdots & u_{nn}
\end{bmatrix},
\tag{7.13.2}
$$

are called lower-triangular and upper-triangular matrices, respectively. Matrices of this form have special properties and are convenient in certain types of problems.

The determinant value of a triangular matrix is equal to the product of the elements on the principal diagonal.

On condition that the leading submatrices of the matrix A are nonsingular, i.e., that

$$
a_{11} \neq 0, \quad \begin{vmatrix} a_{11} & a_{12} \\ a_{21} & a_{22} \end{vmatrix} \neq 0, \quad \cdots,
\tag{7.13.3}
$$

A may be represented as the product of a lower-triangular matrix and an upper-triangular matrix.

Let

$$
A = CB.
\tag{7.13.4}
$$

Partition A into a bordered matrix as follows.

$$
A = \left[\begin{array}{ccc|c}
a_{11} & a_{12} & \cdots & a_{1n} \\
a_{21} & & \cdots & a_{2n} \\
\vdots & & & \vdots \\
a_{n1} & a_{n2} & \cdots & a_{nn}
\end{array}\right] = \begin{bmatrix} A_{n-1} & u \\ v & a_{nn} \end{bmatrix}.
\tag{7.13.5}
$$

Write

$$
C = \begin{bmatrix} C_{n-1} & 0 \\ x & c_{nn} \end{bmatrix} \quad \text{and} \quad B = \begin{bmatrix} B_{n-1} & y \\ 0 & b_{nn} \end{bmatrix}.
\tag{7.13.6}
$$

Thus

$$
CB = \begin{bmatrix} C_{n-1}B_{n-1} & C_{n-1}y \\ xB_{n-1} & xy + c_{nn}b_{nn} \end{bmatrix} = A,
\tag{7.13.7}
$$

and we have

$$
C_{n-1}B_{n-1} = A_{n-1}.
\tag{7.13.8}
$$

From the assumption that $|A_{n-1}| \neq 0$, it follows that $|C_{n-1}| \neq 0$ and $|B_{n-1}| \neq 0$.

Now x and y are found from

$$
x = vB_{n-1}^{-1}, \qquad y = C_{n-1}^{-1}u,
\tag{7.13.9}
$$

and we determine the diagonal elements c_{nn} and b_{nn} from the equation

$$
c_{nn}b_{nn} = a_{nn} - xy.
\tag{7.13.10}
$$

The decomposition of a matrix into the product of lower- and upper-triangular matrices will be unique if we prescribe values for the diagonal elements
of one of the triangular matrices. Thus, if $b_{ii} = 1$, $i = 1, 2, \ldots, n$, then

$$c_{nn} = a_{nn} - xy. \tag{7.13.11}$$

If A can be represented as the product of lower- and upper-triangular matrices,
that is, $A = LU$, then the determinant value of A is given by

$$|A| = |L|\,|U|. \tag{7.13.12}$$

Also, it can easily be shown that the transpose of A is

$$A^t = U^t L^t, \tag{7.13.13}$$

and the inverse of A is

$$A^{-1} = U^{-1} L^{-1}. \tag{7.13.14}$$

Another approach, which is very convenient for machine computation, will
be discussed in connection with the Crout reduction in Chapter 8. We now discuss a special triangular matrix which will be useful to us in Chapter 9. This is
the reduction of the full matrix to the lower Hessenberg matrix.

For any nonsingular matrix P, the matrix PAP^{-1} is similar to A and has the
same eigenvalues.

There is a simple, accurate way in which $\frac{1}{2}(n - 1)(n - 2)$ of the elements of
a full $n \times n$ matrix may be eliminated by similarity transformations. If all the
elements of a matrix above the superdiagonal [the $(i, i + 1)$ elements] are zero,
it is called a lower Hessenberg matrix.

Let us now consider two methods of transforming an $n \times n$ matrix A to the
lower Hessenberg type.

1) Interchange the ith and jth columns of A, and then interchange the ith and
jth rows of the resulting matrix. Add a multiple of row i to row j, and in the
resulting matrix, subtract the same multiple of column j from column i.

These can be expressed in terms of pre- and post-multiplication of A by suitable matrices P and P^{-1}. We eliminate every element in row 1 except for the
first two elements. Then we eliminate row 2 except for the first three elements,
and so on.

2) Suppose

$$|a_{1k}| = \max_j |a_{1j}| \qquad \text{for } j = 2, \ldots, n.$$

If k is not 2, then interchange columns 2 and k, and then rows 2 and k. Now
subtract suitable multiples of column 2 from columns 3 through n to produce
zeros in positions $(1, 3)$, $(1, 4)$, $\ldots$, $(1, n)$. The multipliers will be

$$m_{1j} = \frac{a_{1j}}{a_{12}}, \qquad j = 3, 4, \ldots, n. \tag{7.13.15}$$

Now add these same multiples of rows 3 through n to row 2. This does not destroy
the zeros in row 1, and it gives us a new matrix similar to the original matrix.

Element (1, 2) is called the pivot element in the above transformation. We can now operate in like manner on this new matrix to produce zeros in row 2, using (2, 3) as pivot.

J. H. Wilkinson* discusses the error analysis of this method. Parlett [120] gives a detailed discussion of organizing the computation on a computer.

7.14 TRIDIAGONAL MATRICES

A matrix with nonzero elements on the principal diagonal, the superdiagonal [the $(i, i + 1)$ elements], the subdiagonal [the $(i + 1, i)$ elements], and zeros everywhere else, is called a tridiagonal matrix (7.3.2). We now mention three methods of transforming a matrix to tridiagonal form.

1) The two methods discussed in Section 7.13 for reducing a full matrix to lower Hessenberg type can be extended to produce zero elements below the subdiagonal.

2) Parlett [120] discusses in detail a method which is applicable to any matrix, but is particularly simple for the lower Hessenberg type.

3) If the matrix A is a real symmetric matrix, the orthogonal similarity transformation (7.11.3), as discussed in the Jacobi method in Chapter 9, is also appropriate. The only difference is that we stop the transformation without reducing the elements on the superdiagonal and subdiagonal to zero.

7.15 SUPPLEMENTARY REFERENCES

Matrix analysis in general and a more extensive coverage of the topics presented in this chapter may be found in the following references: Bellman [7], Bodewig [9], Fadeev and Fadeeva [43b], Fox [52b], Householder [77], Perlis [121], Varga [154].

EXERCISES

1. Find $A - B$ when

$$A = \begin{bmatrix} 1.4 & 2.3 & 3.7 \\ 3.3 & 1.6 & 4.3 \\ 2.5 & 1.9 & 4.1 \end{bmatrix} \quad \text{and} \quad B = \begin{bmatrix} -2 & 1 & 3 \\ 4 & 5 & -4 \\ 1 & -3 & 2 \end{bmatrix}.$$

2. Multiply A in Exercise 1 by the scalar 2.

3. Using the two matrices given in Exercise 1, find the product AB.

4. Using the two matrices given in Exercise 1, find the product BA.

5. Derive a proof that, in general, $AB \neq BA$.

---

* J. H. Wilkinson, "Stability of the Reduction of a Matrix to Almost Triangular and Triangular Form by Elementary Similarity Transformations," *J. Assoc. Comp. M.* **6** (1956), pp. 336–359.

6. Given $u = [2, -3, 1]$ and $v = [-3, 2, 1]$, find the scalar product uv.

7. Find the length of vector u given in Exercise 6.

8. If $u = [2, -3, 2]$ and $v = [4, 2, -1]$, show that u and v are orthogonal.

9. Find the determinant value of matrix A given in Exercise 1.

10. Find the inverse of matrix A given in Exercise 1.

11. For the matrix of Exercise 10. Show that $A^{-1}A = I$.

12. Find the eigenvalues and eigenvectors of the matrix A when

$$A = \begin{bmatrix} -1 & 6 \\ 1 & 0 \end{bmatrix}.$$

13. Find the eigenvalues and eigenvectors of A^t. Use the matrix A given in Exercise 12.

14. Show that the eigenvectors of Exercises 12 and 13 are biorthogonal.

15. Show that X is orthogonal when

$$X = \begin{bmatrix} 1/\sqrt{3} & 0 & 1/\sqrt{3} & 1/\sqrt{3} \\ 0 & 1/\sqrt{3} & 1/\sqrt{3} & -1/\sqrt{3} \\ 1/\sqrt{3} & 1/\sqrt{3} & -1/\sqrt{3} & 0 \\ 1/\sqrt{3} & -1/\sqrt{3} & 0 & -1/\sqrt{3} \end{bmatrix}.$$

16. Using the matrix X given in Exercise 15, find the matrix D of Eq. (7.11.3) when

$$A = \begin{bmatrix} 11 & 1 & 6 & 7 \\ 1 & 7 & 2 & -3 \\ 6 & 2 & 14 & 4 \\ 7 & -3 & 4 & 13 \end{bmatrix}.$$

17. Find the determinant value of the matrix X given in Exercise 15.

18. Find the determinant value of the matrix A given in Exercise 16.

19. Show that matrix A given in Exercise 16 is positive definite.

20. Find the norm (7.12.7) of matrix A given in Exercise 16.

21. Find the trace of matrix A given in Exercise 16.

22. Given

$$L = \begin{bmatrix} 1.4 & 0 & 0 \\ 3.3 & -3.82144 & 0 \\ 2.5 & -2.20715 & 0.04654 \end{bmatrix} \quad \text{and} \quad U = \begin{bmatrix} 1 & 1.64286 & 2.64286 \\ 0 & 1 & 1.15701 \\ 0 & 0 & 1 \end{bmatrix},$$

show that LU is equal to the matrix A given in Exercise 1.

23. Find the determinant value of matrix A using the L and U given in Exercise 22.

CHAPTER 8

LINEAR ALGEBRAIC EQUATIONS

8.1 INTRODUCTION

A set of simultaneous linear equations may be represented algebraically by

$$\left.\begin{array}{c} a_{11}x_1 + a_{12}x_2 + \cdots + a_{1n}x_n = b_1 \\ a_{21}x_1 + a_{22}x_2 + \cdots + a_{2n}x_n = b_2 \\ \vdots \qquad\qquad\qquad \vdots \\ a_{n1}x_1 + a_{n2}x_2 + \cdots + a_{nn}x_n = b_n \end{array}\right\} \tag{8.1.1}$$

We write these same equations in matrix notation as

$$\begin{bmatrix} a_{11} & a_{12} & \cdots & a_{1n} \\ a_{21} & a_{22} & \cdots & a_{2n} \\ \vdots & & & \vdots \\ a_{n1} & a_{n2} & \cdots & a_{nn} \end{bmatrix} \begin{bmatrix} x_1 \\ x_2 \\ \vdots \\ x_n \end{bmatrix} = \begin{bmatrix} b_1 \\ b_2 \\ \vdots \\ b_n \end{bmatrix} \tag{8.1.2}$$

or

$$Ax = b, \tag{8.1.3}$$

where A is the coefficient matrix, x is the solution vector, and b is the constant vector.

If the above system is written in the form of the augmented matrix (7.3.4), it is solvable if and only if the rank (Section 7.5) of the coefficient matrix is equal to the rank of the augmented matrix.

Methods of solving the above system are classified as direct, iterative, gradient, and orthogonalization methods. We shall discuss some of the methods in these classifications, and then give a comparison of them.

8.2 METHOD OF DETERMINANTS

Let us assume a system of n equations in n unknowns in the form

$$Ax = b,$$

where A is the coefficient matrix, x is the solution vector, and b is a constant vector. We shall denote the determinant value of A, $|A|$, by Δ. If the determinant of A with its ith column replaced by the b vector is denoted by D_i, then

$$x_i = D_i/\Delta, \qquad i = 1, 2, \ldots, n. \tag{8.2.1}$$

This determinant method is not advised for $n > 8$, say.

Example. Solve the following system of equations by the method of determinants:

$$\begin{aligned}
1.4x_1 + 2.3x_2 + 3.7x_3 &= 6.5, \\
3.3x_1 + 1.6x_2 + 4.3x_3 &= 10.3, \\
2.5x_1 + 1.9x_2 + 4.1x_3 &= 8.8.
\end{aligned} \qquad (8.2.2)$$

Solution. We calculate

$$\Delta = \begin{vmatrix} 1.4 & 2.3 & 3.7 \\ 3.3 & 1.6 & 4.3 \\ 2.5 & 1.9 & 4.1 \end{vmatrix} = -0.249,$$

$$x_1 = \frac{D_1}{\Delta} = \frac{\begin{vmatrix} 6.5 & 2.3 & 3.7 \\ 10.3 & 1.6 & 4.3 \\ 8.8 & 1.9 & 4.1 \end{vmatrix}}{\Delta} = \frac{-0.249}{-0.249} = 1,$$

$$x_2 = \frac{D_2}{\Delta} = \frac{\begin{vmatrix} 1.4 & 6.5 & 3.7 \\ 3.3 & 10.3 & 4.3 \\ 2.5 & 8.8 & 4.1 \end{vmatrix}}{\Delta} = \frac{0.249}{-0.249} = -1,$$

$$x_3 = \frac{D_3}{\Delta} = \frac{\begin{vmatrix} 1.4 & 2.3 & 6.5 \\ 3.3 & 1.6 & 10.3 \\ 2.5 & 1.9 & 8.8 \end{vmatrix}}{\Delta} = \frac{-0.498}{-0.249} = 2.$$

8.3 ELIMINATION, PIVOTING, AND SCALING

Almost all methods for the numerical solution of a system of equations that do not depend on special properties of the matrix such as sparseness, positive definiteness, etc., are variations of elimination or triangularization. They can be thought of as the decomposition of A into a lower-triangular matrix L and an upper-triangular matrix U, so that $A = LU$. The matrices L and U are uniquely determined by A if we specify, for example, that the elements on the main diagonal of L must all be ones. The main diagonal elements of U are then the pivot elements. When we have obtained L and U, the solution of $Ax = b$ is completed by successively solving two triangular systems, $Lz = b$ and $Ux = z$, by successive substitution.

The variation of different methods is principally in the order in which the calculations are done. In the simple Gaussian elimination, as it is usually done, the manipulation of the right-hand side during the "forward pass" is equivalent to solving $Lz = b$, while the "back substitution" is equivalent to solving $Ux = z$.

Elimination of the variables in some predetermined order is not always possible, since this may lead to a zero coefficient for a pivot element. Similarly, when doing the calculations with only finite precision, one should avoid near-zero or comparatively small pivot elements by reordering the matrix and variables as required during the procedure. This leads to consideration of some form of pivotal strategy. It may be impossible to find the best strategy without further assumptions about A.

Two of the most popular and easily programmed pivotal strategies are partial pivoting and complete pivoting. In partial pivoting the columns are considered in consecutive order, and a search is made for the maximum element within the column. The process would stop if every element in the current pivotal column is zero, since the matrix is singular. With complete pivoting, the largest element in the entire unreduced matrix is used for the pivot at each stage.

Since a pivotal strategy usually requires size comparisons between the matrix elements, some form of scaling of the unknowns and equations may be necessary. The need for scaling (other than multiplication by a scalar) usually arises when there is a considerable range in the magnitude among the elements of the matrix. In such a case the smaller elements may be effectively zero. Scaling should not be used blindly. Sometimes scaling sets up a combination of numbers such that no scaling gives the best results. Scaling, in general, is not an easy problem. It is both an art and a science that requires experience, insight, skill and luck. Chapter 10 is devoted exclusively to scaling.

8.4 ITERATIVE IMPROVEMENT

The roundoff error in the calculation of L, U, z, and x causes the solution x_1 to have some error, ϵ_1. If the true solution $A^{-1}b$ is denoted by x, then ϵ_1 is defined by

$$\epsilon_1 = x - x_1. \tag{8.4.1}$$

The error ϵ_1 cannot be calculated because x is not known. However, the residuals r_1, defined by

$$r_1 = b - Ax_1 = A\epsilon_1, \tag{8.4.2}$$

can be computed, at least approximately. Thus ϵ_1 and hence x could be obtained by solving $A\epsilon_1 = r_1$. This system cannot be solved exactly, but an approximate solution $\bar{\epsilon}_1$ can be obtained, and this provides a correction to x_1 and an improved solution $x_2 = x_1 + \bar{\epsilon}_1$. The process is repeated until some kind of convergence criterion is, hopefully, satisfied.

This problem, with scaling, is discussed in detail by Cleve Moler [110]. Moler states that, roughly speaking, we can say that if x_1 is correct to s figures, then $\bar{\epsilon}_1$ will also be correct to s figures and x_2 will be correct to $2s$ figures, x_3 to $3s$ figures, etc. The convergence is therefore linear. If A is so poorly conditioned that $s = 0$, then no improvement and, hence, no convergence is obtained.

The feature that makes this procedure practical is the fact that the matrix A is involved in all the systems that are solved during the iteration. That is,

$$Ax_1 = b, \; A\bar{\epsilon}_1 = r_1, \; A\bar{\epsilon}_2 = r_2, \ldots . \tag{8.4.3}$$

Thus we need only calculate L and U once and save them. Since this calculation takes the greatest part of the time involved, the amount of time taken by solving systems during the iterative improvement is comparatively small.

8.5 GAUSS ELIMINATION

The simplest practical method of solving the set of equations represented by
(8.1.1) is due to Gauss. It consists of dividing the first equation by a_{11} and using
the result to eliminate x_1 from all succeeding equations. Next, the modified
second equation is divided by the coefficient of x_2 and the result is used to eliminate
x_2 from the succeeding equations, and so on. After this elimination has been
effected n times, when $|A| \neq 0$, the resultant set, which is equivalent to the original
one except for roundoff, is of the form

$$
\begin{aligned}
x_1 + a'_{12}x_2 + a'_{13}x_3 + \cdots + a'_{1n}x_n &= b'_1, \\
x_2 + a'_{23}x_3 + \cdots + a'_{2n}x_n &= b'_2, \\
&\vdots \\
x_{n-1} + a'_{n-1,n}x_n &= b'_{n-1}, \\
x_n &= b'_n,
\end{aligned}
\tag{8.5.1}
$$

and the solution is completed by backward substitution.

The case in which $|A| = 0$ is evident through the fact that after r such elimina-
tions, where r is the rank of the coefficient matrix, all coefficients in the $n - r$
succeeding equations will vanish (except for roundoff). Unless all right-hand
members of those equations are also reduced to zeros at that stage, the original
set will be unsolvable. If all those members are zeros, the $n - r$ equations are
reduced to $0 = 0$, and can be ignored. The rth equation would express x_r as
the sum of a specified constant and a certain linear combination of $x_{r+1}, \ldots, x_n$,
and the process of backward substitution finally expresses $x_1, \ldots, x_r$ in similar
form.

Example 1. Solve the system of equations in (8.2.2) by Gauss elimination without pivoting.

Solution.

$$
\begin{aligned}
x_1 + 1.64286x_2 + 2.64286x_3 &= 4.64286, \\
- 3.82144x_2 - 4.42144x_3 &= -5.02144, \\
- 2.20715x_2 - 2.50715x_3 &= -2.80715;
\end{aligned}
\tag{8.5.2}
$$

$$
\begin{aligned}
x_1 + 1.64286x_2 + 2.64286x_3 &= 4.64286, \\
x_2 + 1.15701x_3 &= 1.31042, \\
0.04654x_3 &= 0.09309;
\end{aligned}
\tag{8.5.3}
$$

$$
\begin{aligned}
x_1 + 1.64286x_2 + 2.64286x_3 &= 4.64286, \\
x_2 + 1.15701x_3 &= 1.31402, \\
x_3 &= 2.00021.
\end{aligned}
\tag{8.5.4}
$$

By backward substitution, we obtain

$$
x_2 = -1.00014 \quad \text{and} \quad x_1 = 0.99967.
\tag{8.5.5}
$$

Example 2. Solve the system of Example 1 by Gauss elimination using partial
pivoting.

Solution. Interchanging Equations 1 and 2, we obtain the system

$$3.3x_1 + 1.6x_2 + 4.3x_3 = 10.3,$$
$$1.4x_1 + 2.3x_2 + 3.7x_3 = 6.5, \qquad (8.5.6)$$
$$2.5x_1 + 1.9x_2 + 4.1x_3 = 8.8.$$

Dividing 1 by 3.3 and eliminating x_1 from 2 and 3, we have

$$x_1 + 0.48485x_2 + 1.30303x_3 = 3.12121,$$
$$1.62121x_2 + 1.87576x_3 = 2.13031, \qquad (8.5.7)$$
$$0.68788x_2 + 0.84242x_3 = 0.99698;$$

$$x_1 + 0.48485x_2 + 1.30303x_3 = 3.12121,$$
$$x_2 + 1.15701x_3 = 1.31402, \qquad (8.5.8)$$
$$0.04654x_3 = 0.09309;$$

$$x_1 + 0.48485x_2 + 1.30303x_3 = 3.12121,$$
$$x_2 + 1.15701x_3 = 1.31402, \qquad (8.5.9)$$
$$x_3 = 2.00021.$$

Then by backward substitution, we obtain

$$x_2 = -1.00014 \quad \text{and} \quad x_1 = 0.99880. \qquad (8.5.10)$$

8.6 CROUT REDUCTION

A modification of the Gauss elimination, which is well adapted to high-speed computers and minimizes storage of auxiliary data, is due to P. D. Crout. Starting with the augmented (see Eq. 7.3.4) matrix, $M = [A\!:\!b]$, of the original system, which may be considered as being partitioned into the coefficient array A, and the b column, one determines the elements of an auxiliary matrix $M' = [A'\!:\!b']$, of the same dimensions, which may be considered as being partitioned into a square array A' and a b' column. From this matrix, one then obtains a solution column x.

The instructions for accomplishing this are now given, first verbally, and then in formula.

a) The elements of the first column of M' are identical to the corresponding elements of M; the remaining elements of the first row of M' (to the right of the diagonal element a'_{11}) are each obtained by dividing the corresponding element of M by the diagonal element a'_{11}. Thus,

$$a'_{11} = a_{11}, a'_{21} = a_{21}, \ldots, a'_{n1} = a_{n1},$$
$$a'_{12} = \frac{a_{12}}{a'_{11}}, \ldots, a'_{1n} = a_{1n}/a'_{11}. \qquad (8.6.1)$$

b) Each element on or below the principal diagonal in M' is obtained by subtracting, from the corresponding element in M, the inner product of its own column and its own row in M', with all uncalculated elements taken as zeros.

c) Each element to the right of the principal diagonal in M' is calculated as in (b) and then divided by the diagonal element in its row of M'.

d) The elements of the solution column x are determined in the order x_n, $x_{n-1}, \ldots, x_2, x_1$, from foot to head. The element $x_n = b'_n$. Each succeeding element is obtained as the result of subtracting, from the corresponding element in the b' column, the inner product of its row in A' and the x column, with all uncalculated elements of the x column taken to be zeros.

The preceding instructions may be summarized by the following formulas, in addition to the ones given in (a) above:

$$\text{b)} \qquad a'_{ij} = a_{ij} - \sum_{k=1}^{j-1} a'_{ik}a'_{kj}, \qquad i \geq j, \tag{8.6.2}$$

$$\text{c)} \qquad a'_{ij} = \frac{1}{a'_{ii}}\left[a_{ij} - \sum_{k=1}^{i-1} a'_{ik}a'_{kj}\right], \qquad i < j,$$

$$b'_i = \frac{1}{a'_{ii}}\left[b_i - \sum_{k=1}^{i-1} a'_{ik}b'_k\right], \tag{8.6.3}$$

$$\text{d)} \qquad x_i = b'_i - \sum_{k=i+1}^{n} a'_{ik}x_k. \tag{8.6.4}$$

Example. Solve the example of Section 8.2 by the Crout reduction method.

Solution.

$$M = \begin{bmatrix} 1.4 & 2.3 & 3.7 & \vdots & 6.5 \\ 3.3 & 1.6 & 4.3 & \vdots & 10.3 \\ 2.5 & 1.9 & 4.1 & \vdots & 8.8 \end{bmatrix} = [A \vdots b] \tag{8.6.5}$$

$$a'_{11} = 1.4, \qquad a'_{21} = 3.3, \qquad a'_{31} = 2.5,$$

$$a'_{12} = \frac{2.3}{1.4} = 1.64286, \qquad a'_{13} = \frac{3.7}{1.4} = 2.64286,$$

$$b'_1 = \frac{6.5}{1.4} = 4.64286,$$

$$a'_{22} = a_{22} - a'_{21}a'_{12} = -3.82144,$$

$$a'_{32} = a_{32} - a'_{31}a'_{12} = -2.20715,$$

$$a'_{23} = \frac{1}{a'_{22}}[a_{23} - a'_{21}a'_{13}] = 1.15701,$$

$$b'_2 = \frac{1}{a'_{22}}[b_2 - a'_{21}b'_1] = 1.31402,$$

$$a'_{33} = a_{33} - [a'_{31}a'_{13} + a'_{32}a'_{23}] = 0.04654,$$

$$b'_3 = \frac{1}{a'_{33}}\{b_3 - [a'_{31}b'_1 + a'_{32}b'_2]\} = 2.00021.$$

and
$$M' = \begin{bmatrix} 1.4 & 1.64286 & 2.64286 & \vdots & 4.64286 \\ 3.3 & -3.82144 & 1.15701 & \vdots & 1.31402 \\ 2.5 & -2.20715 & 0.04654 & \vdots & 2.00021 \end{bmatrix} = [A':b']. \qquad (8.6.6)$$

Therefore
$$x_3 = b'_3 = 2.00021,$$
$$x_2 = b'_2 - a'_{23}x_3 = -1.00014,$$
$$x_1 = b'_1 - [a'_{12}x_2 + a'_{13}x_3] = 0.99967.$$

8.7 TRIANGULAR MATRICES FROM CROUT REDUCTION

The Crout reduction provides another method of obtaining upper- and lower-triangular matrices as discussed in Section 7.13. From A', as computed in the previous section, lower- and upper-triangular matrices may be obtained in the form

$$L = \begin{bmatrix} x & 0 & 0 \\ x & x & 0 \\ x & x & x \end{bmatrix} \quad \text{and} \quad U = \begin{bmatrix} 1 & x & x \\ 0 & 1 & x \\ 0 & 0 & 1 \end{bmatrix}. \qquad (8.7.1)$$

For example, from Eq. (8.6.6) we may write

$$L = \begin{bmatrix} 1.4 & 0 & 0 \\ 3.3 & -3.82144 & 0 \\ 2.5 & -2.20715 & 0.04654 \end{bmatrix} \quad \text{and} \quad U = \begin{bmatrix} 1 & 1.64286 & 2.64286 \\ 0 & 1 & 1.15701 \\ 0 & 0 & 1 \end{bmatrix}. \qquad (8.7.2)$$

These are two matrices such that the original matrix $A = LU$. It may also be observed that U is the triangular form obtained in (8.5.4) by Gauss elimination. Matrices of the form,

$$L = \begin{bmatrix} 1 & 0 & 0 \\ x & 1 & 0 \\ x & x & 1 \end{bmatrix} \quad \text{and} \quad U = \begin{bmatrix} x & x & x \\ 0 & x & x \\ 0 & 0 & x \end{bmatrix}, \qquad (8.7.3)$$

are obtained by appropriate modification of the formulas given in Section 8.6. If $A = [a'_{ij}]$, then $A' = [a'_{ij}]$, where

$$a'_{1j} = a_{1j}, \qquad j = 1, 2, \ldots, n,$$
$$a'_{i1} = \frac{a_{i1}}{a_{11}}, \qquad i = 1, 2, \ldots, n,$$
$$a'_{ij} = a_{ij} - \sum_{k=1}^{i-1} a'_{ik}a'_{kj}, \qquad i \le j, \qquad (8.7.4)$$
$$a'_{ij} = \frac{1}{a'_{ii}}\left[a_{ij} - \sum_{k=1}^{i-1} a'_{ik}a'_{kj} \right], \qquad i > j.$$

Lower- and upper-triangular matrices of the form given in (8.7.3) may then be obtained from A'.

8.8 INVERSE METHOD

In Section 7.6 the inverse of a matrix A was discussed. By definition, the inverse A^{-1} is that matrix such that

$$A^{-1}A = AA^{-1} = I.$$

Making use of this fact and multiplying the matrix equation $Ax = b$ by A^{-1}, we obtain

$$A^{-1}Ax = A^{-1}b,$$

or

$$x = A^{-1}b. \tag{8.8.1}$$

Thus, the solution vector x can be obtained by premultiplying the column vector of constants b by A^{-1}.

In Section 7.6, we discussed the possibility of finding the inverse by using the adjoint matrix. A more appropriate method on high-speed digital computers is by means of Gauss elimination or Crout reduction. In the matrix equation $Ax = b$, if the b column consists of the first column of the unit matrix, that is,

$$b = [1, 0, \ldots, 0]^t,$$

and the system is solved by Gauss elimination or Crout reduction, the solution vector x is the first column of A^{-1}. Solving the system again with

$$b = [0, 1, 0, \ldots, 0]^t,$$

the second column of the identity matrix, we obtain the second column of A^{-1}, and so on.

In 1961, J. H. Wilkinson discussed* roundoff errors in matrix inversion. Wilkinson suggests that in floating-point arithmetic additions be done in double precision, divisions be done with a double-precision dividend and single-precision divisor, and multiplication be done in single precision. In some cases, simply reading in the data might be enough to perturb the given system beyond recognition. Wilkinson suggests double-precision numbers throughout, as opposed to better inversion schemes involving more operations. Almost invariably, when Gauss elimination yields poor results, it is due to the matrix of the system rather than the technique used.

Moler [110] suggests a feature which allows exact accumulation of inner products. With this feature, one formulates numerical methods so that the critical arithmetic takes the form of a vector inner product.

Example. Find the inverse of A in Eq. (8.2.2) by the Crout reduction and then obtain the solution of the system.

Solution. Using $c = [1, 0, 0]^t$ in $Ay = c$, and solving by Crout reduction, we obtain

$$y = [6.46633, 11.16539, -9.11710]^t.$$

---

* See pp. 281–330 of No. 3 of the Journal of the Association for Computing Machinery.

Using $c = [0, 1, 0]^t$, we obtain

$$y = [9.63894, 14.09702, -12.41018]^t.$$

Then using $c = [0, 0, 1]^t$, we obtain

$$y = [-15.94444, -24.86055, 21.48689]^t.$$

Therefore

$$A^{-1} = \begin{bmatrix} 6.46633 & 9.63894 & -15.94444 \\ 11.16539 & 14.09702 & -24.86055 \\ -9.11710 & -12.41018 & 21.48689 \end{bmatrix}. \qquad (8.8.2)$$

Now, since $x = A^{-1}b$, if we premultiply $b = [6.5, 10.3, 8.8]^t$ (from Eq. 8.2.2) by the above inverse, we obtain the solution vector x.

8.9 JORDAN ELIMINATION

It is possible to extend the Gauss elimination method so that the equations are reduced to a form in which the matrix is diagonal, and no back substitution is required. The pivots are chosen as in the Gauss method, but elements are also eliminated from the previous pivotal rows, the actual pivots being unaffected since the other elements in previous pivotal columns are zero.

Example. Solve the following system by Jordan elimination:

$$\begin{aligned} 2x_1 + 3x_2 + 2x_3 &= 2, \\ 10x_1 + 3x_2 + 4x_3 &= 16, \\ 3x_1 + 6x_2 + x_3 &= -6. \end{aligned} \qquad (8.9.1)$$

Solution. Forming the augmented matrix $[A \vdots b]$, and applying the Jordan elimination, we obtain the following sequence of matrices:

$$\begin{bmatrix} 2 & 3 & 2 & 2 \\ 10 & 3 & 4 & 16 \\ 3 & 6 & 1 & -6 \end{bmatrix}, \quad \begin{bmatrix} 1 & \frac{3}{2} & 1 & 1 \\ 0 & -12 & -6 & 6 \\ 0 & \frac{3}{2} & -2 & -9 \end{bmatrix}, \quad \begin{bmatrix} 1 & \frac{3}{2} & 1 & 1 \\ 0 & 1 & \frac{1}{2} & -\frac{1}{2} \\ 0 & \frac{3}{2} & 2 & -9 \end{bmatrix},$$

$$\begin{bmatrix} 1 & 0 & \frac{1}{4} & \frac{7}{4} \\ 0 & 1 & \frac{1}{2} & -\frac{1}{2} \\ 0 & 0 & -\frac{11}{4} & -\frac{33}{4} \end{bmatrix}, \quad \begin{bmatrix} 1 & 0 & 0 & 1 \\ 0 & 1 & 0 & -2 \\ 0 & 0 & 1 & 3 \end{bmatrix}.$$

The last matrix is $[I \vdots c]$ and can be written as $Ix = c$ or $x = c$. Therefore, the solution vector x is $[1, -2, 3]^t$ or $x_1 = 1$, $x_2 = -2$, and $x_3 = 3$.

8.10 ITERATIVE METHODS

In most iterative methods the system of equations is solved for the solution vector $x_1, x_2, \ldots, x_n$. Then we start with an arbitrary first approximation and hopefully improve it successively, stopping when the required precision is reached.

We now consider the determination of the condition under which a linear iterative process for determining the solution of $Ax = b$ converges. Suppose the kth approximation to the solution vector x is x_k, and that the $(k + 1)$ approximation to the solution vector is x_{k+1}, as determined by

$$x_{k+1} = H_k x_k + V_k. \tag{8.10.1}$$

This describes a linear iterative process for determining the solution. It leads to a solution only if the process converges. The process is said to be a stationary linear process for H_k and V_k identical for all k. Thus the stationary linear process is

$$x = Hx + V, \tag{8.10.2}$$

so

$$V = (I - H)x = (I - H)A^{-1}b \tag{8.10.3}$$

and

$$x_{k+1} = Hx_k + (I - H)A^{-1}b. \tag{8.10.4}$$

Then

$$(x_{k+1} - A^{-1}b) = H(x_k - A^{-1}b), \tag{8.10.5}$$

and successive applications of the above leads to

$$(x_{k+1} - A^{-1}b) = H^k(x_1 - A^{-1}b). \tag{8.10.6}$$

Now, $x_1 - A^{-1}b$ is a constant vector which is determined by the first approximation. So the convergence of x_{k+1} to x, if it exists, must result from the power sequence H^k. It is possible to prove that convergence is present only when the eigenvalues of H are less than unity in absolute value.

A classical stationary linear iterative process is the so-called Gauss-Seidel method for solving $Ax = b$. Here H is taken to be the matrix $-A_1^{-1}A_2$, where A_1 is the lower-triangular matrix (including the diagonal elements), with its non-zero elements equal to the corresponding elements in A. The matrix A_2 is the upper-triangular matrix with its nonzero elements equal to the corresponding elements in A. Hence, the process converges to a solution if the eigenvalues of $A_1^{-1}A_2$ are less than unity in absolute value.

For the Gauss-Seidel method the system given, (8.1.1), can be written as

$$x_1^{(i+1)} = \frac{1}{a_{11}}(b_1 - a_{12}x_2^{(i)} - a_{13}x_3^{(i)} \cdots - a_{1n}x_n^{(i)}),$$

$$x_2^{(i+1)} = \frac{1}{a_{22}}(b_2 - a_{21}x_1^{(i)} - a_{23}x_3^{(i)} \cdots - a_{2n}x_n^{(i)}), \tag{8.10.7}$$

$$\vdots$$

$$x_n^{(i+1)} = \frac{1}{a_{nn}}(b_n - a_{n1}x_1^{(i)} \cdots - a_{n-1}x_{n-1}^{(i)}).$$

This method is most suitable if the matrix A can be ordered so that each diagonal element is large, compared to all the other elements in its row, i.e., the matrix is strongly diagonal. One possible set of starting values can be obtained by setting all x's in the right members of Eq. (8.10.7) equal to zero.

Iterative methods with extensions and full theoretical and practical details are discussed in R. S. Varga's book, *Matrix Iterative Analysis* (Prentice-Hall, 1962).

8.11 GRADIENT METHODS

The common basis of most gradient methods is the examination of certain functions whose minima are given by the solutions of linear equations. Some of these methods are iterative by truncating an infinite sequence of operations. Others are finite and direct. Gradient methods have been discussed extensively in the literature. We refer particularly to the article by G. E. Forsythe, "Solving Linear Algebraic Equations Can Be Interesting," (*Bull. Amer. Math. Soc.* **59**, 1953, pp. 299–329).

8.12 ORTHOGONALIZATION METHODS

These methods have a common basis in that the required solution, x, of the linear equations $Ax = b$, is obtained as a linear combination of a special set of vectors, whose properties permit easy evaluation of the coefficients of this combination. Such special vectors might satisfy certain orthogonality properties.

However, these methods, even though expressed in different language, are effectively equivalent to one of our various elimination methods, and as such, their practical value for actual computation is very small.

An excellent discussion of this and similar processes is found in M. R. Hestenes, "Inversion of Matrices by Biorthogonalization and Related Results," (*J. Soc. Indust. Appl. Math.* **6**, 1958, pp. 51–90).

8.13 COMPARISON OF METHODS

L. Fox (*An Introduction to Numerical Linear Algebra*, Clarenden Press, Oxford, 1964) gives the following evaluation and comparison of methods:

a) There is no point in evaluating an inverse for the purpose of solving the system $Ax = b$. Elimination and back substitution, or its compact equivalents, are faster, and the inverse should be obtained only if it is needed explicity.

b) The Jordan method is considerably slower than the other elimination methods. Programming for a computer may be easier since no back substitution is required, but computation time may be longer. Also, an error analysis becomes more complicated.

c) For solving a general set of equations, the compact elimination with interchanges is superior to other methods when scalar products can be accumulated accurately, since the "perturbed" equations have smaller upper bounds and neither the arithmetic nor the computer storage is greater than that of lengthy elimination with interchanges.

d) For the symmetric case, the compact elimination with interchanges is recommended, taking no account of symmetry, unless the symmetric matrix is also positive definite. In the latter case the decomposition $A = LL^t$ has significant advantages. The first is that, if every $|a_{rs}| < 1$, then $|l_{rs}| < 1$, and there are no scaling problems at this stage. Moreover, the computed LL^t is then $A + \delta A$, where $|(\delta A)_{rs}|$ does not exceed a single rounding error when scalar products are accumulated accurately. This is not true for the Gauss process with pivots taken down the diagonal, for the multipliers might still exceed unity.

e) There would appear to be no advantage in the use of the orthogonalization methods, in view of their close relationships with the various elimination methods.

EXERCISES

1. Solve the system of equations given in (8.9.1) by the inverse method.

2. Solve the system of Eq. (8.9.1) by Gauss elimination without pivoting.

3. Solve Exercise 2 with partial pivoting.

4. Solve Exercise 2 with complete pivoting.

5. Solve the system of Eq. (8.9.1) by the Crout reduction method.

6. Using A', found in Exercise 5, express A as the product of a lower- and an upper-triangular matrix, $A = LU$.

7. Using the results of Exercise 6, verify that

$$|A| = |L|\,|U|, \qquad A^t = U^t L^t, \qquad A^{-1} = U^{-1} L^{-1}.$$

8. Reordering the system given in Eq. (8.9.1), solve by the Gauss-Seidel method.

9. Show that the following system has no solution:

$$\begin{aligned} -x_1 + 3x_2 + x_3 &= 5, \\ 2x_1 - x_2 - 2x_3 &= 3, \\ x_1 + 4x_2 - x_3 &= 6. \end{aligned}$$

10. Show that the following system has infinitely many solutions:

$$\begin{aligned} x_1 + 3x_2 + x_3 &= 5, \\ 2x_1 - x_2 + 2x_3 &= 3, \\ x_1 + 4x_2 + x_3 &= 6. \end{aligned}$$

CHAPTER 9

EIGENVALUES AND EIGENVECTORS

9.1 INTRODUCTION

The solution of many problems in science, engineering, physics, and statistics involves solving the simple eigenproblem discussed in Section 7.7.

An important problem in dynamics is one in which a system executes small vibrations in the neighborhood of a stable equilibrium position. The equation $|A - \lambda I| = 0$ is called the frequency equation. The n roots λ are called the natural frequencies of the system, and the lowest frequency is called the fundamental frequency. Corresponding to the eigenvalues λ_i are n eigenvectors, $x^{(i)}$, each with n components. These eigenvectors are called the principal modes of oscillation and are proportional to the amplitudes of the principal oscillations. The eigenvector corresponding to the fundamental frequency is called the fundamental mode of oscillation.

Frictional forces are always present in physical systems. In many cases they are so small that we neglect them and treat the system as a conservative one. However, if viscous damping is present in a system and it is so large it cannot be neglected, the pertinent problem may involve solving the general eigenproblem $[A\lambda^2 + B\lambda + C]x = 0$, which usually may be reduced to the simple case. Certain problems in aircraft flutter analysis are special cases of this general problem. Many problems of structural analysis lead to homogeneous problems of free vibrations and buckling. The problems may be expressed as various forms of the above mentioned matrix equations with the associated eigenproblem. Solving the eigenproblem gives eigenvalues which represent natural frequencies or critical loads, and eigenvectors which determine mode shapes of vibration, bending, or buckling.

There is an analogy between mechanical and electrical oscillations if we substitute inductance for inertia, resistance for damping, the reciprocal value of capacitance for elastic restraint, and the impressed electromotive force for the impressed mechanical force. The stability of a system, mechanical or electrical, is associated with the eigenvalues.

Most of these problems are formulated as systems of first- or second-order ordinary differential equations, which are best handled as matrix problems. In a later chapter we will discuss ways to express systems of differential equations in matrix form.

Certain problems in statistics, such as the factor analysis problem, involve finding eigenvalues and eigenvectors.

Thus, the importance of eigenvalues and eigenvectors in a wide range of applications warrants a study of the various methods of solving the eigenproblem.

A method of generating a set of matrices with exact integer elements and known eigenvalues (for use in testing digital computer programs) is given in Appendix D.

9.2 THE CHARACTERISTIC POLYNOMIAL

The simple eigenproblem $Ax = \lambda x$ may be written in the form

$$[A - \lambda_i I]x^{(i)} = 0. \tag{9.2.1}$$

The characteristic polynomial is the determinantal equation, which we write as

$$Q(\lambda) = |A - \lambda I| = 0 \tag{9.2.2}$$

or

$$Q(\lambda) = (-1)^n(\lambda^n - p_1\lambda^{n-1} - p_2\lambda^{n-2} \cdots -p_n), \tag{9.2.3}$$

where

$$\begin{aligned}
p_1 &= a_{11} + a_{22} + \cdots + a_{nn} \\
&= \lambda_1 + \lambda_2 + \cdots + \lambda_n,
\end{aligned} \tag{9.2.4}$$

$$\begin{aligned}
p_k = \ &\text{the sums, with sign } (-1)^{k-1}, \\
&\text{of all the principal minors} \\
&\text{of order } k,
\end{aligned} \tag{9.2.5}$$

and

$$|A| = \lambda_1\lambda_2\lambda_3 \cdots \lambda_n = (-1)^{n-1}p_n. \tag{9.2.6}$$

The coefficient p_1 is the trace or spur of the $n \times n$ matrix A. An important theorem associated with the characteristic polynomial is the Cayley-Hamilton theorem.

Cayley-Hamilton theorem. If $Q(\lambda)$ is the characteristic polynomial of the matrix A, then $Q(A) = 0$, that is, the matrix is a root of its own characteristic equation.

Each λ_i of Eq. (9.2.1) has a corresponding eigenvector $x^{(i)}$. This eigenvector, in general, can be found by solving n homogeneous linear equations in n unknowns. To find all the vectors, one must solve n of these homogeneous systems.

We recall that the transpose of A will have the same eigenvalues as A, but different eigenvectors, except when A is symmetric.

9.3 METHODS

Most methods for computing eigenvalues fall into three main classes: (1) data condensation methods; (2) global iterations; (3) local iterations. In the data condensation methods, there are two separate algorithms. In the first, a finite number of simple transformations are applied to put the relevant information of A into a compact form. In some cases, such as the characteristic polynomial methods, the compact form consists of the coefficients of the characteristic polynomial. Data condensation methods, which ignore the characteristic polynomial, usually reduce A by similarity transformations to tridiagonal form. The second algorithm is one for localizing the eigenvalues from the compact form. When the compact form is the characteristic polynomial, the algorithm is one of finding the roots. Muller's method is a good illustration of this. When the compact form is the tridiagonal form, Givens' method and Householder's method illustrate the algorithm. When the compact form is a lower Hessenberg form, Laguerre's method is used.

The global iteration method consists of a sequence of transformations such that all the eigenvalues are found simultaneously. The Jacobi method is an illustration of this.

A local iteration aims to get one eigenvalue and, if possible, also the corresponding eigenvector at one time. The matrix is then deflated so that this eigenvalue is no longer present, and the process is repeated. R. Von Mises' power method and Wielandt's method are two illustrations of this class.

Some methods handle only symmetric matrices. Some handle only real matrices, while others handle both real and complex. Some methods give more accurate results, depending on the condition of the matrix, while others are faster on a computer.

We now consider some of the best known and most frequently used of these methods.

9.4 JACOBI METHOD FOR REAL SYMMETRIC MATRICES

If $TT^t = I$, that is, if T is an orthogonal matrix, then the roots of TAT^t are the same as those of A, a real symmetric matrix. This is evident, since

$$T[A - \lambda I]T^t = [TAT^t - \lambda I].$$

A simple orthogonal matrix T is given by $T_{ii} = 1$, $(i \neq p, q)$, $T_{ij} = 0$ for all other i, j, except that

$$T_{pp} = \cos\theta, \qquad T_{qq} = \cos\theta,$$
$$T_{pq} = -\sin\theta, \qquad T_{qp} = \sin\theta. \tag{9.4.1}$$

If we form TAT^t, the (p, q) element is given by

$$a_{pq}\cos 2\theta - \tfrac{1}{2}(a_{pp} - a_{qq})\sin 2\theta,$$

and in order for this element to be equal to zero, we must have

$$\tan 2\theta = \frac{2a_{pq}}{a_{pp} - a_{qq}}. \tag{9.4.2}$$

From the values of the $\tan 2\theta$, the values of $\sin \theta$ and $\cos \theta$ for use in Eq. (9.4.1) are determined from the following formulas:

$$R = \sqrt{(a_{pp} - a_{qq})^2 + 4a_{pq}^2}, \tag{9.4.3}$$

$$\sin 2\theta = \frac{2a_{pq}}{R}, \qquad \cos 2\theta = \frac{a_{pp} - a_{qq}}{R}. \tag{9.4.4}$$

Since

$$\tan \theta = \frac{\sin 2\theta}{1 + \cos 2\theta}, \qquad R' = \sqrt{2(1 + \cos 2\theta)}, \tag{9.4.5}$$

then

$$\sin \theta = \frac{|\sin 2\theta|}{R'}, \qquad \cos \theta = \pm \frac{1 + \cos 2\theta}{R'}, \tag{9.4.6}$$

where the sign of $\cos \theta$ is the same as the sign of a_{pq}. This determines an orthogonal matrix T_1. Premultiplying A by T_1 and postmultiplying the result by T_1^t will make a_{pq} and a_{qp} equal to zero.

If we choose a succession of T_i matrices and successively premultiply by T_i and postmultiply by T_i^t, each T_i being chosen to make the largest off-diagonal elements equal to zero, the trace of A remains unchanged at each stage. After k stages, we have

$$T_k T_{k-1} \cdots T_2 T_1 A T_1^t T_2^t \cdots T_k^t = D. \tag{9.4.7}$$

The diagonal elements of D are the eigenvalues of A, and the corresponding columns of

$$T_1^t T_2^t \cdots T_k^t = T^t \tag{9.4.8}$$

are the eigenvectors of A. A discussion of the Jacobi method is found in Bodewig [9].

Example. Find the eigenvalues and eigenvectors of

$$A = \begin{bmatrix} 4 & 2 & 0 \\ 2 & 5 & 3 \\ 0 & 3 & 6 \end{bmatrix} \tag{9.4.9}$$

by the Jacobi method.

Solution. In order to make $a_{12} = a_{21} = 0$, we have $\tan 2\theta = -4$, $\cos 2\theta = -0.24254$, $\sin \theta = 0.78821$, and $\cos \theta = 0.61541$. Therefore,

$$T_1 = \begin{bmatrix} 0.61541 & -0.78821 & 0 \\ 0.78821 & 0.61541 & 0 \\ 0 & 0 & 1 \end{bmatrix}. \tag{9.4.10}$$

Premultiplying A by T_1 and postmultiplying by T_1^t, we obtain

$$A_1 = \begin{bmatrix} 6.56158 & 0 & 2.36463 \\ 0 & 2.43846 & 1.84623 \\ 2.36463 & 1.84623 & 6 \end{bmatrix}. \tag{9.4.11}$$

Now, in order to make $a_{13} = a_{31} = 0$, we have

$$\tan 2\theta = \frac{2(2.36463)}{6.56158 - 6},$$

$T_{22} = 1$, $T_{11} = T_{33} = 0.74764$, and $T_{13} = -T_{31} = -0.66411$. Multiplying appropriately by T_2^t and T_2, we have

$$A_2 = \begin{bmatrix} 8.66209 & 1.22670 & 0 \\ 1.22670 & 2.43846 & 1.38032 \\ 0 & 1.38032 & 3.89958 \end{bmatrix}. \tag{9.4.12}$$

Even though previous zero elements are destroyed, all the off-diagonal elements are decreasing at each stage. Continuing in this manner to obtain T_3, T_4, ..., T_k and multiplying appropriately until all off-diagonal elements are zero, we finally obtain

$$A_k = D = \begin{bmatrix} 8.982623 & 0 & 0 \\ 0 & 4.546986 & 0 \\ 0 & 0 & 1.234820 \end{bmatrix}. \tag{9.4.13}$$

The diagonal elements are the eigenvalues of A. Multiplying the rotation matrices $T_1^t T_2^t T_3^t \cdots T_k^t$ together, we get

$$T^t = \begin{bmatrix} -0.273982 & 0.782786 & 0.505429 \\ -0.672469 & 0.250335 & -0.644010 \\ -0.693540 & -0.551938 & 0.424775 \end{bmatrix}. \tag{9.4.14}$$

The columns of T^t are the eigenvectors of A corresponding to the eigenvalues obtained in D.

9.5 GIVENS' METHOD

Assume that the symmetric matrix A can be changed by some method, such as the Jacobi rotation, to the tridiagonal form:

$$J = \begin{bmatrix} \alpha_1 & \beta_2 & 0 & \\ \beta_2 & \alpha_2 & \beta_3 & \\ 0 & \beta_3 & \alpha_3 & \\ & & & \ddots \\ & & & & \alpha_n \end{bmatrix}. \tag{9.5.1}$$

The values of the leading principal minors may be computed by the Sturm sequence:

$$P_0(\lambda) = 1, \qquad P_1(\lambda) = \alpha_1 - \lambda,$$

$$P_r(\lambda) = (\alpha_r - \lambda)P_{r-1}(\lambda) - \beta_r^2 P_{r-2}(\lambda), \qquad r = 2, 3, \ldots, n. \tag{9.5.2}$$

The nth-degree Sturm function $P_n(\lambda)$ is the characteristic polynomial of A. Its roots may be computed by a polynomial root-finder, such as Bairstow's method. These roots are the eigenvalues of A.

The eigenvectors of A are equal to those of the tridiagonal matrix J, premultiplied by the product S of the rotation matrices.

Another method of finding the eigenvectors is to solve the system of homogeneous linear equations, $[A - \lambda_k I]x^{(k)} = 0$, corresponding to each λ_k. See the example in Section 7.7.

Also, accurate eigenvectors may be found as follows: We transform $[J - \lambda_k I]$ to an upper-triangular matrix U_k so that it corresponds to each λ_k. The equations $U_k x^{(k)} = e$, where e is a vector with all components equal to unity, are solved. The solution $x^{(k)}$ is the eigenvector corresponding to λ_k.

A detailed discussion of this method of finding eigenvalues and eigenvectors, with an extensive error analysis, is found in Givens [58].

Example. By Givens' method, find the eigenvalues and eigenvectors of the example given in Section 7.7:

$$A = \begin{bmatrix} 2 & 3 & 5 \\ 3 & 4 & 6 \\ 5 & 6 & 7 \end{bmatrix}. \tag{9.5.3}$$

Solution. Using a Jacobi rotation to tridiagonalize A, we obtain

$$\tan 2\theta = -2, \sin 2\theta = 2/\sqrt{5}, \cos 2\theta = -1/\sqrt{5},$$
$$\cos \theta = 0.52573, \sin \theta = 0.85065. \tag{9.5.4}$$

Therefore,

$$T_1 = \begin{bmatrix} 0.52573 & 0 & -0.85065 \\ 0 & 1 & 0 \\ 0.85065 & 0 & 0.52573 \end{bmatrix}. \tag{9.5.5}$$

Now, premultiplying A by T_1 and postmultiplying by T_1^t, we obtain

$$J = \begin{bmatrix} 10.09016 & 6.68109 & 0 \\ 6.68109 & 4 & 0.60243 \\ 0 & 0.60243 & -1.09016 \end{bmatrix}. \tag{9.5.6}$$

From (9.5.2) we have

$$\begin{aligned} P_0(\lambda) &= 1, \quad P_1(\lambda) = 10.09016 - \lambda, \\ P_2(\lambda) &= \lambda^2 - 14.09016\lambda - 4.27632, \\ P_3(\lambda) &= 0.99995 + 19.99977\lambda + 13\lambda^2 - \lambda^3. \end{aligned} \tag{9.5.7}$$

Note how $P_3(\lambda)$ compares with Eq. (7.7.7). The roots of $P_3(\lambda)$ are

$$\lambda_1 = 14.39427, \qquad \lambda_2 = -1.34252, \qquad \lambda_3 = -0.051747.$$

Solving $[J - \lambda_i I]y^{(i)}$, for $i = 1, 2, 3$, we obtain

$$y^{(1)} = \begin{bmatrix} 39.89810 \\ 25.70329 \\ 1 \end{bmatrix}, \quad y^{(2)} = \begin{bmatrix} 0.24478 \\ -0.41887 \\ 1 \end{bmatrix}, \quad y^{(3)} = \begin{bmatrix} -1.13548 \\ 1.72367 \\ 1 \end{bmatrix}. \tag{9.5.8}$$

If we form the matrix $[y^{(1)}y^{(2)}y^{(3)}]$, premultiply this matrix by T_1, and normalize each column such that the largest element is unity, we have

$$\begin{bmatrix} 0.58392 & -0.98364 & -0.83983 \\ 0.74577 & -0.57072 & 1 \\ 1 & 1 & -0.25538 \end{bmatrix}, \tag{9.5.9}$$

where the columns are the eigenvectors of the original matrix A, corresponding to λ_1, λ_2, and λ_3, respectively.

9.6 MULLER'S METHOD

This method refers to finding the roots of the characteristic polynomial; it is discussed by David E. Muller [111]. A brief summary of this method is now presented.

To find n solutions of

$$f(x) = a_0 x^n + a_1 x^{n-1} + \cdots + a_n = 0, \tag{9.6.1}$$

one starts with the values x_i, h_i, k_i, $f(x_i)$, $f(x_{i-1})$, and $f(x_{i-2})$. Then k_{i+1} is computed, where

$$k_{i+1} = \frac{-2f(x_i)\,\delta_i}{g_i \pm \sqrt{g_i^2 - 4f(x_i)\,\delta_i k_i[f(x_{i-2})k_i - f(x_{i-1})\,\delta_i + f(x_i)]}}, \tag{9.6.2}$$

and

$$\delta_i = 1 + k_i,$$
$$g_i = f(x_{i-2})k_i^2 - f(x_{i-1})\,\delta_i^2 + f(x_i)(k_i + \delta_i). \tag{9.6.3}$$

Then

$$x_{i+1} = x_i + h_i, \qquad h_{i+1} = k_{i+1}h_i, \qquad f(x_{i+1}) \tag{9.6.4}$$

are computed. The sign in the denominator of k_{i+1} is chosen to make the denominator have the greater modulus.

This gives x_{i+1}, which is the closer of the two roots of the interpolating quadratic through (x_{i-2}, f_{i-2}), (x_{i-1}, f_{i-1}), (x_i, f_i), to x_i. Muller continues the process until x_{i+1} converges, according to a specified criterion, to a root x.

9.7 POWER METHOD AND INVERSE POWER METHOD

These two methods are quite effective when used in conjunction with each other as follows:

a) *Power method.* For some arbitrary vector $x^{(0)} \neq 0$, let

$$y^{(r+1)} = [A - \alpha I]x^{(r)}, \tag{9.7.1}$$
$$x^{(r+1)} = k_{r+1}y^{(r+1)}, \tag{9.7.2}$$

where k_{r+1} is chosen to make the component of $x^{(r+1)}$ of largest absolute value equal to 1, and α is a complex parameter effecting an origin translation which may improve convergence in some cases. One then forms

$$\mu_{r+1} = \frac{\{y^{(r+1)}, x^{(r)}\}}{\{x^{(r)}, x^{(r)}\}},$$

(9.7.3)

where $\{x, y\}$ denotes the inner product of x and y. In general, μ_r approaches an eigenvalue and $x^{(r)}$ approaches the associated eigenvector of $[A - \alpha I]$. The above process is continued until

$$\frac{\|y^{(r+1)} - \mu_{r+1}x^{(r)}\|}{\|x^{(r)}\|} < \epsilon_1$$

(9.7.4)

for some ϵ_1, where $\|x\| = \sqrt{\{x, x\}}$.

When (9.7.4) is satisfied, or after a fixed number of iterations, we switch to the following method.

b) *The inverse power method.* Starting with the vector $x^{(r)}$, the last iterant of the power method, and $\lambda_r = \mu_r + \alpha$, one computes

$$[A - \lambda_r I]y^{(r+1)} = x^{(r)},$$

(9.7.5)

$$\lambda_{r+1} = \frac{\{Ay^{(r+1)}, y^{(r+1)}\}}{\{y^{(r+1)}, y^{(r+1)}\}},$$

(9.7.6)

$$x^{(r+1)} = k_{r+1}y^{(r+1)},$$

(9.7.7)

where we solve for $y^{(r+1)}$, and where k_{r+1} normalizes $x^{(r+1)}$ similar to k_{r+1} in Eq. (9.7.2).

c) Once an approximation to the eigenvalue is found, the matrix is deflated as follows. Suppose

$$Ax = \lambda_1 x.$$

(9.7.8)

Then

$$A_1 y = PAP^{-1}y = \lambda_1 y,$$

(9.7.9)

where $A_1 = PAP^{-1}$, $x = P^{-1}y$. Here P is a permutation matrix chosen such that

$$y = Px = \binom{w}{1},$$

(9.7.10)

where w is an $(n - 1)$ column vector and 1 is a scalar, i.e., the last component of y is 1. Partitioning A_1 conformally with y, we have

$$A_1 = \begin{bmatrix} B & r \\ s & c \end{bmatrix},$$

(9.7.11)

where B is an $(n - 1) \times (n - 1)$ matrix, r is an $(n - 1)$ column vector, s is an $(n - 1)$ row vector, and c is scalar.

Let

$$S = \begin{bmatrix} I_{n-1} & w \\ 0 & 1 \end{bmatrix},$$

(9.7.12)

where I_{n-1} is an $(n-1) \times (n-1)$ identity matrix, and where S is partitioned similar to A_1 in (9.7.11). Clearly

$$S^{-1} = \begin{bmatrix} I_{n-1} & -w \\ 0 & 1 \end{bmatrix}. \tag{9.7.13}$$

Hence we have

$$S^{-1}A_1 Sz = \lambda_1 z, \tag{9.7.14}$$

where

$$Sz = y. \tag{9.7.15}$$

Thus

$$S^{-1}A_1 S = \begin{bmatrix} B - ws & Bw + r - w(sw + c) \\ s & sw + c \end{bmatrix}. \tag{9.7.16}$$

But from Eqs. (9.7.9) and (9.7.11) we have

$$\begin{bmatrix} B & r \\ s & c \end{bmatrix} \begin{bmatrix} w \\ 1 \end{bmatrix} = \begin{bmatrix} Bw + r \\ sw + c \end{bmatrix} = \begin{bmatrix} \lambda_1 w \\ \lambda_1 \end{bmatrix}. \tag{9.7.17}$$

Hence (9.7.16) becomes

$$S^{-1}A_1 S = \begin{bmatrix} B - ws & 0 \\ s & \lambda_1 \end{bmatrix},$$

and since $S^{-1}A_1 S$ is similar to A, we see that $B - ws$ is an $(n-1) \times (n-1)$ matrix whose eigenvalues are the same as those of A, except for λ_1. We find the next eigenvalue by repeating the entire process, using $[B - ws]$ in place of A.

The power method has the advantage that it will always converge provided that there is one eigenvalue furthest away from α. The convergence may be slow. The inverse power method, however, requires $|\alpha_0 - \lambda_1|$ to be sufficiently small for convergence, but the convergence is usually rapid. The two methods are used in conjunction in an effort to utilize their respective advantages.

For diagonalizable matrices, the over-all method works quite well. For non-diagonalizable matrices, however, the determination of multiple roots may be a problem. The method usually finds roots but appears to exhibit clusters of roots rather than multiple roots. In practice, roundoff error in the data will usually perturb multiple roots into clusters. Thus the method might give reasonable roots even here.

Finally, once a root has been found to some degree of accuracy, the original $n \times n$ matrix is deflated to a $(n-1) \times (n-1)$ matrix, and the process is repeated. Although this may introduce some error in practice, the results have been quite good, in general. A discussion of the power and inverse power method is found in Bodewig [9].

Example. Find the eigenvalues and eigenvectors of (9.5.3) by the power and inverse power methods.

Solution. Using $\alpha = 1$ and $x^{(1)} = [1, 1, 1]^t$, we obtain

$$y^{(2)} = [A - \alpha I]x^{(1)} = [0, 12, 17]^t,$$

$$\lambda_2 = \mu_2 + \alpha = \frac{\{y^{(2)}, x^{(1)}\}}{\{x^{(1)}, x^{(1)}\}} + 1 = \frac{38}{3} + 1 = 13.66666,$$

$$\frac{\|y^{(2)} - \mu_2 x^{(1)}\|^2}{\|x^{(1)}\|^2} = \frac{32.66666}{3} \neq \epsilon,$$

$$x^{(2)} = \begin{bmatrix} 0.52942 \\ 0.70588 \\ 1 \end{bmatrix}, \quad y^{(3)} = [A - \alpha I]x^{(2)} = \begin{bmatrix} 7.64706 \\ 9.70588 \\ 12.88235 \end{bmatrix},$$

$$\lambda_3 = \mu_3 + \alpha = \frac{\{y^{(3)}, x^{(2)}\}}{\{x^{(2)}, x^{(2)}\}} + 1 = \frac{23.78201}{1.77855} + 1 = 14.37160,$$

$$\frac{\|y^{(3)} - \mu_3 x^{(2)}\|^2}{\|x^{(2)}\|^2} = \frac{0.63331}{1.77855} \neq \epsilon.$$

After five iterations, we have

$$x^{(5)} = \begin{bmatrix} 0.58421 \\ 0.74601 \\ 1 \end{bmatrix}, \quad y^{(6)} = [A - \alpha I]x^{(5)} = \begin{bmatrix} 7.82226 \\ 9.99069 \\ 13.39716 \end{bmatrix},$$

$$\lambda_6 = \mu_6 + \alpha = \frac{\{y^{(6)}, x^{(5)}\}}{\{x^{(5)}, x^{(5)}\}} + 1 = \frac{25.42024}{1.89784} + 1 = 14.39427,$$

$$\frac{\|y^{(6)} - \mu_6 x^{(5)}\|^2}{\|x^{(5)}\|^2} = \frac{0.19269 \times 10^{-4}}{1.89784} < \epsilon, \quad x^{(6)} = \begin{bmatrix} 0.58387 \\ 0.74573 \\ 1 \end{bmatrix}.$$

Now going to the inverse power method, we obtain

$$x^{(1)} = x^{(6)}, \quad \lambda_1 = \lambda_6, \quad [A - \lambda_1 I]y^{(2)} = x^{(1)},$$

$$y^{(2)} = \begin{bmatrix} 844775.35 \\ 1078925.5 \\ 1446719.2 \end{bmatrix} = \begin{bmatrix} 0.58387 \\ 0.74573 \\ 1 \end{bmatrix},$$

$$\lambda_2 \quad \frac{\{Ay^{(2)}, y^{(2)}\}}{\{y^{(2)}, y^{(2)}\}} = \frac{27.30804}{1.89715} = 14.39427,$$

$$\frac{\|y^{(2)} - \lambda_1 x^{(1)}\|^2}{\|x^{(1)}\|^2} = \frac{0.12790 \times 10^{-12}}{1.89715} < \epsilon.$$

Therefore

$$\lambda_1 = 14.39427.$$

Solving $[A - \lambda_1]x^{(1)} = 0$, we get

$$x^{(1)} = \begin{bmatrix} 0.58392 \\ 0.74577 \\ 1 \end{bmatrix}.$$

Deflating A, we obtain

$$A_1 = \begin{bmatrix} -0.91962 & -0.50355 \\ -0.72887 & -0.47464 \end{bmatrix}.$$

Repeating the entire process with A_1 and A_2, we obtain

$$\lambda_2 = -1.34252, \qquad x^{(2)} = \begin{bmatrix} -0.98364 \\ -0.57072 \\ 1 \end{bmatrix},$$

and

$$\lambda_3 = -0.051747, \qquad x^{(3)} = \begin{bmatrix} 3.28861 \\ -3.91580 \\ 1 \end{bmatrix} = \begin{bmatrix} -0.83983 \\ 1 \\ -0.25538 \end{bmatrix}.$$

9.8 LAGUERRE'S METHOD

The following is a summary of the application of Laguerre's method to the eigenvalue problem as given by Parlett [120].

Given an approximation z to a root of a polynomial $P(z)$, then Laguerre's method uses $P(z)$, $P'(z)$, and $P''(z)$ to obtain a better approximation. Defining

$$s_1(z) = \frac{P'(z)}{P(z)}, \qquad s_2(z) = \frac{[P'(z)]^2 - P(z)P''(z)}{[P(z)]^2}, \tag{9.8.1}$$

Parlett proceeds to derive the formula

$$z_{i+1} = z_i - \frac{n}{s_1 \pm \sqrt{(n-1)(ns_2 - s_1^2)}}, \tag{9.8.2}$$

where the square root which maximizes the absolute value of the denominator is chosen. The term z_{i+1} is called the Laguerre iterate of z_i for the polynomial P. The transition from z_i to z_{i+1} is one Laguerre iteration.

The following properties have been proven for polynomials of degree n with real coefficients and real roots.

1) The real line is divided into n abutting intervals, each containing one root (t intervals if there are only t distinct roots), and from any initial point in such an interval, the Laguerre iterates converge monotonically to the root therein.

2) If the root is single, then convergence is cubic. If the root is of multiplicity $k(k > 1)$, then convergence is linear.

3) Laguerre iterations are invariant under all Mobius transformations,

$$x' = \frac{ax + b}{cx + d}.$$

Extensions of these results can be made to the complex domain.

If H is a lower Hessenberg matrix (see Chapter 6), the determinant of $[H - zI]$ is found by Gaussian elimination, plane rotations, or Hyman's method. Hyman's method uses the superdiagonal elements $(h_{i,i+1})$ as pivots, and this keeps any complex numbers confined to the diagonal.

Let $H = (h_{ij})$, $v_i = -h_{i,i+1} \neq 0$ $(i = 1, 2, \ldots, n - 1)$, and $v_n = 1$. Essentially, Hyman's method consists of eliminating the first column of H except for the last element, which is called $f(z)$. Then,

$$\det[H - zI] = \left(\prod_{i=1}^{n-1} v_i\right) f(z). \tag{9.8.3}$$

This constant nonzero coefficient of $f(z)$ is ignored since it will eventually cancel out in the homogeneous expressions $s_1(z)$ and $s_2(z)$.

We put $u_1 = 1$ and calculate $u_2, \ldots, u_n$ from

$$u_{i+1} = (h_{i1}u_1 + h_{i2}u_2 + \cdots + h_{ii}u_i - zu_i)/v_i. \tag{9.8.4}$$

Then, since $v_n = 1$, $u_{n+1} = P(z)$. From the above formula for u_{i+1}, we have

$$u'_{i+1} = (h_{i1}u'_1 + h_{i2}u'_2 + \cdots + h_{ii}u'_i - zu'_i - u_i)/v_i, \tag{9.8.5}$$

$$u''_{i+1} = (h_{i1}u''_1 + h_{i2}u''_2 + \cdots + h_{ii}u''_i - zu''_i - 2u'_i)/v_i, \tag{9.8.6}$$

$$u'_{n+1} = P(z), \qquad u''_{n+1} = P''(z).$$

To start the Laguerre iteration, Parlett uses

$$s_1(0) = -\sum_{i=1}^{n} \lambda_i = -\text{trace}(H), \tag{9.8.7}$$

$$s_2(0) = \sum_{i=1}^{n} \lambda_i^2 = \text{trace}(H^2). \tag{9.8.8}$$

To find an initial approximation to an eigenvalue, he uses

$$z_0 = -(1/n)\{s_1(0) \pm \sqrt{(n - 1)[ns_2(0) + s_1^2(0)]}\}. \tag{9.8.9}$$

As the initial approximation for the first eigenvalue, Parlett uses $2z_0$, but for the remaining eigenvalues he uses z_0 as determined by Eq. (9.8.9). As each eigenvalue is found, $s_1(0)$ and $s_2(0)$ can be adjusted by the following subtraction method.

Suppose we have found j roots $\lambda_1, \lambda_2, \ldots \lambda_j$; then s_1 and s_2 for the reduced polynomial of degree $n - j$ are given by

$$s_1^{(n-j)} = \sum_{k=1}^{j} \lambda_k - \text{trace}(H), \tag{9.8.10}$$

$$s_2^{(n-j)} = \text{trace}(H^2) - \sum_{k=1}^{j} \lambda_k^2. \tag{9.8.11}$$

The criterion which Parlett uses to stop iteration on any particular root is

$$|z_i - z_{i-1}| < \max(\epsilon |z_i|, k \, |\text{largest eigenvalue}|), \tag{9.8.12}$$

where ϵ and k are input parameters.

Only a general summary of the Laguerre method has been given here. Parlett [120] gives not only comprehensive details of the theory, but also details for a computer program.

This method is an excellent one for finding the roots of a polynomial from the companion matrix.

Example. Find the eigenvalues of (9.5.3) by the Laguerre method.

Solution. By the method of Section 7.13, the matrix A is transformed to the lower Hessenberg matrix:

$$H = \begin{bmatrix} 2 & 5 & 0 \\ 6.8 & 10.6 & 2.04 \\ 3 & 6 & 0.4 \end{bmatrix}.$$

Then

$$s_1^{(3)} = -13, \qquad s_2^{(3)}(0) = 209, \qquad z_0 = 28.84366;$$

$$s_1(0) = 0.136942, \qquad s_2(0) = 0.00708475, \qquad z_1 = 14.39750;$$

$$s_1(0) = 309.37028, \qquad s_2(0) = 95627.864, \qquad z_2 = \lambda_1 = 14.39427;$$

$$s_1^{(2)}(0) = 1.39427, \qquad s_2^{(2)}(0) = 1.80504, \qquad z_0 = \lambda_2 = -1.34252;$$

$$s_1^{(1)}(0) = 0.051747, \qquad s_2^{(1)}(0) = 0.0026780, \qquad z_0 = \lambda_3 = -0.05175.$$

9.9 HOUSEHOLDER'S METHOD

The very successful method of Givens for finding the eigenvalues and eigenvectors of a general symmetric matrix is based on the reduction of the matrix to tridiagonal form. This is effected by means of a similarity transformation with an orthogonal matrix. In the Givens' method, the orthogonal matrix is obtained as the product of a number of simple orthogonal matrices known as plane rotations. In 1959 Householder described an alternative method of reduction to tridiagonal form in which the orthogonal matrix is obtained as the product of a number of simple orthogonal matrices which are not plane rotations. According to Wilkinson [163], it is the fastest and most accurate of known methods, it is somewhat simpler, and it requires less storage in a computer than Givens' method. The basic feature of the Householder method is that each transformation produces a complete row of zeros in the appropriate positions, without affecting previous rows. Only $n - 2$ transformations are required, although each requires more calculation than the Givens' method.

Consider the transformation sequence

$$A_k = P_k A_{k-1} P_k, \qquad A_0 = A, \tag{9.9.1}$$

where

$$P_k = I - 2w^{(k)} w^{(k)^t}, \qquad w^{(k)^t} w^{(k)} = 1. \tag{9.9.2}$$

Apart from this normalization, the elements of the vector $w^{(k)}$ are chosen so that A will have zeros, except in the tridiagonal positions, in every spot of a particular row. The matrix P_k is symmetric and orthogonal, since

$$P_k^t P_k = (I - 2w^{(k)}w^{(k)^t})(I - 2w^{(k)}w^{(k)^t})$$
$$= I - 4w^{(k)}w^{(k)^t} + 4w^{(k)}w^{(k)^t}$$
$$= I, \tag{9.9.3}$$

by virtue of the normalization of $w^{(k)}$. This is the desirable orthogonal transformation, and typically, for a matrix of order 4, the choice of suitable $w^{(k)}$ to produce the required zeros is as follows:

In the first transformation $A_1 = P_1 A_0 P_1$, we produce zeros in the positions $(1, 3)$ and $(1, 4)$ of the first row of A_1. For this purpose, take $w^{(1)^t} = (0, w_2, w_3, w_4)$, such that $w_2^2 + w_3^2 + w_4^2 = 1$. The corresponding matrix P_1 is

$$P_1 = \begin{bmatrix} 1 & 0 & 0 & 0 \\ 0 & 1 - 2w_2^2 & -2w_2w_3 & -2w_2w_4 \\ 0 & -2w_2w_3 & 1 - 2w_3^2 & -2w_3w_4 \\ 0 & -2w_2w_4 & -2w_3w_4 & 1 - 2w_4^2 \end{bmatrix}. \tag{9.9.4}$$

Here $P_1 A_0$ leaves unchanged the first row of A_0, and the $(1, 3)$ and $(1, 4)$ elements of $A_1 = P_1 A_0 P_1$ are, respectively,

$$a_{13}^{(1)} = -2w_2w_3a_{12} + (1 - 2w_3^2)a_{13} - 2w_3w_4a_{14}$$
$$= a_{13} - 2w_3(w_2a_{12} + w_3a_{13} + w_4a_{14}), \tag{9.9.5}$$
$$a_{14}^{(1)} = -2w_2w_4a_{12} - 2w_3w_4a_{13} + (1 - 2w_4^2)a_{14}$$
$$= a_{14} - 2w_4(w_2a_{12} + w_3a_{13} + w_4a_{14}). \tag{9.9.6}$$

The element $(1, 2)$ is given by

$$a_{12}^{(1)} = (1 - 2w_2^2)a_{12} - 2w_2w_3a_{13} - 2w_2w_4a_{14}$$
$$= a_{12} - 2w_2(w_2a_{12} + w_3a_{13} + w_4a_{14}). \tag{9.9.7}$$

The sum of the squares of these elements is $a_{12}^2 + a_{13}^2 + a_{14}^2$, so that if $a_{13}^{(1)}$ and $a_{14}^{(1)}$ are reduced to zero, we must have

$$a_{13} - 2mw_3 = 0, \qquad a_{14} - 2mw_4 = 0, \tag{9.9.8}$$

where

$$m = w_2a_{12} + w_3a_{13} + w_4a_{14}, \tag{9.9.9}$$

and then

$$a_{12} - 2mw_2 = \pm(a_{12}^2 + a_{13}^2 + a_{14}^2)^{1/2}. \tag{9.9.10}$$

From Eqs. (9.9.10) and (9.9.8) we obtain

$$w_2^2 = \frac{1}{2}\left\{1 \pm \frac{a_{12}}{(a_{12}^2 + a_{13}^2 + a_{14}^2)^{1/2}}\right\}, \tag{9.9.11}$$

$$w_3 = \pm \frac{a_{13}}{2w_2(a_{12}^2 + a_{13}^2 + a_{14}^2)^{1/2}}, \qquad w_4 = \pm \frac{a_{14}}{2w_2(a_{12}^2 + a_{13}^2 + a_{14}^2)^{1/2}}. \tag{9.9.12}$$

The sign of Eq. (9.9.11) is chosen to be that of a_{12}, so that w_2 is as large as possible in order to avoid difficulty in the division by w_2 in Eq. (9.9.12).

The matrix now has zeros in elements (1, 3), (1, 4), (3, 1), and (4, 1), and we proceed, in exactly the same way, to eliminate the required elements of the second row. The vector $w^{(2)t} = (0, 0, w_3, w_4)$, with a notation whose ambiguity should not cause trouble, and the matrix P_2 is given by

$$
P_2 = \begin{bmatrix} 1 & 0 & 0 & 0 \\ 0 & 1 & 0 & 0 \\ 0 & 0 & 1 - 2w_3^2 & -2w_3 w_4 \\ 0 & 0 & -2w_3 w_4 & 1 - 2w_4^2 \end{bmatrix}. \tag{9.9.13}
$$

And $P_2 A P_2$ leaves unchanged both the leading submatrix of order 2 and the zeros in the first row and first column. The extension to the general case is obvious.

When we have the final tridiagonal matrix A_{n-2}, we compute its roots by the method of Givens and obtain the vectors of A_{n-2} in exactly the same way. We recover the vectors of A by premultiplying the vector matrix of A_{n-2} with the successive P_k in the order $P_{n-2}, P_{n-3}, \ldots, P_2, P_1$.

A discussion of Householder's method is given by Wilkinson [163].

Example. Find the eigenvalues and eigenvectors of (9.5.3) by Householder's method.

Solution. Applying Householder's method of reduction to tridiagonal form, we obtain

$$
\begin{bmatrix} 2 & -5.83095 & 0 \\ -5.83095 & 11.5 & 1.5 \\ 0 & 1.5 & -0.5 \end{bmatrix}.
$$

Using the Sturm sequence of Section 9.5, we obtain the same characteristic equation as found by Givens' method. Therefore, the eigenvalues and the eigenvectors are the same.

9.10 SUPPLEMENTARY REFERENCES

In this chapter we discussed, with special references, seven of the most popular methods for solving eigenproblems. Some of the most significant contributions to the eigenvalue problem were made with the development of the LR-algorithm by Rutishauser, the QR-algorithm by Francis, and the QD-algorithm. A thorough and practical discussion of these algorithms is not possible here. Wilkinson [164] devotes nearly one hundred pages in Chapter 8 to a discussion of the algorithms. An excellent discussion of the QD-algorithm is given by Peter Henrici in the *National Bureau of Standards Applied Mathematics Series* **49**. Additional methods, as well as the ones discussed above, may be found in Faddeev and Fadeeva [43b], Modern Computing Methods [109], Osborn [116], Perlis [121], Wilkinson [162], and the following:

a) "Applications of Advanced Numerical Analysis to Digital Computer Problems," Summer Session, University of Michigan (1958), 101–152.

b) S. H. CRANDALL, "Iterative Procedures Related to Relaxation Method for Eigenvalue Problems," *Proc. Royal Soc.* (London) **207** (1951) 416–423.

c) W. GIVENS, "Computation of Plane Unitary Rotations Transforming a General Matrix to Triangular Form," *J. S.I.A.M.*, **6** (1958), 26.

d) C. LANCZOS, "An Iteration Method for the Solution of the Eigenvalue Problem of Linear Differential and Integral Operations," *J. Research Natl. Bur. Standards* **45** (1950) 255.

e) R. VON MISES and H. GEIRINGER, *Z. Angew. Math. Mech.*, **9** (1929) 28–77.

f) D. V. WIDDER, *Advanced Calculus*, Prentice-Hall, New York, 1947.

g) H. WIELANDT, "Beitrage Zur Math. Behandlung Komplexer Eigenwert problems," V, *Aerodynamische Versuchsanstalt Gottingen*, Report B44/J/37, 1944.

h) J. H. WILKINSON, "The Calculation of the Latent Roots and Vectors of Matrices on the Pilot Model of the A.C.E., " *Proc. Camb. Phil. Soc.* **50** (1954) 536–566.

i) J. H. WILKINSON, "Stability of the Reduction of a Matrix to Almost Triangular and Triangular Forms," *J.A.C.M.* **6** (1959) 336.

EXERCISES

1. By Jacobi's method, find the eigenvalues and eigenvectors of

$$\begin{bmatrix} 11 & 1 & 6 & 7 \\ 1 & 7 & 2 & -3 \\ 6 & 2 & 14 & 4 \\ 7 & -3 & 4 & 13 \end{bmatrix}.$$

2. By Givens' method, find the eigenvalues and eigenvectors of the matrix given in Exercise 1.

3. Find the eigenvalues and eigenvectors of

$$\begin{bmatrix} 2 & 3 & 2 \\ 10 & 3 & 4 \\ 3 & 6 & 1 \end{bmatrix}.$$

   by the power method and inverse power method.

4. By Laguerre's method, find the eigenvalues of the matrix given in Exercise 3.

CHAPTER 10

SCALING OF MATRICES

10.1 INTRODUCTION

The need for scaling, other than multiplication by a scalar, usually arises when there is a considerable range in the magnitude among the elements of the matrix. In such a case, the smaller elements are effectively zero. If such elements are intended to be effectively zero, no scaling should be attempted. However, if these elements are just as important as the other elements in the matrix, scaling should be considered.

We should not use scaling blindly; it sometimes sets up a combination of numbers such that no scaling gives the better result. We should always use the simplest and least time-consuming method of scaling a matrix, if it will condition the matrix properly.

Scaling a matrix prior to an operation consists of multiplying each element of the matrix by some predetermined number x_{ij}. This predetermined number need not be the same for each element, but in the methods described below, it is restricted by its relation to other x_{ij} for the matrix being scaled. Some methods require that the result of the operation also be scaled. This will be called compensatory scaling.

Scaling, in general, is a difficult problem. There are no explicit rules for when and how to scale though some adeptness in the art can be acquired through experience. Since scaling is used most often with large matrices on a digital computer, much of what follows in this chapter is oriented toward digital computer programming.

10.2 SCALING MATRICES ON A DIGITAL COMPUTER

When we use a desk calculator to calculate solutions, scaling can be used for a given arithmetic operation. Problem solving on the computer, however, is different. Unless the programmer allows the computer to consume more time testing the result than was spent in the operation, he has no such access to the result of a particular arithmetic operation.

Some computers have variable word length. It is possible, limited, of course, by the size of the computer storage, to set word length such that all significant digits arising in computation can be retained and used. However, most computers used to solve matrix problems have fixed word length.

When a computer program is used to scale a matrix, the number base of the computer should be considered. If it is not, the result of an operation on the scaled matrix may be entirely different from the true result of that operation on the original matrix. Scaling without consideration of the number base can cause elements of the original matrix to lose significance. Scaling of floating-point numbers should be accomplished by changing the characteristic, leaving the mantissa intact.

10.3 METHODS OF SCALING MATRICES

The remainder of this chapter will be devoted to various methods of scaling matrices. First, we shall discuss the method of scalar multiplication, which can be used in solving determinant, inverse, simultaneous linear equations, and eigenvalue problems, and shall give the associated compensatory scaling of the result. Then, we shall discuss two general methods that are useful in solving determinant, inverse, and simultaneous linear equations problems, and give the compensatory scaling of the results. Finally, we shall discuss two general methods that are useful in solving eigenvalue problems and give the compensatory scaling of the results.

10.4 SCALAR MULTIPLICATION

One simple method of scaling a matrix consists of multiplying each element of the matrix A (or the augmented matrix $[A \vdots b]$ for the solution of a set of simultaneous equations) by some number c. This is equivalent to premultiplying or post-multiplying A by C, a diagonal matrix with diagonal elements of c.

This method is particularly useful when the elements of a matrix are considerably larger or considerably smaller than 1. The object of this scaling is to prevent underflow or overflow (thus losing significance) in a computer during repeated multiplication.

a) Determinant:
   Given A, find $|A|$.
   Found: $|AC|$.   (10.4.1)
   Compensatory scaling: $|AC|(c^n)^{-1} = |A|(c^n)(c^n)^{-1} = |A|$.
b) Inverse:
   Given A, find A^{-1}.
   Found: $[AC]^{-1}$.   (10.4.2)
   Compensatory scaling: $C[AC]^{-1} = CC^{-1}A^{-1} = A^{-1}$.
c) Systems of Linear Equations:
   Given $Ax = b$, find x.
   Found: x.   (10.4.3)
   Compensatory scaling: none, since $C[A \vdots b]$ is a row operation.
d) Eigenvalue Problem:
   Given $Ax = \lambda x$, find λ, x.
   Found: λ', x, such that $[cA]x = \lambda'x$.   (10.4.4)
   Compensatory scaling: $\lambda = (1/c)\lambda'$.

10.5 EQUILIBRATION

This method is defined by Moler [110] as the multiplication of each row of a matrix A by some constant c_i, such that

$$\tfrac{1}{2} \leq \max_i |c_i A_{ij}| \leq 1, \qquad i = 1, 2, \ldots, n. \tag{10.5.1}$$

This is equivalent to premultiplying A by a diagonal matrix C of dimension n, which has c_i as its diagonal elements. A more elaborate method, also called equilibration, can be found in Wilkinson [162].

a) Determinant:
   Given A, find $|A|$.
   Found:

$$\left(|A| \prod_{i=1}^{n} c_i\right). \tag{10.5.2}$$

   Compensatory scaling:

$$\left(|A| \prod_{i=1}^{n} c_i\right)\left(\prod_{i=1}^{n} c_i\right)^{-1} = |A|.$$

b) Inverse:
   Given A, find A^{-1}.
   Found: $[CA]^{-1}$. \hfill (10.5.3)
   Compensatory scaling: $[CA]^{-1}C = A^{-1}C^{-1}C = A^{-1}$.
c) Systems of Equations:
   Given $Ax = b$, find x.
   Found: x. \hfill (10.5.4)
   Compensatory scaling: none, since $C[A \,\vdots\, b]$ is a row operation.

10.6 LINEAR PROGRAM METHOD

The linear program method [Section 10.9(a)] finds diagonal matrices R and S such that the expression

$$\frac{\max |r_i a_{ij} s_j|}{\min |r_i a_{ij} s_j|}, \qquad i = 1, 2, \ldots, m, \qquad j = 1, 2, \ldots, n, \tag{10.6.1}$$

is minimized, where A is an $m \times n$ matrix. The algorithm for finding R and S is:

I. *Initialization*

1) Let c_{ij} equal characteristic $(\log_b |a_{ij}|)$, where b is the number base of the computer. If $a_{ij} = 0$, let c_{ij} equal some unique number designating a nonentry.

2) Let

$$u_i = -\min_j c_{ij}, \qquad i = 1, \ldots, m,$$

$$v_j = -\min_i (u_i + c_{ij}), \qquad j = 1, \ldots, n,$$

$$\omega = \max_{i,j} (u_i + v_j + c_{ij}).$$

If $\omega = 0$, nothing can be accomplished by proceeding to the computation section.

II. *Computation*

In the description below, the terms entry, row, and column all refer to the current array $(u_i + v_j + c_{ij})$. Certain rows and columns will be marked during the course of computation. Some system for designating whether a row or column is marked and/or freshly marked should be set up.

1) Let p be the maximum of all the entries, and choose a particular entry e of value p. Erase all row and column marks.

2) Mark the row in which e lies.

3) Repeat the following two steps in order until there are either no freshly marked rows or no freshly marked columns. (The row containing e is called "freshly marked" after application of step 2, and any other row or column marked in the immediately preceding application of 3a or 3b is called freshly marked.)

a) For each freshly marked row, mark each unmarked column having an entry of value 0 in that row.

b) For each freshly marked column, mark each unmarked row having an entry of value p or $p - 1$ in that column.

4) When step 3 is finished:

a) If the column containing e is unmarked, define $u_i = u_i - 1$ for marked i, u_i for unmarked i and $v_j = v_j + 1$ for marked j, v_j for unmarked j, and return to step 1 with the new array $(u_i + v_j + c_{ij})$.

b) If the column containing e is marked, the value p is the minimum sought. Let

$$R_i = b^{u_i}, \qquad i = 1, \ldots, m,$$
$$S_j = b^{v_j}, \qquad j = 1, \ldots, n,$$

where b is the number base of the computer.

The authors of this method suggest a way to decrease the number of iterations while increasing the time per iteration. In step 4(a), if the column containing e is unmarked, let

$$u_i = u_i - \alpha \quad \text{for marked } i$$
$$= u_i \quad \text{for unmarked } i,$$
$$v_j = v_j + \alpha \quad \text{for marked } j$$
$$= v_j \quad \text{for unmarked } j.$$

The number α is chosen in the following manner. Let q be the smallest entry value in the subarray of marked rows and unmarked columns, and let p' be the largest entry value in the subarray of unmarked rows and marked columns. Then $\alpha = \min(q, [(p - p')/2])$. If the subarray of unmarked rows and marked columns determining p' is empty, the second quantity in the minimand should be ignored.

a) Determinant:
   Given A, find $|A|$.
   Found:

$$|RAS| = |A| \left(\prod_{i=1}^{n} r_i \right) \left(\prod_{i=1}^{n} s_i \right). \tag{10.6.2}$$

Compensatory scaling:

$$|RAS| \left(\prod_{i=1}^{n} r_i\right)^{-1} \left(\prod_{i=1}^{n} s_i\right)^{-1} = |A|.$$

b) Inverse:

Given A, find A^{-1}.

Found: $[RAS]^{-1}$.   (10.6.3)

Compensatory scaling: $S[RAS]^{-1}R = A^{-1}$.

c) Systems of Equations:

Given $Ax = b$, find x.

Found: Since the augmented matrix $[A : b]$ was scaled, we found y such that $[RAT]y = [Rbs_n]$, s_n a constant, and

$$S = \left[\begin{array}{c|c} T & 0 \\ \hline 0 & s_n \end{array}\right].$$

Compensatory scaling: $x = [Ty]/s_n$.   (10.6.4)

Example. Let

$$A = \begin{bmatrix} 2^2 & 2^{-5} & -2^6 & -2^{-8} \\ -2^6 & 2^0 & 0 & 2^{-5} \\ 2^{-3} & -2^{-8} & 2^2 & -2^{-12} \\ -2^{10} & 2^3 & 2^{14} & 2^0 \end{bmatrix}.$$

Assume the number base of the computer is 2, and that 2^{-300} is a number impossible to represent by ordinary means within the computer. Since -300 would not occur otherwise in the characteristic log matrix, it is used to represent 0 and we calculate as follows.

Initialization:

Step 1:

$$C = \begin{bmatrix} 2 & -5 & 6 & -8 \\ 6 & 0 & -300 & -5 \\ -3 & -8 & 2 & -12 \\ 10 & 3 & 14 & 0 \end{bmatrix}.$$

Step 2: $u_1 = 8$, $u_2 = 5$, $u_3 = 12$, $u_4 = 0$.

$$C' = [c_{ij} + u_i] = \begin{bmatrix} 10 & 3 & 14 & 0 \\ 11 & 5 & -300 & 0 \\ 9 & 4 & 14 & 0 \\ 10 & 3 & 14 & 0 \end{bmatrix}.$$

$v_1 = -9$, $v_2 = -3$, $v_3 = -14$, $v_4 = 0$.

$$C' = [c_{ij} + u_i + v_j] = \begin{bmatrix} 1 & 0 & 0 & 0 \\ 2 & 2 & -300 & 0 \\ 0 & 1 & 0 & 0 \\ 1 & 0 & 0 & 0 \end{bmatrix}.$$

Thus $\omega = 2$, and the computation section begins.

Computation:

Step 1: $p = 2$, $e = c'_{21}$.
Step 2: mark row 2.
Step 3a: mark column 4.
Step 3b: no mark.
Step 4a: $u_2 = 4$, $v_4 = 1$.

Hence

$$C' = [c_{ij} + u_i + v_j] = \begin{bmatrix} 1 & 0 & 0 & 1 \\ 1 & 1 & -300 & 0 \\ 0 & 1 & 0 & 1 \\ 1 & 0 & 0 & 1 \end{bmatrix}.$$

Step 1: $p = 1$, $e = c'_{11}$.
Step 2: mark row 1.
Step 3a: mark column 2, column 3.
Step 3b: mark row 2, row 3, row 4.
Step 3a: mark column 1, column 4.
Step 4b: end.

The scaled matrix A' therefore is

$$A' = \begin{bmatrix} 2^1 & 2^0 & -2^0 & -2^1 \\ -2^1 & 2^1 & 0 & 2^0 \\ 2^0 & -2^1 & 2^0 & -2^1 \\ -2^1 & 2^0 & 2^0 & 2^1 \end{bmatrix}.$$

10.7 OSBORNE'S METHOD

The method of Osborne [Section 10.9(b)] attempts to reduce the Euclidean norm of the matrix. Given matrix A, find a diagonal matrix S, such that SAS^{-1} is more nearly symmetric than the original matrix. Of course the method is useless if the matrix A is already symmetric. The transformed matrix, $B = SAS^{-1}$, may be multiplied by some scalar α, so that the median element $(\alpha B)_m$ is equal to or greater than $\frac{1}{2}$ and less than 1. This operation will be called "medianation."

Given A, set $S_i = 1$, $i = 1, 2, \ldots, n$, and repeat the following sequences of instructions until no change in S can be made:

1) $i = 1$.

2) $TI = \left(\sum_{k=1}^{n} {}' a_{ik}^2 \right)^{1/2}$, $TJ = \left(\sum_{k=1}^{n} {}' a_{ki}^2 \right)^{1/2}$,

where $\sum'$ denotes omission of diagonal element from the summation.

3) If TI or $TJ = 0$, go to 7. Otherwise,

$$NI = \log_b TI,$$
$$NJ = \log_b TJ,$$
$$NCH = |NI - NJ|/2,$$

where b is the number base of the computer.

4) If $NCH = 0$, go to 7.

5) If $NI < NJ, T = b^{NCH}$.
   If $NI > NJ, T = b^{-NCH}$.
   $S_i = S_i T$.

6) For $k = 1, 2, \ldots, n$, except $k = i$,
   $A_{i,k} = A_{i,k} T, \quad A_{k,i} = A_{k,i}/T$.

7) If $i = n, i = i + 1$, go to 2.
   If $i = n$, this iteration is completed.

Eigenvalue Problem:
Given $Ax = \lambda x$, find λ, x.
Found: λ', y, such that $\alpha SAS^{-1}y = \lambda'y$.   (10.7.1)
Compensatory scaling: $\lambda = (^1/\alpha)\lambda', x = S^{-1}y$.

10.8 MODIFIED OSBORNE'S METHOD

This method is the same as in Section 10.7 with two exceptions:

1) Only two iterations are made.

2) Step 3 is changed as follows:

$$TI = \max(a_{ik}), \quad i \neq k,$$
$$TJ = \max(a_{ki}), \quad i \neq k.$$

The results given in (10.7.1) are the same.

10.9 COMMENTS AND SUPPLEMENTARY REFERENCES

Multiplication by a scalar is the simplest of the methods. Equilibration is simpler than the linear program method. Since equilibration is a row operation, it does its best work when one or more rows of the matrix are affecting the norm significantly.

The operation and the method that will be used for the operation on the scaled matrix should be considered. Scalar multiplication should probably be used in conjunction with other methods to make the exponents of the matrix center about some number. The linear program method causes the exponents of each of the elements of the matrix to be equal to or greater than zero. If a matrix were scaled by the linear program method and immediately operated on to find its determinant, there is a strong possibility overflow would occur. In most cases, centering the exponents about zero could prevent this.

References for the linear program method and Osborne's method are

a) D. FULKERSON and P. WOLFE, "An Algorithm for Scaling Matrices," *S.I.A.M. Review*, **4**, 3 (1962) 142–146.

b) E. E. OSBORNE, "On Pre-Conditioning of Matrices," *Journal of A.C.M.*, **7**, 4 (1960) 338–345.

CHAPTER 11

INTRODUCTION TO COMPLEX VARIABLES

11.1 DEFINITIONS

In this chapter we present a synopsis of some important definitions and theorems from the theory of functions of a complex variable. This synopsis will provide a background for the Laplace transform. For a more extensive study of these topics, the reader is referred to the supplementary reading list in Section 11.11.

A set of points in the complex plane is any collection of points. This set may consist of a finite or infinite number of points. Thus, $(2, 3)$, $(-4, 5)$, $(-3, -5)$ is a finite set, whereas the points (x, y), satisfying the inequality $2x^2 + 3y^2 < 35$, form an infinite set.

A set S is bounded if a positive real number M can be found such that $|z| = |x + iy| = \sqrt{x^2 + y^2} < M$ for all points z of S.

An ϵ-neighborhood of a point z_0 is the set of points inside a circle with center z_0 and radius $\epsilon > 0$, i.e., it is the set of points z which satisfy the inequality

$$|z - z_0| < \epsilon.$$

If every point z of a set S has a neighborhood lying entirely within the set, then S is said to be an open set. Examples of open sets are the sets of points satisfying the inequalities

$$\text{Re}(z) = x > 0, \quad \text{Im}(z) = y < \tfrac{1}{4}, \quad x^4 + y^4 < 4. \tag{11.1.1}$$

If the set of points not in S is an open set, then S is called a closed set. Thus the set of points satisfying the following conditions

$$x^2 + y^2 = 9, \quad 5x^2 + 4y^2 \geq 20, \quad \text{Re}(z) \leq 9, \tag{11.1.2}$$

are examples of closed sets.

A set S is called a connected set if it is possible to join any two points of the set by a polygonal arc lying entirely within the set. An open connected set is called a region.

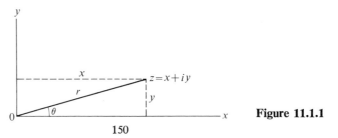

Figure 11.1.1

Complex numbers lend themselves to a geometrical representation if we agree to call x the abscissa and y the ordinate of a point with respect to a rectangular coordinate system which is known as the complex plane (Fig. 11.1.1). To the number $z = x + iy$ there corresponds a point (x, y) and conversely. Sometimes it is convenient to think of a complex number emanating from the origin 0 and terminating at the point (x, y). In this way we establish a one-to-one correspondence between the totality of vectors in the complex plane and the complex numbers. The length of the vector is called the modulus or absolute value of z and is denoted by $|z|$ or r:

$$|z| = r = \sqrt{x^2 + y^2}. \tag{11.1.3}$$

It is obvious that $x = r \cos \theta$ and $y = r \sin \theta$, and hence

$$z = x + iy = r(\cos \theta + i \sin \theta). \tag{11.1.4}$$

This is known as the polar form of the complex number, and θ is called the argument of z.

11.2 ELEMENTARY FUNCTIONS OF A COMPLEX VARIABLE

If complex variables z and w are so related that for each value of z in a given region of the complex plane there corresponds one value of w, then w is a single-valued function of z. However, if more than one value of w corresponds to each value of z, then $w = f(z)$ is multiple valued.

Elementary functions of a complex variable are defined so that these functions reduce to the corresponding functions of a real variable when z becomes x.

A polynomial is defined as a function of the form

$$P(z) = a_0 z^n + a_1 z^{n-1} + \cdots + a_{n-1} z + a_n, \tag{11.2.1}$$

where $a_0, a_1, \ldots, a_n$ may be complex and n is a positive integer.

A rational function of z is defined as the quotient of two polynomials and e^z is defined as a power series.

The convergence of a power series of the form

$$\sum_{n=0}^{\infty} a_n (z - z_0)^n \tag{11.2.2}$$

can be investigated by tests analogous to those in elementary calculus for real variables. In the real case, the interval of convergence of a power series is the entire x-axis, a portion of it, or a single point on it. In the complex case the region of convergence is the interior of a circle with, possibly, some of the points on the circle. For example, $\sum_{n=0}^{\infty} x^n$ has for its interval of convergence $-1 < x < 1$, whereas $\sum_{n=0}^{\infty} z^n$ has for its region of convergence the interior of the circle $|z| = 1$.

It can be shown that convergent power series enjoy the following properties inside their circles of convergence: (a) they represent continuous functions, (b) the series can be differentiated or integrated term by term, and the resulting series has the same radius of convergence as the original series, (c) term by term multiplication of the series is a valid operation.

We define the exponential function e^z by the power series

$$e^z = 1 + z + \frac{z^2}{2!} + \frac{z^3}{3!} + \cdots + \frac{z^n}{n!} + \cdots \tag{11.2.3}$$

The Cauchy ratio test shows that it converges for all complex values of z.

The trigonometric functions, trigonometric identities, and hyperbolic functions are defined exactly as in the case of real variables.

By expanding e^{iz} in a power series and separating the real and imaginary parts, we easily show that

$$e^{iz} = \cos z + i \sin z. \tag{11.2.4}$$

This is known as Euler's formula. In a similar manner

$$e^{-iz} = \cos z - i \sin z. \tag{11.2.5}$$

Euler's formula permits one to write a complex number z in the form

$$z = x + iy = r(\cos \theta + i \sin \theta) = re^{i\theta}. \tag{11.2.6}$$

The logarithm of z is defined as the inverse of the exponential function. If

$$w = \ln z, \tag{11.2.7}$$

then

$$z = e^w. \tag{11.2.8}$$

If $w = u + iv$, then

$$z = e^w = e^{u+iv} = e^u \cdot e^{iv} = e^u(\cos v + i \sin v), \tag{11.2.9}$$

$$x = e^u \cos v, \qquad y = e^u \sin v, \tag{11.2.10}$$

$$|z|^2 = x^2 + y^2 = e^{2u} \cos^2 v + e^{2u} \sin^2 v = e^{2u}, \tag{11.2.11}$$

$$\tan v = y/x. \tag{11.2.12}$$

Thus $u = \ln |z|$, $v = \arctan y/x = \theta \pm 2k\pi$, $(k = 0, 1, 2, \ldots)$, where $\ln |z| = \ln r$ is the ordinary real logarithm, and θ is defined to lie in the interval $-\pi < \theta \leq \pi$. Therefore

$$\ln z = \ln |z| + i(\theta \pm 2k\pi), \qquad k = 0, 1, 2, \ldots \tag{11.2.13}$$

When $k = 0$, one obtains the principal value of the logarithm. We observe that $\ln z$ is an infinitely many-valued function defined for all values of z except $z = 0$.

11.3 LIMIT, CONTINUITY, AND ANALYTICITY OF FUNCTIONS OF A COMPLEX VARIABLE

The function $w = f(z)$, defined in some region R, has the limit w_0, $\lim_{z \to z_0} f(z) = w_0$, if, corresponding to every positive number ϵ, there exists a positive number δ, such that $|f(z) - w_0| < \epsilon$ whenever $0 < |z - z_0| < \delta$.

If the complex number $z = x + iy$ represents a point in the z-plane with coordinates x and y, then the corresponding value of $w = f(z) = u + iv$ can be represented by a point in the w-plane with coordinates u and v. If z traces out a curve in the z-plane, then w traces out a corresponding curve in the w-plane.

The preceding definition of a limit can be interpreted geometrically as follows. Corresponding to $\epsilon > 0$, there exists a $\delta > 0$ such that for all points $z \neq z_0$ lying within the circle of radius δ and center z_0 in the z-plane, the corresponding points w lie within the circle of radius ϵ and center w_0 in the w-plane.

If $f(z_0)$ exists, and for each $\epsilon > 0$ there exists a $\delta > 0$ such that

$$|f(z) - f(z_0)| < \epsilon$$

when $|z - z_0| < \delta$, then $f(z)$ is continuous at the point z_0. This is equivalent to the statements: $f(z_0)$ exists, $\lim_{z \to z_0} f(z)$ exists; and $\lim_{z \to z_0} f(z) = f(z_0)$. If $f(z)$ is continuous at every point in the region R, then it is continuous in the region R.

The derivative of $w = f(z)$ at z_0 is defined as

$$\frac{dw}{dz} = f'(z_0) = \lim_{z \to z_0} \frac{f(z) - f(z_0)}{z - z_0} = \lim_{\Delta z \to 0} \frac{f(z_0 + \Delta z) - f(z_0)}{\Delta z},$$

$$(11.3.1)$$

where we require that the limit exist and be the same, regardless of the direction in which z tends to z_0 or $\Delta z \to 0$.

This requirement is rather severe and restricts the class of functions which possess a derivative. However, the class of functions having derivatives is still very broad.

A function $f(z)$ which is single valued in a region R and possesses a unique derivative at each point of R is analytic in R. It is analytic at a point z_0 if z_0 lies inside some region where $f(z)$ is analytic.

Since the derivative is to exist and be unique for all modes of approach of Δz to zero, if we allow $\Delta z \to 0$ along a line parallel to the y-axis, then we have $\Delta x = 0$ and $\Delta z = i \Delta y$. So for $w - u(x, y) + iv(x, y)$, we have

$$\frac{dw}{dz} = \lim_{\Delta y \to 0} \frac{u(x, y + \Delta y) - u(x, y)}{i \Delta y} + i \lim_{\Delta y \to 0} \frac{v(x, y + \Delta y) - v(x, y)}{i \Delta y},$$

$$\frac{dw}{dz} = -i \frac{\partial u}{\partial y} + \frac{\partial v}{\partial y}. \qquad (11.3.2)$$

Letting $\Delta z \to 0$ along a line parallel to the x-axis, we have $\Delta y = 0$ and $\Delta z = \Delta x$. Thus

$$\frac{dw}{dz} = \lim_{\Delta x \to 0} \frac{u(x + \Delta x, y) - u(x, y)}{\Delta x} + i \lim_{\Delta x \to 0} \frac{v(x + \Delta x, y) - v(x, y)}{\Delta x},$$

$$\frac{dw}{dz} = \frac{\partial u}{\partial x} + i \frac{\partial v}{\partial x}. \qquad (11.3.3)$$

It follows that since

$$\frac{dw}{dz} = \frac{\partial v}{\partial y} - i\frac{\partial u}{\partial x} = \frac{\partial u}{\partial x} + i\frac{\partial v}{\partial x},$$

then

$$\frac{\partial u}{\partial x} = \frac{\partial v}{\partial y}, \qquad \frac{\partial v}{\partial x} = -\frac{\partial u}{\partial y}. \tag{11.3.4}$$

These equations are known as the Cauchy-Riemann equations.

We can show that the necessary and sufficient conditions for w to be analytic in R are that u and v satisfy the Cauchy-Riemann equations and the four partial derivatives exist and be continuous in R.

Suppose that the partial derivatives of second order exists. Then

$$\frac{\partial^2 u}{\partial x^2} = \frac{\partial^2 v}{\partial x\,\partial y}, \qquad \frac{\partial^2 u}{\partial y^2} = \frac{\partial^2 v}{\partial y\,\partial x}. \tag{11.3.5}$$

Now if, in addition, the second-order partial derivatives are assumed to be continuous, then the order of differentiation is immaterial and

$$\frac{\partial^2 u}{\partial x^2} + \frac{\partial^2 u}{\partial y^2} = 0, \qquad \frac{\partial^2 v}{\partial x^2} + \frac{\partial^2 v}{\partial y^2} = 0. \tag{11.3.6}$$

Hence the real and imaginary parts of an analytic function must satisfy Laplace's equation.

Since Laplace's equation occurs frequently in two-dimensional problems in hydrodynamics, elasticity, electrostatics, etc., the connection between analytic functions and Laplace's equation makes the study of functions of a complex variable of great importance in applied mathematics.

11.4 LINE INTEGRALS OF COMPLEX FUNCTIONS

Let C be any continuous curve of finite length joining the two points z_0 and z_n, and let $f(z) = u(x, y) + iv(x, y)$ be a continuous function defined at all points of C. Then

$$\int_C f(z)\,dz = \int_C (u\,dx - v\,dy) + i\int_C (v\,dx + u\,dy). \tag{11.4.1}$$

Hence, a line integral of a function of a complex variable can be evaluated by finding the values of two real line integrals. The value of this integral depends, in general, on the function $f(z)$ and the path C.

We can then obtain a related inequality

$$\left| \int_C f(z)\,dz \right| \leqq \int_C |f(z)|\,|dz|, \tag{11.4.2}$$

which is of some importance. Now $|dz| = ds$, so that if $f(z)$ is bounded on C, that is, $|f(z)| < M$, where M is a constant, then

$$\left| \int_C f(z)\,dz \right| \leqq M\int_C ds \leqq ML \tag{11.4.3}$$

where L is the length of the curve C.

11.5 CAUCHY'S INTEGRAL THEOREM

A continuous closed curve C which does not cross itself, and is such that parallels to the x- and y-axes cut it in at most two points is called a simple closed curve.

If, in the process of describing the curve C, an observer proceeds so that the region enclosed is to his left, then we say that the curve has been traversed in the positive direction.

Regions more complicated than those enclosed by simple curves can, in general, be decomposed into regions bounded by simple closed curves by introducing suitable cross cuts.

If a region R has the property that any closed curve lying in R can be shrunk continuously to a point without crossing the boundary of R, then the region is said to be simply connected.

When closed curves are contained within closed curves, the region is said to be multiply connected. These can be made simply connected by introducing cross cuts.

In order to prove Cauchy's integral theorem we make use of:

Green's theorem. If $P(x, y)$, $Q(x, y)$, $\partial P/\partial y$, and $\partial Q/\partial x$ are continuous single-valued functions in a simply connected region R bounded by a closed curve C, where C is included in R, then

$$\int_C (P\,dx + Q\,dy) = \iint_R \left(\frac{\partial Q}{\partial x} - \frac{\partial P}{\partial y}\right) dx\,dy. \tag{11.5.1}$$

Suppose that R is a simply connected region, C a closed contour lying entirely within R, and $f(z) = u + iv$ an analytic function in R. Then u, v, and their first-order partial derivatives are continuous in R, and by Green's theorem,

$$\int_C f(z)\,dz = \int_C (u\,dx - v\,dy) + i\int_C (v\,dx + u\,dy),$$

$$= \iint_R \left(-\frac{\partial v}{\partial x} - \frac{\partial u}{\partial y}\right) dx\,dy + i\iint_R \left(-\frac{\partial v}{\partial y} + \frac{\partial u}{\partial x}\right) dx\,dy. \tag{11.5.2}$$

Since we assumed that $f(z)$ was analytic, $\partial u/\partial x = \partial v/\partial y$, $\partial u/\partial y = -\partial v/\partial x$, and, hence, the double integrals in Eq. (11.5.2) vanish identically. Therefore,

$$\int_C f(z)\,dz = 0. \tag{11.5.3}$$

This result is known as Cauchy's integral theorem.

Suppose that two distinct curves C_1 and C_2 join the points z_0 and z_1. Then assuming $f(z)$ is analytic within the region enclosed by the curves and on the curves themselves, we have, by Cauchy's theorem,

$$\int_{C_1} f(z)\,dz = \int_{C_2} f(z)\,dz. \tag{11.5.4}$$

This states that the value of the integral $\int_{z_0}^{z_1} f(\xi)d\xi$ is independent of the path joining z_0 to z_1. Also, if a simple closed curve C' lies entirely within a simple closed curve C, then, introducing a cross cut, we have

$$\int_C f(z)\,dz = \int_{C'} f(z)\,dz. \tag{11.5.5}$$

11.6 CAUCHY'S INTEGRAL FORMULA

Let $f(z)$ be an analytic function in the region R bounded by a closed curve C, and let z_0 be any point inside R. With z_0 as center, draw a circle C' with radius ρ entirely within R. It is clear that $f(z)/(z - z_0)$ is analytic in the region bounded by C and C'. Hence, by Eq. (11.5.5), it follows that

$$\int_C \frac{f(z)}{z - z_0}\,dz = \int_{C'} \frac{f(z)}{z - z_0}\,dz. \tag{11.6.1}$$

Now

$$\int_C \frac{f(z)}{z - z_0}\,dz = \int_{C'} \frac{f(z_0)}{z - z_0}\,dz + \int_{C'} \frac{f(z) - f(z_0)}{z - z_0}\,dz. \tag{11.6.2}$$

On the circle C', we have

$$z = z_0 + \rho e^{i\theta} \qquad \text{and} \qquad dz = \rho i e^{i\theta}\,d\theta.$$

Therefore,

$$\int_{C'} \frac{f(z_0)}{z - z_0}\,dz = f(z_0) \int_0^{2\pi} \frac{\rho i e^{i\theta}\,d\theta}{\rho e^{i\theta}} = 2\pi i f(z_0). \tag{11.6.3}$$

Since $f(z)$ is continuous, corresponding to any $\epsilon > 0$, we can take ρ so small that for any z on C', $|f(z) - f(z_0)| < \epsilon$. Therefore, by Eq. (11.4.3),

$$\left| \int_{C'} \frac{f(z) - f(z_0)}{z - z_0}\,dz \right| \leqq \frac{\epsilon}{\rho}(2\pi\rho) = 2\pi\epsilon,$$

that is,

$$\int_{C'} \frac{f(z) - f(z_0)}{z - z_0}\,dz = 0. \tag{11.6.4}$$

Therefore, from Eq. (11.6.2), we obtain

$$\int_C \frac{f(z)}{z - z_0}\,dz = 2\pi i f(z_0). \tag{11.6.5}$$

This is Cauchy's integral formula. We note that the value of $f(z_0)$ at any point z_0 within C can be obtained from the given boundary values of $f(z)$ on C.

For some purposes it is desirable to express Eq. (11.6.5) in a more convenient form, that is,

$$f(z) = \frac{1}{2\pi i} \int_C \frac{f(\xi)}{\xi - z}\,d\xi. \tag{11.6.6}$$

If we differentiate both sides of (11.6.6), assuming differentiation under the integral sign is permissible, we obtain

$$f'(z) = \frac{1}{2\pi i} \int_C \frac{f(\xi)}{(\xi - z)^2} d\xi. \tag{11.6.7}$$

In a similar manner

$$f^{(n)}(z) = \frac{n!}{2\pi i} \int_C \frac{f(\xi)}{(\xi - z)^{n+1}} d\xi. \tag{11.6.8}$$

11.7 TAYLOR'S SERIES

Let $f(z)$ be analytic in a region R, and let z_0 be the center of a circle C of radius r lying entirely within R. Then

$$f(z) = \frac{1}{2\pi i} \int_C \frac{f(\xi)}{\xi - z} d\xi = \frac{1}{2\pi i} \int_C \frac{f(\xi)\,d\xi}{(\xi - z_0) - (z - z_0)}$$

$$= \frac{1}{2\pi i} \int_C \frac{f(\xi)}{\xi - z_0} \left(\frac{1}{1 - (z - z_0)/(\xi - z_0)} \right) d\xi$$

$$= \frac{1}{2\pi i} \int_C \frac{f(\xi)}{\xi - z_0} \left[1 + \frac{z - z_0}{\xi - z_0} + \cdots + \left(\frac{z - z_0}{\xi - z_0} \right)^{n-1} \right.$$

$$\left. + \frac{(z - z_0)^n}{(\xi - z)(\xi - z_0)^{n-1}} \right] d\xi$$

$$= f(z_0) + (z - z_0)f'(z_0) + \frac{(z - z_0)^2}{2!} f''(z_0) + \cdots$$

$$+ \frac{(z - z_0)^{n-1}}{(n - 1)!} f^{(n-1)}(z_0) + R_n, \tag{11.7.1}$$

where

$$R_n = \frac{(z - z_0)^n}{2\pi i} \int_C \frac{f(\xi)\,d\xi}{(\xi - z_0)^n(\xi - z)}. \tag{11.7.2}$$

The series (11.7.1), called a Taylor series, converges to $f(z)$ for every z inside any circle C lying wholly within the region R in which $f(z)$ is analytic.

11.8 LAURENT SERIES

Let $f(z)$ be analytic in the annular region bounded by the concentric circles C_1 and C_2 whose common center is z_0 and whose radii are r_1, r_2. Introducing a cross cut connecting C_1 and C_2 and using Cauchy's integral formula, we have

$$f(z) = \frac{1}{2\pi i} \int_{C_2} \frac{f(\xi)\,d\xi}{\xi - z} - \frac{1}{2\pi i} \int_{C_1} \frac{f(\xi)\,d\xi}{\xi - z}, \tag{11.8.1}$$

where z is any point within the annular region. Then,

$$\frac{1}{2\pi i} \int_{C_2} \frac{f(\xi)\, d\xi}{\xi - z} = \sum_{n=0}^{\infty} a_n (z - z_0)^n, \tag{11.8.2}$$

where

$$a_n = \frac{1}{2\pi i} \int_{C_2} \frac{f(\xi)\, d\xi}{(\xi - z_0)^{n+1}}, \qquad n = 0, 1, 2, \dots \tag{11.8.3}$$

Now

$$-\frac{1}{2\pi i} \int_{C_1} \frac{f(\xi)\, d\xi}{\xi - z} = \frac{1}{2\pi i} \int_{C_1} \frac{f(\xi)\, d\xi}{(z - z_0) - (\xi - z_0)}$$

$$= \frac{1}{2\pi i} \int_{C_1} \frac{f(\xi)}{z - z_0} \left[\frac{1}{1 + (\xi - z_0)/(z - z_0)} \right] d\xi$$

$$= \frac{1}{2\pi i} \int_{C_1} \frac{f(\xi)}{z - z_0} \left[1 + \frac{\xi - z_0}{z - z_0} + \left(\frac{\xi - z_0}{z - z_0} \right)^2 + \cdots \right.$$

$$\left. + \left(\frac{\xi - z_0}{z - z_0} \right)^{n-1} + \frac{(\xi - z_0)^n}{(z - z_0)^{n-1}(z - \xi)} \right] d\xi. \tag{11.8.4}$$

The nth term of Eq. (11.8.4) tends to zero as n approaches infinity. Therefore,

$$-\frac{1}{2\pi i} \int_{C_1} \frac{f(\xi)\, d\xi}{\xi - z_0} = \sum_{n=1}^{\infty} \frac{1}{2\pi i} \int_{C_1} \frac{f(\xi)(\xi - z_0)^{n-1}}{(z - z_0)^n} d\xi. \tag{11.8.5}$$

If we set

$$a_{-n} = \frac{1}{2\pi i} \int_{C_1} \frac{f(\xi)\, d\xi}{(\xi - z_0)^{-n+1}}, \qquad n = 1, 2, 3, \dots \tag{11.8.6}$$

and combine (11.8.5) with (11.8.2), we may write (11.8.1) as

$$f(z) = \sum_{n=0}^{\infty} a_n (z - z_0)^n + \sum_{n=1}^{\infty} a_{-n} (z - z_0)^{-n}. \tag{11.8.7}$$

We write Eq. (11.8.7) briefly as

$$f(z) = \sum_{n=-\infty}^{\infty} a_n (z - z_0)^n, \qquad r_1 < |z - z_0| < r_2. \tag{11.8.8}$$

This is known as the Laurent series expansion of $f(z)$. If each a_{-n} is zero, then (11.8.8) is a Taylor series. Also, since (11.8.2) converges everywhere inside C_2, and (11.8.5) converges everywhere outside C_1, the sum of the two series, Eq. (11.8.8), converges in the annular region between C_1 and C_2.

11.9 SINGULARITIES

Points at which $f(z)$ ceases to be analytic are called singular points. By the definition of an analytic function, a point z can be singular if: (1) the derivative fails to exist at z, (2) z is such that it cannot be made the interior point of a region where $f(z)$ is single valued.

For example, if $f(z) = 1/(z - 2)(z + 3i)$, $z = 2$ and $z = -3i$ are singular points because $f'(2)$ and $f'(-3i)$ fail to exist. If $f(z) = (z - 2i)^{3/2}$, $z = 2i$ is a singular point because it cannot be made the interior point of a region where $(z - 2i)^{3/2}$ is single valued.

Singularities of the first category are of two types: (1) poles or nonessential singularities and (2) essential singularities. To the second category belong the so-called branch points. At these, the derivative may or may not exist. It can be shown, however, that a derivative of some order will fail to exist.

Suppose that z_0 is an isolated singularity of $f(z)$. This means there is a neighborhood of z_0 throughout which $f(z)$ is analytic except at z_0. In the Laurent expansion of $f(z)$, if the number of terms involving $(z - z_0)$ to a negative exponent is finite, then z_0 is said to be a pole. Moreover, if $a_{-m}(m \geq 1)$ is the last nonzero coefficient, then $z = z_0$ is a pole of order m. If the function is redefined by multiplying by $(z - z_0)^m$, then $(z - z_0)^m f(z)$ is analytic at $z = z_0$, and

$$\lim_{z \to z_0} (z - z_0)^m f(z) = a_{-m} \neq 0.$$

In this case, z_0 is called a removable singularity.

If the number of negative powers of $(z - z_0)$ in the Laurent expansion is infinite, then $z = z_0$ is said to be an essential singularity. This singularity is not removable.

Branch points are characteristic of multiple-valued functions. By definition, a branch point is one such that if a point traces out a small closed path (circle) surrounding it but not enclosing any other singular points, then the value of the function after a complete circuit is no longer the same as it was initially. The theorems so far assumed the function to be analytic. For these theorems to apply, when multiple-valued functions arise, it is necessary to make them single valued. This is done by selecting one branch of the function and introducing cuts or barriers so that it is impossible to draw closed curves around the branch points.

11.10 RESIDUES AND CAUCHY'S RESIDUE THEOREM

Assume that the function $f(z)$ is expanded in a Laurent series about the isolated singularity $z = z_0$. Then

$$f(z) = \sum_{n=1}^{\infty} a_{-n}(z - z_0)^{-n} + \sum_{n=0}^{\infty} a_n(z - z_0)^n. \tag{11.10.1}$$

The coefficient

$$a_{-1} = \frac{1}{2\pi i} \int_C f(z) \, dz, \tag{11.10.2}$$

where C is a curve enclosing $z = z_0$, but no other singularities of $f(z)$, is called the residue of $f(z)$ at $z = z_0$. We shall denote it by $\text{Res}(z_0)$ whenever it is clear what function is being referred to.

Assume now that C is a closed curve enclosing a finite number of singularities $z_1, z_2, \ldots, z_n$, and let $C_1, C_2, \ldots, C_n$ be circles lying within C and having centers

$z_1, z_2, \ldots, z_n$. Then an extension of Eq. (11.5.5) gives

$$\int_C f(z)\, dz = \int_{C_1} f(z)\, dz + \int_{C_2} f(z)\, dz + \cdots + \int_{C_n} f(z)\, dz. \qquad (11.10.3)$$

But

$$\int_{C_k} f(z)\, dz = 2\pi i \operatorname{Res}_{z_k} f(z).$$

Therefore,

$$\int_C f(z)\, dz = 2\pi i \sum_{k=1}^{n} \operatorname{Res}_{z_k} f(z). \qquad (11.10.4)$$

This is known as Cauchy's residue theorem.

Although Formula (11.10.2) can be used to compute the residue of a function at a given point, it may be that the Laurent expansion is easier to obtain. For example, the residue of

$$f(z) = \frac{3z}{(z+2)^2} = \frac{3}{z+2} - \frac{6}{(z+2)^2}$$

at $z = -2$ is 3.

In other cases we may proceed as follows. If $f(z)$ has a pole of order k at $z = z_0$, then its Laurent expansion is

$$f(z) = \frac{a_{-k}}{(z-z_0)^k} + \frac{a_{-k+1}}{(z-z_0)^{k-1}} + \cdots + \frac{a_{-1}}{z-z_0}$$
$$+ a_0 + a_1(z-z_0) + a_2(z-z_0)^2 + \cdots \qquad (11.10.5)$$

In order to obtain a_{-1} let us multiply (11.10.5) by $(z-z_0)^k$, $z \neq z_0$. We get

$$(z-z_0)^k f(z) = a_{-k} + a_{-k+1}(z-z_0) + \cdots$$
$$+ a_{-1}(z-z_0)^{k-1} + a_0(z-z_0)^k + \cdots \qquad (11.10.6)$$

Differentiating (11.10.6) $k - 1$ times with respect to z, and taking the limit as $z \to z_0$, we obtain

$$\lim_{z \to z_0} \frac{d^{k-1}}{dz^{k-1}} [(z-z_0)^k f(z)] = (k-1)! a_{-1}. \qquad (11.10.7)$$

Therefore,

$$\operatorname{Res}(z_0) = \frac{1}{(k-1)!} \lim_{z \to z_0} \frac{d^{k-1}}{dz^{k-1}} [(z-z_0)^k f(z)]. \qquad (11.10.8)$$

If $z = z_0$ is a simple pole ($k = 1$), then

$$\operatorname{Res}(z_0) = \lim_{z \to z_0} (z-z_0) f(z). \qquad (11.10.9)$$

In this case, we can derive a convenient formula by writing $f(z) = P(z)/Q(z)$ and applying l'Hôpital's rule:

$$\lim_{z \to z_0} \frac{(z-z_0)P(z)}{Q(z)} = \lim_{z \to z_0} \frac{(z-z_0)P'(z) + P(z)}{Q'(z)} = \frac{P(z_0)}{Q'(z_0)}.$$

Therefore,

$$\text{Res}(z_0) = \frac{P(z_0)}{Q'(z_0)}, \qquad P(z_0) \neq \infty. \qquad (11.10.10)$$

Example 1. Find the residues of

$$f(z) = \frac{e^{-z}}{z^2 - 4}$$

at its poles.

Solution. The function $f(z)$ has simple poles at $z = \pm 2$. For the residues we have

$$\text{Res}(2) = \lim_{z \to 2} (z - 2)f(z) = \lim_{z \to 2} \frac{e^{-z}}{z + 2} = \frac{e^{-2}}{4},$$

$$\text{Res}(-2) = \lim_{z \to -2} (z + 2)f(z) = \lim_{z \to -2} \frac{e^{-z}}{z - 2} = -\frac{e^2}{4}.$$

Example 2. For the function

$$f(z) = \frac{1}{z(z - 2)^2}$$

there is a simple pole at $z = 0$ and a double pole at $z = 2$. We have

$$\text{Res}(0) = \lim_{z \to 0} zf(z) = \lim_{z \to 0} \frac{1}{(z - 2)^2} = \frac{1}{4},$$

$$\text{Res}(2) = \lim_{z \to 2} \frac{d}{dz}\left(\frac{1}{z}\right) = \lim_{z \to 2} \left(-\frac{1}{z^2}\right) = -\frac{1}{4}.$$

Example 3. Find residues of $f(z) = \sin z/z^3$ at its poles.

Solution. In this case $\lim_{z \to 0} z^3 f(z) = 0$, and hence $z = 0$ is not a triple pole. If we define

$$g(z) = \sin z/z, \qquad z \neq 0,$$
$$= 1, \qquad z = 0,$$

then $f(z) = g(z)/z^2$ and, since $z^2 f(z) = g(z)$ is analytic at $z = 0$ and

$$\lim_{z \to 0} z^2 f(z) = \lim_{z \to 0} g(z) = 1,$$

then $f(z)$ has a double pole at $z = 0$. Therefore,

$$\text{Res}(0) = \lim_{z \to 0} \frac{d}{dz} [z^2 f(z)] = \lim_{z \to 0} [g(z)]$$

$$= \lim_{z \to 0} \frac{z \cos z - \sin z}{z} = \lim_{z \to 0} \frac{-z \sin z}{z}$$

$$= \lim_{z \to 0} (-\sin z) = 0.$$

11.11 SUPPLEMENTARY REFERENCES

a) R. V. CHURCHILL, *Introduction to Complex Variables and Applications*, McGraw-Hill, New York, 1948.

b) K. KNOPP, *Theory of Functions*, Dover Press, New York, 1945.

c) W. R. LEPAGE, *Complex Variables in Linear Systems Analysis*, McGraw-Hill, New York, 1959.

d) S. SESHU and N. BALABANIAN, *Linear Network Analysis*, Wiley, New York, 1959.

e) E. C. TITCHMARSH, *Theory of Functions*, Oxford University Press, Oxford, 1932.

f) E. T. WHITTAKER and G. N. WATSON, *Modern Analysis*, Cambridge University Press, London, 1927.

EXERCISES

1. Show that the following functions satisfy the Cauchy-Riemann equations and Laplace's equation: (a) $\sinh z$, (b) $\tan z$, (c) $\ln z$, (d) e^z.

2. Show that the value of $\int_i^1 (z^2 - z + 1)\, dz$ along the circle $x^2 + y^2 = 1$ is $\frac{1}{3}(1 - 2i)$.

3. Show that the value of $\int_{-i}^i [(1 + z)/z]\, dz$ along the right half of the circle $x^2 + y^2 = 1$ is $i(2 + \pi)$.

4. Find the Laurent expansion of $f(z) = 1/(z - 1)(z - 3)$ which is valid for the ring $1 < |z| < 3$.

5. Show that $f(z) = (2z - 1)/(z^3 + 1)$ has poles at $z = -1$ and $z = \frac{1}{2}(1 \pm i\sqrt{3})$.

6. Show that $f(z) = \sin [1/(z - i)]$ has an essential singularity at $z = i$.

7. Show that $f(z) = \ln(z^2 - 1)$ has branch points at $z = \pm 1$.

8. Show that $\cos \sqrt{1 - z}$ has no singularities.

9. Show that $f(z) = \tan^{-1} (z + i)$ has branch points at $z = 0$ and $z = -2i$.

10. Find the values of the residues of the following functions at each of their poles:

a) $f(z) = \dfrac{z^2 - 2z + 3}{(z + 1)(z - 2)}$,

b) $f(z) = \dfrac{e^{3z}}{z^3 - 8}$,

c) $f(z) = \dfrac{z + 1}{z^2(z - 2)^2}$,

d) $f(z) = \dfrac{\sin 2z}{z^4}$.

CHAPTER 12

INTRODUCTION TO THE LAPLACE TRANSFORM

12.1 DEFINITION

The operation of multiplying a function $F(t)$ of the real variable t, $t > 0$, by e^{-st} (where s is the complex variable $x + iy$), and integrating the result with respect to t from zero to infinity to generate a new function $f(s)$ is called the Laplace transformation of $F(t)$. Symbolically

$$f(s) = \int_0^\infty F(t)e^{-st}\, dt. \tag{12.1.1}$$

This is often abbreviated as $f(s) = \mathcal{L}\{F(t)\}$, and $f(s)$ is called the Laplace transform of $F(t)$.

In the definition of the Laplace transform, $F(t)$ may be a complex-valued function of the real variable t. Such a function can be treated by resolving it into real and imaginary parts, each of which is now a real function of the real variable t.

Since the upper limit of the integral defining $\mathcal{L}\{F(t)\}$ is infinite, the integral is an improper integral. Also, it can be improper because $F(t)$ has discontinuities over the range of integration and, in particular, at the origin. We now discuss the conditions that $F(t)$ must satisfy in order for its Laplace transform to exist.

12.2 EXISTENCE OF LAPLACE TRANSFORMS

The integral defining the Laplace transform may fail to exist for several reasons. For instance, $F(t)$ may have infinite discontinuities in the interval of integration, or it may increase so rapidly that the multiplier e^{-st} cannot dampen it sufficiently for convergence of the integral. To ensure convergence of the integral, we state certain sufficient conditions on $F(t)$ which will be satisfied by most functions arising in the solution of physical problems.

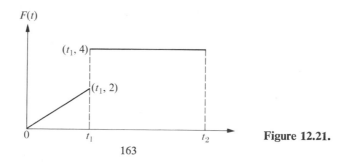

Figure 12.21.

163

A function $F(t)$ is sectionally continuous over a finite interval if that interval can be divided into a finite number of subintervals, and if, over each of these subintervals, $F(t)$ is continuous and has finite limits as t approaches either end of the subinterval from the interior. The function shown in Fig. 12.2.1 is sectionally continuous in the interval $(0, t_2)$. Since

$$\lim_{t \to t_1 -} F = 2 \quad \text{and} \quad \lim_{t \to t_1 +} F = 4$$

(where $t \to t_1 -$ and $t \to t_1 +$ mean that t approaches t_1 from the left and right, respectively), $F(t)$ is discontinuous at t_1 and has a finite jump.

A function $F(t)$ is of exponential order as $t \to \infty$ if there is a constant c, such that the product $e^{-ct}|F(t)|$ is bounded for all $t > T$, where T is a finite number. If M is a bound, then

$$|F(t)| < Me^{ct} \quad \text{for } t > T. \tag{12.2.1}$$

When this inequality is satisfied, we say that $F(t)$ is of the order of e^{ct}, or

$$F(t) = 0(e^{ct}).$$

The function $F(t) = $ constant is of exponential order with $c = 0$, as are $e^{at} \cos bt$ with $c > a$, $t^n(n \geq 0)$ with $c > 0$, and $t^2 \sin t$ with $c > 0$. The function e^{t^2} is not of exponential order. All bounded functions are of exponential order with $c = 0$.

Now, if $F(t)$ is (a) sectionally continuous over any finite interval for $t \geq 0$ and (b) of exponential order as t becomes infinite, then

$$\int_0^\infty |e^{-st}F(t)|\, dt = \int_0^\infty e^{-xt}|F(t)|\, dt$$

$$= \int_0^T e^{-xt}|F(t)|\, dt + \int_T^\infty e^{-xt}|F(t)|\, dt$$

$$= \int_0^T e^{-xt}|F(t)|\, dt + M\int_T^\infty e^{-(x-c)t}\, dt. \tag{12.2.2}$$

The first integral on the right exists because it is the sum of integrals over the separate subintervals in which the function is continuous, and the second integral exists if $x = \text{Re}(s) > c$. It follows that $\mathcal{L}\{F(t)\}$ converges absolutely when $\text{Re}(s) > c$. We can relax these conditions by allowing $F(t)$ to have certain infinite discontinuities at $t = 0$. Precisely, if $F(t)$ is sectionally continuous in any finite range for which $t > 0$, and if $F(t) = 0(e^{ct})$ and $t^n F(t)$ is bounded near $t = 0$, when n is a number less than one, then its transform still exists.

12.3 TRANSFORMS OF SIMPLE FUNCTIONS

We can determine the Laplace transform of simple functions by direct integration. If $F(t)$ is a rational fraction, we may resolve it into its partial fractions and integrate term by term. By the application of the Laplace transform, ordinary differential equations are reduced to algebraic equations of the transform. This method is discussed in detail in the chapter on transfer functions. The transforms of many of the frequently occurring functions of engineering and physics are tabulated in Appendix E.

Two theorems which are useful in finding some transforms follow.

Linearity theorem. The Laplace transformation is a linear transformation for which superposition holds. It follows from the integral definition of the transform that

$$\mathcal{L}[c_1F_1(t) + c_2F_2(t)] = c_1f_1(s) + c_2f_2(s). \tag{12.3.1}$$

Shifting theorem (in the s-plane). This theorem states that if $f(s)$ is the transform of $F(t)$, then $f(s - a)$ is the transform of $e^{at}F(t)$. That is,

$$\mathcal{L}[e^{at}F(t)] = f(s - a). \tag{12.3.2}$$

Example 1. Find the Laplace transform of $F(t) = t$.

Solution.

$$f(s) = \int_0^\infty te^{-st}\, dt = \frac{e^{-st}}{s^2}(-st - 1)\Big]_0^\infty = \frac{1}{s^2}.$$

Example 2. Find the Laplace transform of $F(t) = \sin \omega t$.

Solution.

$$f(s) = \mathcal{L}\{\sin \omega t\} = \mathcal{L}\left\{\frac{e^{i\omega t} - e^{-i\omega t}}{2}\right\} = \frac{1}{2i}\left(\frac{1}{s - i\omega} - \frac{1}{s + i\omega}\right) = \frac{\omega}{s^2 + \omega^2}.$$

Example 3. Find the transform of te^{-at}.

Solution. The transform $f(s)$ of t is $\dfrac{1}{s^2}$. Hence, by (12.3.2)

$$\mathcal{L}\{te^{-at}\} = \frac{1}{(s + a)^2}.$$

12.4 TRANSFORMS OF DERIVATIVES

If $\lim_{t \to \infty} e^{-st}f(t) = 0$, then $\mathcal{L}\{f(t)\} = f(s)$, and the Laplace transform of the derivative $f'(t)$ is given by the equation

$$\mathcal{L}\{f'(t)\} = sf(s) - f(0). \tag{12.4.1}$$

This is easily shown as follows:

$$\int_0^\infty e^{-st}f'(t)\, dt = e^{-st}f(t)\Big]_0^\infty + s\int_0^\infty e^{-st}f(t)\, dt$$
$$= -f(0) + sf(s).$$

If $\lim_{t \to \infty} e^{-st} f'(t) = 0$, the transform of the second derivative is

$$\int_0^\infty e^{-st} f''(t)\, dt = e^{-st} f'(t) \Big]_0^\infty + s \int_0^\infty e^{-st} f'(t)\, dt$$

$$= -f'(0) + s\mathcal{L}\{f'(t)\}$$

$$= s^2 f(s) - sf(0) - f'(0). \tag{12.4.2}$$

For the transform of the nth derivative, this procedure is repeated n times, and

$$\mathcal{L}\{f^{(n)}(t)\} = s^n f(s) - s^{n-1} f(0) - \cdots - sf^{(n-2)}(0) - f^{(n-1)}(0). \tag{12.4.3}$$

This equation is valid only if $f(t)$ and its first $(n-1)$-derivatives are continuous.

12.5 THE INVERSE TRANSFORMATION

The solution of many problems depends on finding the inverse Laplace transform. Consider, for example, the differential equation

$$\frac{d^2 y}{dt^2} + a^2 y = f(t), \tag{12.5.1}$$

where $f(t)$ is called the driving or forcing function. Applying the Laplace transformation, we get

$$s^2 y(s) - sy(0) - y'(0) + a^2 y(s) = f(s). \tag{12.5.2}$$

Solving for $y(s)$, we get

$$y(s) = \frac{sy(0) + y'(0)}{s^2 + a^2} + \frac{f(s)}{s^2 + a^2}. \tag{12.5.3}$$

This equation is called the subsidiary equation of the differential equation. Here $y(s)$ is the response transform, $f(s)$ is the driving transform, and $s^2 + a^2$ is the characteristic function of the system. The first term on the right, being a function of the initial conditions, is the transform of the transient solution. The second term, which is independent of the initial conditions, is the transform of the steady-state solution. The inverse Laplace transform of $y(s)$ is the time response or solution of the differential equation.

This operation, abbreviated by

$$\mathcal{L}^{-1}\{y(s)\} = y(t), \tag{12.5.4}$$

can be performed in some cases by looking up the function $y(t)$ corresponding to the transform $y(s)$ in the table of transforms.

In general, the transform is of the form

$$y(s) = \frac{P(s)}{Q(s)}, \tag{12.5.5}$$

where $P(s)$ and $Q(s)$ are polynomials in s, and $Q(s)$ is generally of higher degree than $P(s)$. The procedure is then to factor $Q(s)$ and express $y(s)$ in terms of partial fractions, such as

$$y(s) = \frac{C_1}{s - s_1} + \frac{C_2}{s - s_2} + \cdots + \frac{C_n}{s - s_n}. \qquad (12.5.6)$$

We can then solve for C_i algebraically. However, we shall develop a more rapid method of determining C_i that is most suitable for numerical computation. The method is based on the theory of residues, discussed in the previous chapter, and leads easily to the inverse transform.

12.6 INVERSE TRANSFORM BY METHOD OF RESIDUES

a) *Simple poles*. If the transform $P(s)/Q(s)$ can be written in the form of Eq. (12.5.6), where $s_1, s_2, \ldots, s_n$, are all different, then $y(s)$ is said to have n simple or first-order poles. To determine the constants C_i, we have

$$C_i = \lim_{s-s_i} \frac{(s - s_i)P(s)}{Q(s)} = \frac{P(s)}{Q'(s)}\bigg]_{s=s_i}. \qquad (12.6.1)$$

Since

$$\mathcal{L}^{-1}\left\{\frac{1}{s - s_i}\right\} = e^{s_i t},$$

the inverse transform for the case of simple poles becomes

$$y(t) = \sum_{i=1}^{n} C_i e^{s_i t}. \qquad (12.6.2)$$

b) *Complex poles*. For the case of complex conjugate roots, that is, if s_k, $s_{k+1} = A_k \pm B_k i$, then

$$C_k = \frac{P(s)}{Q'(s)}\bigg]_{s=s_k} = C_k + D_k i. \qquad (12.6.3)$$

Applying formula (12.6.2), we write the exponential form in polar form

$$2R_k e^{A_k t} \cos (B_k t \pm \theta_k), \qquad (12.6.4)$$

where,

$$R_k = \sqrt{C_k^2 + D_k^2}, \qquad (12.6.5)$$

$$\theta = \arctan \frac{|D_k|}{|C_k|}, \qquad 0 \le \theta \le \frac{\pi}{2},$$

$$\theta_k = 0, \quad \text{if } D_k = 0,$$

$$\theta_k = \frac{\pi}{2}, \quad \text{if } C_k = 0, \qquad (12.6.6)$$

$$\theta_k = \theta, \quad \text{if } C_k \text{ is } +,$$

$$\theta_k = \pi - \theta, \quad \text{if } C_k \text{ is } -;$$

the positive sign of θ_k is used in Formula (12.6.4) if $A_k + B_k i$ gives $C_k + D_k i$, and the negative sign is used if $A_k + B_k i$ gives $C_k - D_k i$.

c) *Multiple- or high-order poles.* If $P(s)/Q(s)$ has a high-order pole s_k of multiplicity m, then the residue at s_k is

$$\frac{1}{(m-1)!} \lim_{s \to s_k} \frac{d^{m-1}}{ds^{m-1}} \left[(s - s_k)^m \frac{e^{st}P(s)}{Q(s)} \right]. \tag{12.6.7}$$

If $(s - s_k)^m[P(s)/Q(s)] = F(s)$, then Eq. (12.6.7) is written in the form

$$\frac{1}{(m-1)!} \left[\frac{d^{m-1}}{ds^{m-1}} \{e^{st}F(s)\} \right]_{s=s_k} = \left\{ \frac{e^{st}}{(m-1)!} [t + D]^{m-1} F \right\}_{s=s_k}. \tag{12.6.8}$$

Therefore, in general, the inverse transform $y(t)$ is equal to the sum of the residues at simple poles added to the sum of the residues at complex poles added to the sum of the residues at multiple poles. This is illustrated very comprehensively in the chapter on transfer functions.

12.7 CERTAIN PROPERTIES OF THE LAPLACE TRANSFORMATION

Certain properties of the Laplace transformation are summarized in the following theorems:

Initial-value theorem. If $f(t)$ and $f'(t)$ are Laplace transformable, then the behavior of $f(t)$ in the neighborhood of $t = 0$ corresponds to the behavior of $sf(s)$ in the neighborhood of $s = \infty$. That is

$$\lim_{s \to \infty} sf(s) = \lim_{t \to 0} f(t). \tag{12.7.1}$$

Final-value theorem. If $f(t)$ and $f'(t)$ are Laplace transformable, and the limit of $f(t)$ as $t \to \infty$ exists, then the behavior of $f(t)$ in the neighborhood of $t = \infty$ corresponds to the behavior of $sf(s)$ in the neighborhood of $s = 0$. That is,

$$\lim_{s \to 0} sf(s) = \lim_{t \to \infty} f(t). \tag{12.7.2}$$

Differentiation theorem. If $f(t)$ and $f'(t)$ are Laplace transformable, and if $sf(s)$ has a denominator of higher degree than the numerator, then the multiplication of $f(s)$ by s corresponds to the differentiation of $f(t)$ with respect to t. That is,

$$sf(s) = \mathcal{L}\{f'(t)\}. \tag{12.7.3}$$

Integration theorem. If $\mathcal{L}\{f(t)\} = f(s)$ exists, then the division of $f(s)$ by s corresponds to integration of $f(t)$ with respect to t between the limits of 0 and t. That is

$$\frac{1}{s} f(s) = \mathcal{L}\left\{ \int_0^t f(t)\, dt \right\}. \tag{12.7.4}$$

Multiplication of f(t) by t. If $\mathcal{L}\{f(t)\} = f(s)$, then

$$\mathcal{L}\{tf(t)\} = -(d/ds)[f(s)]. \qquad (12.7.5)$$

Division of f(t) by t. If $\mathcal{L}\{f(t)\} = f(s)$, then

$$\mathcal{L}\left\{\frac{f(t)}{t}\right\} = \int_s^{\infty} f(s)\, ds. \qquad (12.7.6)$$

12.8 CERTAIN BASIC FUNCTIONS

In many of the problems in applied mathematics, electrical and mechanical systems are encountered with forces acting on them. Some of the basic forcing functions encountered are given as follows.

a) *Unit-step function.* The unit-step function, shown in Fig. 12.8.1, is defined by

$$\begin{aligned} U(t - a) &= 0, &\quad t < a, \\ &= 1, &\quad t > a. \end{aligned}$$

Its transform, by the definition, is

$$\mathcal{L}\{U(t - a)\} = (1/s)e^{-as}. \qquad (12.8.1)$$

In the special case $a = 0$, we have

$$\mathcal{L}\{U(t)\} = 1/s. \qquad (12.8.2)$$

Any function $f(t)$ multiplied by $U(t - a)$ will have a value of zero for $t < a$ and $f(t)$ in the region $t > a$.

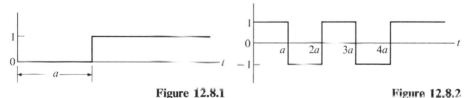

Figure 12.8.1   Figure 12.8.2

b) *Square wave or meander function.* The square wave, shown in Fig. 12.8.2, is expressed by the equation

$$f(t) = U(t) - 2U(t - a) + 2U(t - 2a) - 2U(t - 3a) + 2U(t - 4a) - \cdots \qquad (12.8.3)$$

Its transform, obtained by using (12.8.1), is

$$\begin{aligned} f(s) &= \frac{1}{s} - 2\frac{1}{s}e^{-as} + 2\frac{1}{s}e^{-2as} - 2\frac{1}{s}e^{-3as} + \cdots \\ &= \frac{1}{s}[1 - 2e^{-as}(1 - e^{-as} + e^{-2as} - e^{-3as} + \cdots)] \\ &= \frac{1}{s}\left(1 - \frac{2e^{-as}}{1 + e^{-as}}\right) = \frac{1}{s}\left(\frac{1 - e^{-as}}{1 + e^{-as}}\right) = \frac{1}{s}\tanh\frac{as}{2}. \qquad (12.8.4) \end{aligned}$$

c) *Unit impulse function.* Combining two-step functions of height $1/c$ as shown in Fig. 12.8.3, and approaching a limit as $c \to 0$, we obtain another important quantity known as the unit impulse. Expressed mathematically, the unit impulse is given by the following limit:

$$U'(t - a) = \lim_{c \to 0} \left[\frac{1}{c} U(t - a) - \frac{1}{c} U(t - a - c) \right]. \qquad (12.8.5)$$

Its value is unity at $t = a$ and zero everywhere else. Its transform can be obtained by substituting (12.8.1) in (12.8.5), using l'Hôpital's rule to determine an indeterminant quantity, and allowing c to approach zero. Thus

$$\mathcal{L}\{U'(t - a)\} = \lim_{c \to 0} \left[\frac{e^{-as} - e^{-(a+c)s}}{cs} \right]$$

$$= e^{-as} \qquad (12.8.6)$$

Among physicists, the unit impulse is known as the *Dirac-δ function.*

Additional basic functions are given as exercises at the end of the chapter.

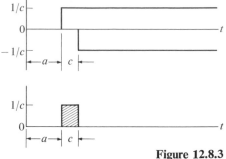

Figure 12.8.3

12.9 SHIFTING THEOREM IN THE *t*-PLANE

The shifting theorem in the *s*-plane, sometimes called the first shifting theorem, was given in Eq. (12.3.2). The shifting theorem in the *t*-plane, sometimes called the second shifting theorem, states that if the inverse transformation of $f(s)$ is $f(t)$, then the inverse transformation of $e^{-as}f(s)$ is $f(t - a)U(t - a)$. That is

$$\mathcal{L}^{-1}\{e^{-as}f(s)\} = f(t - a)U(t - a). \qquad (12.9.1)$$

12.10 SUPPLEMENTARY REFERENCES

a) R. V. Churchill, *Modern Operational Mathematics in Engineering*, McGraw-Hill, New York, 1951.

b) S. Seshu and N. Balabanian, *Linear Network Analysis*, Wiley, New York, 1959.

c) D. V. Widder, *Laplace Transform*, Princeton University Press, Princeton, 1941.

EXERCISES

1. Show that $\mathcal{L}\{e^{-at} \sin \omega t\} = \omega/[(s + a)^2 + \omega^2]$.
2. Show that $\mathcal{L}\{t^n/n!\} = 1/s^{n+1}$.
3. Show that $\mathcal{L}\{t \sin \omega t\} = 2\omega s/(s^2 + \omega^2)^2$.
4. Show that $\mathcal{L}^{-1}\{(s - 1)/s(s + 2)\} = -\frac{1}{2} + \frac{3}{2}e^{-2t}$.

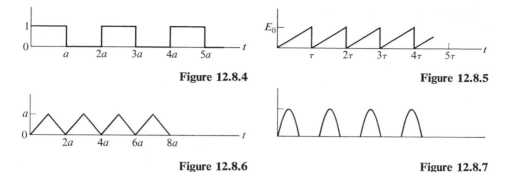

Figure 12.8.4

Figure 12.8.5

Figure 12.8.6

Figure 12.8.7

5. Show that $\mathcal{L}^{-1}\{1/s^2(s^2 + \omega^2)\} = (1/\omega^3)(\omega t - \sin \omega t)$.

6. Show that $\mathcal{L}^{-1}\{(s + 2)/(s + 3)(s + 1)^2\} = (\frac{1}{4} + \frac{1}{2}t)e^{-t} - \frac{1}{4}e^{-3t}$.

7. Show that the transform of the function shown in Fig. 12.8.4 is $f(s) = 1/s(1 + e^{-as})$.

8. Show that the transform of the *saw-tooth wave* shown in Fig. 12.8.5 is

$$f(s) = E_0\left[\frac{1}{\tau s^2} - \frac{e^{-\tau s}}{s(1 - e^{-\tau s})}\right].$$

9. Show that the transform of the *triangular wave* shown in Fig. 12.8.6 is

$$f(s) = (1/s^2) \tanh (as/2).$$

10. Show that the transformation of the *half-wave rectification* of sin ωt shown in Fig. 12.8.7 is

$$f(s) = \frac{\omega}{(s^2 + \omega^2)(1 - e^{-\pi s/\omega})}.$$

The period is $2\pi/\omega$ and the function is defined as

$$f(t) = \sin \omega t, \qquad 0 \leq t \leq \frac{\pi}{\omega},$$

$$= 0, \qquad \frac{\pi}{\omega} \leq t \leq \frac{2\pi}{\omega}.$$

11. The *full-wave rectification* of sin ωt is obtained by addition of the curve of Fig. 12.8.7 and the same curve shifted to the right by π/ω. Show that its transform is

$$f(s) = \frac{\omega}{s^2 + \omega^2} \coth \frac{\pi s}{2\omega}.$$

CHAPTER 13

DIFFERENCE EQUATIONS

13.1 INTRODUCTION

A large number of applied and theoretical problems are eventually reduced to differential equations. The solution of many of these equations can be expressed explicitly in terms of elementary functions or special functions. However, a multitude of differential equations encountered cannot be solved explicitly in terms of these functions. The situation with respect to nonlinear differential equations, and particularly partial differential equations, is even more complicated. Explicit methods do not apply. This does not mean that explicit methods have lost their value. They remain a very powerful and necessary tool for qualitative investigations and the study of ideal problems. However, in addition to analytical methods, numerical methods are encountered more and more frequently. Great impetus has been given to numerical techniques with the advent of high-speed computing machines.

The numerical solution of differential equations by the method of finite differences is an example of this. The differential equation is replaced by a finite difference equation. Brief mention of this was made in Sections 1.7 and 1.8. The numerical solution of ordinary differential equations, nonlinear ordinary differential equations, boundary-value problems, partial differential equations, digital filtering, and integral equations may be accomplished by finite difference methods. It is the purpose of this chapter to establish a very basic background in finite difference schemes for the study of these topics. It is not the intent to develop extensive theoretical considerations. This has been well done in entire books on the subject, such as the ones listed in the supplementary references at the end of this chapter.

13.2 SIMPLE DIFFERENCE EQUATIONS AND THEIR ORDER

In Section 4.3 we considered formulas for expressing derivatives in terms of finite differences. From Formula (4.3.2) we have

$$hy'_n = \Delta y_n = y_{n+1} - y_n$$

or

$$y'_n = \frac{y_{n+1} - y_n}{h}.$$

(13.2.1)

Also, from Formula (4.3.10) we have

$$hy'_n = \mu \, \delta y_n = \frac{y_{n+1} - y_{n-1}}{2}$$

or

$$y'_n = \frac{y_{n+1} - y_{n-1}}{2h}. \tag{13.2.2}$$

From Formula (4.3.8) we have

$$h^2 y''_n = \delta^2 y_n = y_{n+1} - 2y_n + y_{n-1}$$

or

$$y''_n = \frac{y_{n+1} - 2y_n + y_{n-1}}{h^2}. \tag{13.2.3}$$

Now, let us consider the first-order ordinary differential equation

$$y' + ky = f(x), \tag{13.2.4}$$

where k is a constant. If $y'(x_n) = y'_n$, $y(x_n) = y_n$, and $f(x_n) = f_n$, we may write the above equation as

$$y'_n + ky_n = f_n. \tag{13.2.5}$$

Replacing y'_n by the right member of Eq. (13.2.1), we obtain

$$\frac{y_{n+1} - y_n}{h} + ky_n = f_n.$$

Simplifying, we have

$$\frac{1}{h} y_{n+1} - \frac{1}{h} y_n + ky_n = f_n$$

or

$$\frac{1}{h} y_{n+1} + \left(k - \frac{1}{h} \right) y_n = f_n.$$

Letting $(k - 1/h) = a_0$ and $1/h = a_1$, we have

$$a_0 y_n + a_1 y_{n+1} = f_n. \tag{13.2.6}$$

A unique solution of this equation requires the value of y at one point. Such an equation is called a difference equation of first order.

If we replace the derivative y'_n by the right member of (13.2.2), and simplify, we obtain

$$\frac{y_{n+1} - y_{n-1}}{2h} + ky_n = f_n,$$

$$\frac{1}{2h} y_{n+1} - \frac{1}{2h} y_{n-1} + ky_n = f_n.$$

Letting $-1/2h = a_0$, $k = a_1$, $1/2h = a_2$, we have

$$a_0 y_{n-1} + a_1 y_n + a_2 y_{n+1} = f_n. \tag{13.2.7}$$

A unique solution of this equation requires the value of y at two consecutive points. Such an equation is called a difference equation of second order.

Now, considering the second-order differential equation

$$y'' + by' + cy = f(x), \tag{13.2.8}$$

where b and c are constants, we write this equation as

$$y_n'' + by_n' + cy_n = f_n. \tag{13.2.9}$$

Substituting for y_n' and y_n'' from (13.2.2) and (13.2.3), and simplifying, we obtain

$$\frac{y_{n+1} - 2y_n + y_{n-1}}{h^2} + b\frac{y_{n+1} - y_{n-1}}{2h} + cy_n = f_n.$$

Letting

$$\left(\frac{1}{h^2} - \frac{b}{2h}\right) = a_0, \quad \left(c - \frac{2}{h^2}\right) = a_1, \quad \left(\frac{1}{h^2} + \frac{b}{2h}\right) = a_2,$$

we have

$$a_0 y_{n-1} + a_1 y_n + a_2 y_{n+1} = f_n. \tag{13.2.10}$$

Again, we have a second-order difference equation.

13.3 SOLUTION OF FIRST-ORDER DIFFERENCE EQUATIONS

To obtain a unique solution of $a_0 y_n + a_1 y_{n+1} = f_n$, it is sufficient to know the value of y at any one point. Our equation can then be written in the form of the recursion formula

$$y_{n+1} = \frac{1}{a_1}(f_n - a_0 y_n), \tag{13.3.1}$$

from which we calculate y_{n+1}, y_{n+2}, etc.

Let $y_n^{(1)}$ and $y_n^{(2)}$ be any two given solutions of the equation

$$a_0 y_n + a_1 y_{n+1} = f_n.$$

Subtracting the two equations

$$a_0 y_n^{(1)} + a_1 y_{n+1}^{(1)} = f_n, \quad a_0 y_n^{(2)} + a_1 y_{n+1}^{(2)} = f_n, \tag{13.3.2}$$

we see that $y_n^{(1)} - y_n^{(2)} = \bar{y}_n$ satisfies the homogeneous equation

$$a_0 \bar{y}_n + a_1 \bar{y}_{n+1} = 0.$$

Use u_n to denote the solution of the homogeneous equation $a_0 u_n + a_1 u_{n+1} = 0$ that satisfies the condition $u_0 = 1$. For arbitrary α, $\bar{u}_n = \alpha u_n$ will also be a solution. Any solution of our homogeneous equation will be of this form. Each solution is uniquely determined by its value at $n = 0$. Therefore, if two solutions $u_n^{(1)}$ and $u_n^{(2)}$ are equal at the point zero, they will also be equal for all n. The equality $\bar{y}_0 = \bar{u}_0 = \alpha u_0$ may always be satisfied by the proper choice of α. Thus, we write the general solution of $a_0 y_n + a_1 y_{n+1} = f_n$ in the form

$$y_n = y_n^{(1)} + \alpha u_n, \tag{13.3.3}$$

where $y_n^{(1)}$ is a particular solution and u_n is the solution of the homogeneous equation $a_0 u_n + a_1 u_{n+1} = 0$, which satisfy the condition $u_0 = 1$.

Beginning with the homogeneous equation $a_0 y_n + a_1 y_{n+1} = 0$, and since

$$y_{n+1} = -\frac{a_0}{a_1} y_n, \qquad (13.3.4)$$

the solution has the form of the geometric progression

$$y_n = K\left(-\frac{a_0}{a_1}\right)^n. \qquad (13.3.5)$$

At the point $n = 0$ this has the value $y_0 = K$. The solution u_n, satisfying the condition $u_0 = 1$, is obtained by setting $K = 1$. Thus

$$u_n = \left(-\frac{a_0}{a_1}\right)^n, \qquad (13.3.6)$$

and therefore

$$y_n = y_n^{(1)} + \alpha u_n = y_n^{(1)} + \alpha\left(-\frac{a_0}{a_1}\right)^n. \qquad (13.3.7)$$

13.4 SOLUTION OF SECOND-ORDER DIFFERENCE EQUATIONS

A unique solution of the equation

$$a_0 y_{n-1} + a_1 y_n + a_2 y_{n+1} = f_n \qquad (13.4.1)$$

requires the value of y at two consecutive points. This equation can be written in the form of the recursion formula

$$y_{n+1} = \frac{1}{a_2}(f_n - a_1 y_n - a_0 y_{n-1})$$

from which we can calculate y_{n+1}, y_{n+2}, etc.

We write the general solution of Eq. (13.4.1) in the form

$$y_n = y_n^{(1)} + \alpha u_n + \beta v_n, \qquad (13.4.2)$$

where $y_n^{(1)}$ is any particular solution of Eq. (13.4.1), and u_n and v_n are solutions of the homogeneous equation which satisfy the conditions

$$u_0 = 1, \qquad u_1 = 0, \qquad v_0 = 0, \qquad v_1 = 1. \qquad (13.4.3)$$

Any solution of a homogeneous equation of second order has the form

$$y_n = \alpha u_n + \beta v_n. \qquad (13.4.4)$$

Beginning with the homogeneous equation,

$$a_0 y_{n-1} + a_1 y_n + a_2 y_{n+1} = 0, \qquad (13.4.5)$$

we assume a solution of the form

$$y_n = \alpha r^n. \qquad (13.4.6)$$

Substituting in the difference equation, we will have a solution if r is a root of the quadratic

$$a_0 + a_1 r + a_2 r^2 = 0. \tag{13.4.7}$$

a) If the roots r_1 and r_2 are real and distinct, we can find, in the form of a geometric progression, two independent particular solutions

$$y_n^{(1)} = \alpha_1 r_1^n, \qquad y_n^{(2)} = \alpha_2 r_2^n,$$

where α_1 and α_2 are arbitrary. The sum of these two solutions,

$$y_n = \alpha_1 r_1^n + \alpha_2 r_2^n, \tag{13.4.8}$$

will be a solution. We attempt to use as solutions, u_n and v_n as defined above, which satisfy the conditions $u_0 = 1$, $u_1 = 0$, $v_0 = 0$, $v_1 = 1$. This can be done by setting

$$u_n = \frac{r_2}{r_2 - r_1} r_1^n - \frac{r_1}{r_2 - r_1} r_2^n \tag{13.4.9}$$

and

$$v_n = -\frac{1}{r_2 - r_1} r_1^n + \frac{1}{r_2 - r_1} r_2^n. \tag{13.4.10}$$

b) If the roots are repeated, one particular solution can be found in the form

$$y_n = \alpha_1 r_1^n. \tag{13.4.11}$$

To find a second solution, we substitute

$$y_n = x_n r_1^n \tag{13.4.12}$$

in Eq. (13.4.5) and obtain

$$a_0 x_{n-1} + a_1 r_1 x_n + a_2 r_1^2 x_{n+1} = 0. \tag{13.4.13}$$

The product of the roots of (13.4.7) is equal to a_0/a_2, and the sum (with opposite sign) of the roots is equal to a_1/a_2.

Since both roots are equal to r_1,

$$\frac{a_0}{a_2} = r_1^2 \quad \text{and} \quad \frac{a_1}{a_2} = -2r_1. \tag{13.4.14}$$

Therefore, Eq. (13.4.13) becomes

$$a_2 r_1^2 x_{n-1} - 2a_2 r_1^2 x_n + a_2 r_1^2 x_{n+1} = 0$$

or

$$x_{n-1} - 2x_n + x_{n+1} = 0. \tag{13.4.15}$$

Rewriting this as

$$(x_{n-1} - x_n) - (x_n - x_{n+1}) = 0, \tag{13.4.16}$$

we see that

$$x_{n-1} - x_n = \alpha \quad \text{and} \quad x_n = \alpha n + \beta, \tag{13.4.17}$$

where α and β are arbitrary.

We can now write a solution of (13.4.5) for multiple roots as

$$y_n = \alpha n r_1^n + \beta r_1^n. \tag{13.4.18}$$

The u_n and v_n obtained from this by a proper choice of α and β are

$$u_n = -nr_1^n + r_1^n \quad \text{and} \quad v_n = \frac{1}{r_1}nr_1^n = nr_1^{n-1}. \tag{13.4.19}$$

c) If the roots of $a_0 + a_1 r + a_2 r^2 = 0$ are complex, we write r_1 and r_2 as

$$r_1 = \sqrt{(a_0/a_2)}(\cos\theta + i\sin\theta), \tag{13.4.20}$$

$$r_2 = \sqrt{(a_0/a_2)}(\cos\theta - i\sin\theta). \tag{13.4.21}$$

Therefore,

$$r_1^n = (\sqrt{a_0/a_2})^n(\cos n\theta + i\sin n\theta) \tag{13.4.22}$$

and

$$r_2^n = (\sqrt{a_0/a_2})^n(\cos n\theta - i\sin n\theta). \tag{13.4.23}$$

Substituting into (13.4.9) and (13.4.10) for u_n and v_n, we obtain

$$u_n = -(\sqrt{a_0/a_2})^n \frac{\sin(n-1)\theta}{\sin\theta}, \tag{13.4.24}$$

$$v_n = (\sqrt{a_0/a_2})^{n-1} \frac{\sin n\theta}{\sin\theta}. \tag{13.4.25}$$

Even though the roots are complex, u_n and v_n are real, since they are solutions of real equations and satisfy real conditions ($n = 0$ and $n = 1$ are real).

Substituting the values of r_1^n and r_2^n from (13.4.22) and (13.4.23) into the equation

$$y_n = \alpha_1 r_1^n + \alpha_2 r_2^n,$$

we get

$$y_n = k_1(\sqrt{a_0/a_2})^n \cos n\theta + k_2(\sqrt{a_0/a_2})^n \sin n\theta,$$

$$\cos\theta = -a_1/2\sqrt{a_0 a_2}. \tag{13.4.26}$$

13.5 CONVERGENCE AND ORDER OF ACCURACY

We now give a brief consideration to the convergence and order of accuracy of difference equations of the type discussed.

a) *First-Order Equations.* The simplest difference equation for $y' + ky = 0$ is

$$\frac{y_i - y_{i-1}}{h} + ky_{i-1} = 0, \tag{13.5.1}$$

with initial conditions $y(0) = b$, $0 \leqq x \leqq 1$, $x_0 = 0$, $x_n = 1$. We have

$$y_i = (1 - kh)y_{i-1} = (1 - k/n)y_{i-1} \tag{13.5.2}$$

or

$$y_i = (1 - k/n)^i b. \tag{13.5.3}$$

Since $x_i = i/n$,

$$y_i = (1 - k/n)^{nx_i} b. \tag{13.5.4}$$

The true solution is $y(x) = be^{-kx}$, and at x_i, it assumes the value be^{-kx_i}. The error estimate at the point x_i is

$$E(x_i) = [(1 - k/n)^{nx_i} - e^{-kx_i}]b. \tag{13.5.5}$$

We can show that

$$(1 - k/n)^{nx_i} = e^{-kx_i} + \tfrac{1}{2}hk^2 x_i e^{-kx_i} + 0(h^2).$$

Therefore,

$$E(x_i) = \tfrac{1}{2}hbk^2 x_i e^{-kx_i} + 0(h^2) = 0(h). \tag{13.5.6}$$

The error goes to zero as $h \to 0$, and the magnitude of the error is of first order in h.

b) *Second-Order Equations.* In order that the solution of the second-order difference equation

$$\frac{y_{n+1} - y_{n-1}}{2h} + ky_n = 0 \tag{13.5.7}$$

converge to the true solution $y = be^{-kx}$ of the differential equation, it is necessary that

$$\frac{r_1 y_0 - y_1}{r_2 - r_1} \to 0 \quad \text{and} \quad \frac{r_2 y_0 - y_1}{r_2 - r_1} \to b. \tag{13.5.8}$$

If the initial value y_0 is given with an accuracy of order h^2, the error in the solution will also be of order h^2. If it is of order h in initial conditions, the error will also be order h in the solution. The difference equation in (13.5.7) has a higher rate of convergence than (13.5.1), in that the residual term is of order h^2 instead of h.

c) *Higher-Order Equations.* A more general discussion of convergence and instability of higher-order difference equations was given in Section 1.8.

13.6 EXAMPLES OF DIFFERENCE EQUATIONS

We now consider several examples of difference equations and their solutions.

Example 1. Find the general solution of

$$y_{n+3} - 6y_{n+2} + 12y_{n+1} - 8y_n = 0.$$

Solution. Assume a solution of the form $y_n = r^n$. Then we have

$$r^3 - 6r^2 + 12r - 8 = 0 \quad \text{and} \quad r = 2, 2, 2.$$

Therefore, $y_n = (A + nB + n^{(2)}C)2^n$, where $n^{(2)} = n(n - 1)$.

Example 2. Solve $y_{n+2} - 4y_{n+1} + 13y_n = 0$.

Solution. $r^2 - 4r + 13 = 0$, $r = 2 \pm 3i$. Therefore,

$$y_n = A(2 + 3i)^n + B(2 - 3i)^n$$

or

$$y_n = 13^{n/2}(C \cos n\theta + D \sin n\theta),$$

where $\theta =$ principal value, $-\pi/2 \leq \theta \leq \pi/2$, of $\tan^{-1}(\tfrac{3}{2})$ or $\tan^{-1}(-\tfrac{3}{2})$.

Example 3. Solve the nonhomogeneous difference equation

$$y_{n+2} - 7y_{n+1} + 10y_n = 12 \cdot 4^n.$$

Solution. First solving the homogeneous equation, we obtain $y_n = A2^n + B5^n$. Now, assuming a particular solution of the form $y_n = C4^n$, and substituting in the difference equation, we have

$$C4^n[4^2 - 7 \cdot 4 + 10] = 12 \cdot 4^n \qquad \text{or } C = -6.$$

Therefore, we have

$$y_n = A2^n + B5^n - 6 \cdot 4^n.$$

Example 4. Solve $y_{n+2} - 7y_{n+1} + 10y_n = 12 \cdot 5^n$, where the right-hand member satisfies the homogeneous equation.

Solution. The solution of the homogeneous equation is $y_n = A2^n + B5^n$. Assuming a particular solution of the form $y_n = Cn5^n$, and substituting in the difference equation, we get $C = \frac{4}{5}$. Therefore, the general solution is

$$y_n = A2^n + B5^n + \tfrac{4}{5}n5^n.$$

Example 5. Solve $y_{n+2} - 4y_n = 9n^2$, where the right-hand member is a polynomial.

Solution. The solution of the homogeneous equation is $y_n = A2^n + B(-2)^n$. Assuming a particular solution of the form $y_n = Cn^2 + Dn + E$, and substituting in the difference equation, we get $C = -3$, $D = -4$, $E = -\frac{20}{3}$. Therefore, we have the general solution

$$y_n = A2^n + B(-2)^n - 3n^2 - 4n - \tfrac{20}{3}.$$

13.7 PARTIAL DIFFERENTIAL EQUATIONS AND FINITE DIFFERENCES

In mathematical physics one often encounters partial differential equations of various types. Many of these equations cannot be solved explicitly or in an elementary manner. The numerical solutions of these equations is discussed in a later chapter. We are concerned here with obtaining the approximating difference equations to a particular partial differential equation. We shall limit ourselves at this time to the consideration of two very simple cases using the following difference approximations for the partial derivatives:

$$\frac{\partial y}{\partial t} = \frac{y(t + k, x) - y(t, x)}{k}, \tag{13.7.1}$$

$$\frac{\partial^2 y}{\partial t^2} = \frac{y(t + k, x) - 2y(t, x) + y(t - k, x)}{k^2}, \tag{13.7.2}$$

$$\frac{\partial^2 y}{\partial x^2} = \frac{y(t, x + h) - 2y(t, x) + y(t, x - h)}{h^2}. \tag{13.7.3}$$

13.8 SIMPLE WAVE EQUATION

Let us consider the simple wave equation $y_{tt} = y_{xx}$ with initial conditions

$$y(x, 0) = f(x) \quad \text{and} \quad y_t(x, 0) = g(x).$$

Substituting for the second partial derivatives from the previous section, we have

$$\frac{y(x, t + k) - 2y(x, t) + y(x, t - k)}{k^2}$$
$$= \frac{y(x + h, t) - 2y(x, t) + y(x - h, t)}{h^2}. \quad (13.8.1)$$

Simplifying, we obtain

$$y(x, t + k) = 2y(x, t) - y(x, t - k) + (k/h)^2[y(x + h, t)$$
$$- 2y(x, t) + y(x - h, t)], \quad (13.8.2)$$

and the initial conditions are written in the form

$$y_t(x, t) = \frac{y(x, t + k) - y(x, t)}{k}.$$

Therefore,

$$y_t(x, 0) = \frac{y(x, k) - y(x, 0)}{k} = g(x) \quad (13.8.3)$$

or

$$y(x, k) = kg(x) + f(x), \quad (13.8.4)$$

since

$$y(x, 0) = f(x). \quad (13.8.5)$$

Beginning with the grid points $(x_0 + rh, 0)$ on the initial line, the values at the grid points on the lines $t = k, 2k, 3k$, etc. can be calculated successively from these equations.

We can show that (13.8.2) converges to the true solution as h approaches zero, provided that

$$k/h < 1. \quad (13.8.6)$$

Otherwise, the finite difference approximation is unstable.

13.9 SIMPLE HEAT EQUATION

Now let us consider the simple heat equation $y_t = y_{xx}$ with initial condition $y(x, 0) = f(x)$. Substituting for the partial derivatives from Section 13.7, we have

$$\frac{y(x, t + k) - y(x, t)}{k} = \frac{y(x + h, t) - 2y(x, t) + y(x - h, t)}{h^2}. \quad (13.9.1)$$

Letting $k/h^2 = \lambda$, we rewrite the above equation as

$$y(x, t + k) = \lambda y(x + h, t) + (1 - 2\lambda)y(x, t) + \lambda y(x - h, t). \quad (13.9.2)$$

Starting with the initial values $y(x, 0) = f(x)$, we successively calculate the values of y at the grid points $t = k, 2k, \ldots$, from the above difference equation.

We can show that the above numerical solution converges to the true solution as h approaches zero, provided that

$$\lambda \leqq \tfrac{1}{2}. \tag{13.9.3}$$

Otherwise, the finite difference approximation is unstable.

13.10 SUPPLEMENTARY REFERENCES

A more extensive treatment of difference equations and finite difference approximations may be found in Collatz [20], Forsythe [45], Fox [52], Henrici [70], Milne [106], and S. Godunov and V. Ryabenki, *Theory of Difference Schemes, An Introduction*, North-Holland, Amsterdam, 1964.

EXERCISES

Find the general solution of each of the following difference equations:

1. $y_{n+4} - 5y_{n+2} + 4y_n = 0.$
2. $y_{n+2} - 4y_{n+1} + 4y_n = 0.$
3. $y_{n+2} + 2y_{n+1} + 2y_n = 0.$
4. $y_{n+2} - a^2 y_n = a^n.$
5. $y_{n+1} - ay_n = b^n.$
6. $y_{n+2} + a^2 y_n = a^n.$
7. $y_{n+2} - 4y_n = n.$
8. $y_{n+2} - y_n = n^2.$

CHAPTER 14

ORDINARY DIFFERENTIAL EQUATIONS

14.1 INTRODUCTION

The solutions of many problems arising in mathematical physics, dynamics, and other branches of science and engineering, involve ordinary differential equations or partial differential equations. Often it is necessary to solve systems of coupled differential equations. Mechanical systems or electrical systems may lead to analogous sets of differential equations. In this chapter we shall consider the numerical solution of ordinary differential equations, initial-value and boundary-value, by finite difference schemes. Then we shall consider the matrix form of systems of ordinary differential equations, particularly of second order with constant coefficients, and the matrix exponential method. The matrix form will establish a background for the next chapter, which discusses computer methods for finding transform functions, inverse transforms, doing transfer function analyses, and root locus studies. Finally, we consider a brief survey of nonlinear ordinary differential equations and supplementary references.

14.2 PICARD'S METHOD OF SUCCESSIVE APPROXIMATION

This method will be used to develop some of the finite difference schemes to be considered. The differential equation of the form

$$\frac{dy}{dx} = f(x, y), \qquad y(x_0) = y_0 \tag{14.2.1}$$

is first transformed into the integral equation

$$y(x) = y_0 + \int_{x_0}^{x} f[x, y(x)] \, dx. \tag{14.2.2}$$

Successive functions approximating $y(x)$ near $x = x_0$ are generated by the iteration

$$y^{(k+1)}(x) = y_0 + \int_{x_0}^{x} f[x, y^{(k)}(x)] \, dx. \tag{14.2.3}$$

The initial approximation $y^{(0)}(x)$ is conveniently taken to be the constant y_0 or the linear function $y_0 + y_0'(x - x_0)$, where y_0' is determined from the differential equation.

We could estimate the accuracy afforded by a member of the sequence of approximations at a certain number of points $x_1, x_2, \ldots$ by comparing calculated values at those points with values calculated from the preceding approximation.

We can start the iteration over at each step by reinitializing. Thus, the form for the kth iteration at the $(n + 1)$-step is written as

$$y_{n+1}^{(k)} = y_n + \int_{x_n}^{x} f[x, y_{n+1}^{(k-1)}] \, dx. \tag{14.2.4}$$

While Picard's method is of great theoretical importance, the explicit evaluation of the integral in (14.2.3) is often prohibitive or impossible.

14.3 FINITE DIFFERENCE SCHEMES

In Section 1.8, Euler's formula was introduced and used as a first-order finite difference equation to find the numerical solution of a first-order differential equation. Also, using a central difference form for the second derivative, a second-order difference scheme was used to find the numerical solution of a given second-order differential equation. Then a higher-order difference scheme was used and a brief discussion given on the stability of difference schemes. We shall now consider finite difference methods for solving ordinary differential equations in greater detail. Initial-value problems will be discussed first, and then boundary-value problems will be considered.

14.4 OPEN TYPE FORMULAS

If the value at the current point depends only on one or more previously calculated points, the formula being used is called an open type formula. If it depends on a value of the current point being calculated, it is called a closed type formula. Given the simple initial-value problem

$$\frac{dy}{dx} = y'(x) = f(x), \qquad y(x_0) = y_0, \tag{14.4.1}$$

if the ordinates $y_n, y_{n-1}, y_{n-2}, \ldots, y_1, y_0$ are known, then

$$y_k' = f(x_k). \tag{14.4.2}$$

In general, if the derivative is a function of x and y, then

$$y_k' = f(x_k, y_k).$$

From Eq. (3.5.6), we have Newton's backward-difference formula and

$$y_{n+s}' = y_n' + s\nabla y_n' + \frac{s(s + 1)}{2!} \nabla^2 y_n' + \cdots + \frac{s(s + 1) \cdots (s + N - 1)}{N!} \nabla^N y_n', \tag{14.4.3}$$

where $s = (x - x_n)/h$. Using Picard's formula in the form

$$y_{n+1} = y_n + \int_{x_n}^{x_n+h} y'(x) \, dx, \tag{14.4.4}$$

and substituting (14.4.3), we obtain

$$y_{n+1} = y_n + h \int_0^1 y'_{n+s} \, ds = y_n + h \sum_{k=0}^{N} a_k \nabla^k y'_n, \tag{14.4.5}$$

where $a_0 = 1$,

$$a_k = \int_0^1 \frac{s(s+1)\cdots(s+k-1)}{k!} \, ds, \qquad k > 0. \tag{14.4.6}$$

The error term truncating with the Nth difference is

$$E_N = h^{N+2} \int_0^1 \frac{s(s+1)\cdots(s+N)}{(N+1)!} y^{(N+2)}(\xi) \, ds, \tag{14.4.7}$$

or, since the coefficient of $y^{(N+2)}$ does not change sign in $(0, 1)$,

$$E_N = a_{N+1} h^{N+2} y^{(N+2)}(\xi). \tag{14.4.8}$$

Computing the first few coefficients in (14.4.5), we have

$$y_{n+1} = y_n + h(1 + \tfrac{1}{2}\nabla + \tfrac{5}{12}\nabla^2 + \tfrac{3}{8}\nabla^3 + \tfrac{251}{720}\nabla^4 + \cdots)y'_n. \tag{14.4.9}$$

More generally, substituting Eq. (14.4.3) in

$$y_{n+1} = y_{n-p} + h \int_{-p}^1 y'_{n+s} \, ds, \tag{14.4.10}$$

we can calculate the ordinate following the nth ordinate in terms of the ordinate calculated p steps previously, and in terms of $N + 1$ already calculated values of y'. Note that $p = 0$ gives Eq. (14.4.9). The formulas most frequently used are those for $p = 1$, 3, and 5. These values of p give the following formulas:

$$y_{n+1} = y_{n-1} + h(2 + 0\nabla + \tfrac{1}{3}\nabla^2 + \tfrac{1}{3}\nabla^3 + \tfrac{29}{90}\nabla^4 + \cdots)y'_n, \tag{14.4.11}$$

$$y_{n+1} = y_{n-3} + h(4 - 4\nabla + \tfrac{8}{3}\nabla^2 + 0\nabla^3 + \tfrac{14}{45}\nabla^4 + \cdots)y'_n, \tag{14.4.12}$$

$$y_{n+1} = y_{n-5} + h(6 - 12\nabla + 15\nabla^2 - 9\nabla^3 + \tfrac{33}{10}\nabla^4 + 0\nabla^5 + \cdots)y'_n. \tag{14.4.13}$$

The error associated by terminating with the Nth difference is given by

$$E = h^{N+2} \int_{-p}^1 \frac{s(s+1)\cdots(s+N)}{(N+1)!} y^{(N+2)}(\xi) \, ds. \tag{14.4.14}$$

Note that the coefficient of the pth difference is zero. Retaining only the first p differences, we get the following formulas:

$$y_{n+1} = y_{n-1} + 2hy'_n + (h^3/3)y^{(3)}(\xi), \tag{14.4.15}$$

$$y_{n+1} = y_{n-3} + 4h(y'_n - \nabla y'_n + \tfrac{2}{3}\nabla^2 y'_n) + (14h^5/45)y^{(5)}(\xi), \tag{14.4.16}$$

$$y_{n+1} = y_{n-5} + 6h(y'_n - 2\nabla y'_n + \tfrac{5}{2}\nabla^2 y'_n - \tfrac{3}{2}\nabla^3 y'_n + \tfrac{11}{20}\nabla^4 y'_n) + (14h^7/140)y^{(7)}(\xi). \tag{14.4.17}$$

14.5 CLOSED TYPE FORMULAS

If the right-hand member of Eq. (14.4.3) is replaced by the interpolating polynomial agreeing with y' at $x_{n+1}, x_n, x_{n-1}, \ldots, x_{n-N+1}$, we have

$$y'_{n+s} = y'_{n+1} + (s - 1)\nabla y'_{n+1} + \frac{(s - 1)s}{2!}\nabla^2 y'_{n+1} + \cdots$$

$$+ \frac{(s - 1)s(s + 1)\cdots(s + N - 2)}{N!}\nabla^N y'_{n+1}, \qquad (14.5.1)$$

where $s = (x - x_n)/h$. If this approximating polynomial is used in (14.4.10)
with $p = 0, 1, 3, 5$, we obtain the following formulas:

$$y_{n+1} = y_n + h(1 - \tfrac{1}{2}\nabla - \tfrac{1}{12}\nabla^2 - \tfrac{1}{24}\nabla^3 - \tfrac{19}{720}\nabla^4 - \cdots)y'_{n+1}, \qquad (14.5.2)$$

$$y_{n+1} = y_{n-1} + h(2 - 2\nabla + \tfrac{1}{3}\nabla^2 + 0\nabla^3 - \tfrac{1}{90}\nabla^4 - \cdots)y'_{n+1}, \qquad (14.5.3)$$

$$y_{n+1} = y_{n-3} + h(4 - 8\nabla + \tfrac{20}{3}\nabla^2 - \tfrac{8}{3}\nabla^3 + \tfrac{14}{45}\nabla^4 - 0\nabla^5 - \cdots)y'_{n+1}, \qquad (14.5.4)$$

$$y_{n+1} = y_{n-5} + h(6 - 18\nabla + 27\nabla^2 - 24\nabla^3 + \tfrac{123}{10}\nabla^4 - \tfrac{33}{10}\nabla^5 + \cdots)y'_{n+1}. \qquad (14.5.5)$$

The error associated with retaining only the first N differences is

$$E = h^{N+2}\int_{-p}^{1} \frac{(s - 1)s(s + 1)\cdots(s + N - 1)}{(N + 1)!} y^{(N+2)}(\xi)\,ds. \qquad (14.5.6)$$

14.6 EULER'S METHOD

If Formula (14.4.9) is truncated with no differences, we have

$$y_{n+1} = y_n + hy'_n \qquad (14.6.1)$$

and

$$E = \tfrac{1}{2}h^2 y^{(2)}(\xi) = 0(h^2).$$

This is Euler's formula as derived and discussed in Section 1.8.

14.7 MODIFIED EULER OR HEUN METHOD

If Formula (14.5.2) is truncated after the first difference, we have

$$y_{n+1} = y_n + h(1 - \tfrac{1}{2}\nabla)y'_{n+1}$$
$$= y_n + hy'_{n+1} - \tfrac{1}{2}h\nabla y'_{n+1}$$
$$= y_n + \tfrac{1}{2}h(y'_n + y'_{n+1}), \qquad (14.7.1)$$

and $E = -\tfrac{1}{12}h^3 y^{(3)}(\xi)$. This formula uses the average of the slopes at x_n and
x_{n+1} to get an improved value of y_{n+1}. This improved value of y_{n+1} is then
used in Eq. (14.4.2) to get an improved value of y'_{n+1}. This process can be continued until no improvement is shown in y_{n+1}.

14.8 ADAMS' METHOD

The so-called Adams' method is given by Eq. (14.4.9), which is truncated to a suitable number of terms. That is,

$$y_{n+1} = y_n + h(1 + \tfrac{1}{2}\nabla + \tfrac{5}{12}\nabla^2 + \tfrac{3}{8}\nabla^3 + \tfrac{251}{720}\nabla^4 + \cdots)y_n', \quad (14.8.1)$$

where the error associated with retaining through the Nth difference is given by

$$E = a_{N+1}h^{N+2}y^{(N+2)}(\xi), \qquad a_{N+1} = \int_0^1 \frac{s(s+1)\cdots(s+N)}{(N+1)!}\,ds. \quad (14.8.2)$$

14.9 MODIFIED ADAMS OR ADAMS-BASHFORTH METHOD

In this method, Formula (14.4.9),

$$y_{n+1} = y_n + h(1 + \tfrac{1}{2}\nabla + \tfrac{5}{12}\nabla^2 + \tfrac{3}{8}\nabla^3 + \cdots)y_n', \quad (14.9.1)$$

is used as a predictor to get a value of y_{n+1}. This value is then used to evaluate the derivative at y_{n+1}, and substituting in Eq. (14.5.2), we get

$$y_{n+1} = y_n + h(1 - \tfrac{1}{2}\nabla - \tfrac{1}{12}\nabla^2 - \tfrac{1}{24}\nabla^3 - \cdots)y_{n+1}'. \quad (14.9.2)$$

The second formula is used as a corrector to get an improved value of y_{n+1}. This is an example of a predictor-corrector method, and the iteration can be continued until no further improvement is shown in y_{n+1}.

14.10 A SIMPLE PREDICTOR-CORRECTOR METHOD

As a simple predictor, one can use Eq. (14.4.15) to find

$$y_{n+1} = y_{n-1} + 2hy_n', \qquad E = (h^3/3)y^{(3)}(\xi). \quad (14.10.1)$$

This uses the slope at the middle of the double interval to avoid bias as much as possible. However, we need two points to get started. To get the second point we can use Euler's formula (14.6.1) or the first four terms of a Taylor's series. Then we can use the modified Euler's formula (14.7.1),

$$y_{n+1} = y_n + (h/2)(y_n' + y_{n+1}'), \qquad E = -(h^3/12)y^{(3)}(\xi), \quad (14.10.2)$$

as a corrector to improve the value of y_{n+1}. Iteration with these two formulas can be continued until no further improvement is shown in y_{n+1}.

14.11 MILNE METHODS

We now present two predictor-corrector methods proposed by W. E. Milne for the solution of a first-order differential equation.

a) Milne proposes to use (14.4.16),

$$y_{n+1} = y_{n-3} + 4h(y_n' - \nabla y_n' + \tfrac{2}{3}\nabla^2 y_n') + (14h^5/45)y^{(5)}(\xi), \quad (14.11.1)$$

as a predictor in order to get improved values of the derivative to use in

$$y_{n+1} = y_{n-1} + 2h(y'_{n+1} - \nabla y'_{n+1} + \tfrac{1}{6}\nabla^2 y'_{n+1}) - (h^5/90)y^{(5)}(\xi) \qquad (14.11.2)$$

as a corrector. The corrector formula is a modified form of Simpson's rule.

b) In another method (14.4.17),

$$y_{n+1} = y_{n-5} + 6h(y'_n - 2\nabla y'_n + \tfrac{5}{2}\nabla^2 y'_n - \tfrac{3}{2}\nabla^3 y'_n + \tfrac{11}{20}\nabla^4 y'_n) + \tfrac{41}{140}h^7 y^{(7)}(\xi) \tag{14.11.3}$$

is used as a predictor, and

$$y_{n+1} = y_{n-3} + 4h(y'_{n+1} - 2\nabla y'_{n+1} + \tfrac{5}{3}\nabla^2 y'_{n+1} - \tfrac{2}{3}\nabla^3 y'_{n+1}$$
$$+ \tfrac{7}{90}\nabla^4 y'_{n+1}) - (8h^7/945)y^{(7)}(\xi) \qquad (14.11.4)$$

is used as a corrector.

These methods possess the advantage that the truncation errors in each step are proportional to h^5 and h^7, respectively. On the other hand, they have a much greater tendency toward instability than many of the other methods.

14.12 RUNGE-KUTTA METHODS

The Runge-Kutta methods for finding the numerical solution of differential equations have been very popular. They have proven, in general, to be quite stable and accurate. Two of the best known of these methods are the so-called third-order accuracy formulas and the fourth-order accuracy formulas. Given the initial-value problem

$$y' = F(x, y), \qquad y(x_0) = y_0, \qquad (14.12.1)$$

we have

a) *Third-order accuracy formulas:*

$$y_{n+1} = y_n + \tfrac{1}{6}(k_0 + 4k_1 + k_2) + 0(h^4),$$
$$k_0 = hF(x_n, y_n), \qquad k_1 = hF(x_n + \tfrac{1}{2}h, y_n + \tfrac{1}{2}k_0) \qquad (14.12.2)$$
$$k_2 = hF(x_n + h, y_n + 2k_1 - k_0),$$

and

b) *Fourth-order accuracy formulas:*

$$y_{n+1} = y_n + \tfrac{1}{6}(k_0 + 2k_1 + 2k_2 + k_3) + 0(h^5),$$
$$k_0 = hF(x_n, y_n), \qquad k_1 = hF(x_n + \tfrac{1}{2}h, y_n + \tfrac{1}{2}k_0), \qquad (14.12.3)$$
$$k_2 = hF(x_n + \tfrac{1}{2}h, y_n + \tfrac{1}{2}k_1), \qquad k_3 = hF(x_n + h, y_n + k_2).$$

14.13 NORDSIECK'S METHOD

A general-purpose method for the numerical integration of a system of ordinary differential equations has been proposed by Arnold Nordsieck. The method was proved to be quite reliable and efficient. It operates with the current values of the higher derivatives of a polynomial approximating the solution. It has a high degree of stability, incorporates automatic starting and automatic choice and revision of interval size, minimizes the amount of computation for a specified accuracy of solution, and applies to any system of differential equations with continuous derivatives or piecewise continuous with finite jumps. A detailed discussion of this method with specifications for a computer program is found in *Mathematics of Computation*, January, 1962, pp. 22–49.

14.14 HIGHER-ORDER EQUATIONS

Higher-order equations can, in general, be reduced to a system of first-order equations. One of the previous first-order methods can then be applied to the system of equations. For example, if we are given the second-order equation

$$y'' = F(x, y, y'), \qquad y(x_0) = y_0, \qquad y'(x_0) = y'_0, \qquad (14.14.1)$$

we can let $y' = u$ and rewrite the given equation with initial conditions in the following form:

$$y' = u, \qquad y(x_0) = y_0;$$
$$u' = F(x, y, u), \qquad u(x_0) = y'_0. \qquad (14.14.2)$$

Instead of a single second-order equation, we now have two coupled first-order equations. Euler's formula for this system is

$$y_{n+1} = y_n + hy'_n = y_n + hu_n,$$
$$u_{n+1} = u_n + hu'_n = u_n + hF(x_n, y_n, u_n). \qquad (14.14.3)$$

If Heun's method, Adams' method, or a predictor-corrector method is used, we use Eq. (14.14.3) to obtain the required number of starting values. Other special formulas are found in Milne [106].

14.15 LINEAR EQUATIONS WITH VARIABLE COEFFICIENTS

Finite difference schemes can be applied to linear equations with variable coefficients. The previous methods can be modified to include the values of the variable coefficients at each step. Schemes requiring more work, but giving more accuracy by using difference correction terms, such as the following, can be used.

a) For the first-order equation

$$y' + f(x)y = k(x), \qquad (14.15.1)$$

we have the recurrence relation

$$y_{n+1}(1 + \tfrac{1}{2}hf_{n+1}) - y_n(1 - \tfrac{1}{2}hf_n) + Cy_{n+1/2} = \tfrac{1}{2}h(k_n + k_{n+1}), \quad (14.15.2)$$

where $C = \tfrac{1}{12}\delta^3 - \tfrac{1}{120}\delta^5 + \tfrac{1}{840}\delta^7 - \ldots$, and $Cy_{n+1/2}$ is the difference correction term. If the initial value y_0 is known, the difference correction term is ignored, and the recurrence relation is applied until the required number of ordinates is obtained to compute the differences, $Cy_{n+1/2}$. These differences are then used in the difference formula to obtain better approximations to y.

b) For the second-order equation

$$y'' + f(x)y = k(x), \qquad (14.15.3)$$

we have the recurrence relation

$$(1 + \tfrac{1}{12}h^2 f_{n+1})y_{n+1} - (2 - \tfrac{10}{12}h^2 f_n)y_n + (1 + \tfrac{1}{12}h^2 f_{n-1})y_{n-1}$$
$$+ Cy_n = \tfrac{1}{12}h^2(k_{n+1} + 10k_n + k_{n-1}),$$

where

$$\qquad (14.15.4)$$

$$C = \frac{1}{240}\delta^6 - \frac{13}{15120}\delta^8 + \cdots.$$

With two initial values y_0 and y_1 the computation may be started. We ignore the correction differences until a sufficient number of y-values has been computed to include them.

c) For the second-order equation

$$y'' + f(x)y' + g(x)y = k(x), \qquad (14.15.5)$$

we have the recurrence relation

$$(1 + \tfrac{1}{2}hf_n)y_{n+1} - (2 - h^2 g_n)y_n + (1 - \tfrac{1}{2}hf_n)y_{n-1} + Cy_n = h^2 k_n,$$

where

$$C = (-\tfrac{1}{12}\delta^4 + \tfrac{1}{90}\delta^6 - \cdots) + hf_n(-\tfrac{1}{6}\mu\delta^3 + \tfrac{1}{30}\mu\delta^5 - \cdots). \quad (14.15.6)$$

We start the computation with two initial conditions and compute the difference correction term as for Eq. (14.15.4).

14.16 UNSTABLE FINITE DIFFERENCE SCHEMES

In Section 1.8, we considered the stability of a particular finite difference scheme, and discussed, in general, the stability of a higher-order difference equation. This was further amplified in Section 13.5.

More specifically, if the finite difference equation is of higher order than the differential equation it represents, then we may introduce additional unwanted solutions that are increasing.

Also, if the differential equation has some solutions which decrease very rapidly compared with the others, then it may happen that only the latter are adequately represented by the finite-difference equation, while the former are transformed into increasing functions.

Example. $y' = -\lambda y, y(0) = 1 \quad (\lambda > 0).$ (14.16.1)

Solution. This first-order equation has the solution $y = e^{-\lambda x}$. Assume a predictor-corrector method which uses

$$y_{n+1} = y_n + \tfrac{1}{3}h(y'_{n+1} - 4y'_n + y'_{n-1}) \qquad (14.16.2)$$

as a corrector. From (14.16.1) and (14.16.2) we obtain the second-order difference equation

$$(1 + \tfrac{1}{3}\lambda h)y_{n+1} + \tfrac{4}{3}\lambda hy_n - (1 - \tfrac{1}{3}\lambda h)y_{n-1} = 0. \tag{14.16.3}$$

The general solution of this difference equation is

$$y_n = Ar_1^n + Br_2^n, \tag{14.16.4}$$

where A and B are constants, and

$$r_1, r_2 = (-\tfrac{2}{3}\lambda h \pm \sqrt{1 + \tfrac{1}{3}\lambda^2 h^2})/(1 + \tfrac{1}{3}\lambda h). \tag{14.16.5}$$

The root r_1 gives a good approximation to the true solution. However, $|r_2|$ is always greater than unity, so an unwanted increasing solution has been introduced and the method is unstable.

14.17 BOUNDARY-VALUE PROBLEMS

The problems we have considered thus far have been of the initial-value type, i.e., starting values at a given point. We now consider the same types of differential equations with conditions given at two different points or boundaries. These conditions may be functional values, y_0 and y_n, at the endpoints of a range x_0 and x_n. Instead of functional values, one or both of the conditions may involve a derivative value y_0' and y_n'. We shall consider the simplest case first, that is, with the endpoints given. For illustration we use the general second-order differential equation given in (4.15.5) with the associated finite-difference relation given in (4.15.6). If we disregard the difference corrections, there are $n - 1$ equations in the $n + 1$ unknowns $y_0, y_1, \ldots, y_n$. However, we know y_0 and y_n and can substitute them in the $n - 1$ equations, which we then write as

$$
\begin{aligned}
-(2 - h^2 g_1)y_1 + (1 + \tfrac{1}{2}hf_1)y_2 &= h^2 k_1 - Cy_1 - (1 - \tfrac{1}{2}hf_1)y_0, \\
(1 - \tfrac{1}{2}hf_2)y_1 - (2 - h^2 g_2)y_2 + (1 + \tfrac{1}{2}hf_2)y_3 &= h^2 k_2 - Cy_2, \\
(1 - \tfrac{1}{2}hf_3)y_2 - (2 - h^2 g_3)y_3 + (1 + \tfrac{1}{2}hf_3)y_4 &= h^2 k_3 - Cy_3, \\
&\;\;\vdots \\
(1 - \tfrac{1}{2}hf_{n-2})y_{n-3} - (2 - h^2 g_{n-3})y_{n-2} + (1 + \tfrac{1}{2}hf_{n-3})y_{n-1} &= h^2 k_{n-2} - Cy_{n-2}, \\
(1 - \tfrac{1}{2}hf_{n-1})y_{n-2} - (2 - h^2 g_{n-1})y_{n-1} &= h^2 k_{n-1} - Cy_{n-1} - (1 + \tfrac{1}{2}hf_{n-1})y_n,
\end{aligned}
\tag{14.17.1}
$$

or, since we know the f_i, g_i, k_i, and h, the coefficients of the y_i are constants, and we write the above equations in the form

$$
\begin{bmatrix}
a_{11} & a_{12} & 0 & 0 & \cdots & 0 \\
a_{21} & a_{22} & a_{23} & 0 & \cdots & 0 \\
0 & a_{32} & a_{33} & a_{34} & & \vdots \\
\vdots & & & & a_{n-2,\,n-1} & \\
0 & \cdots & & a_{n-1,\,n-2} & a_{n-1,\,n-1}
\end{bmatrix}
\begin{bmatrix}
y_1 \\ y_2 \\ \vdots \\ \\ y_{n-1}
\end{bmatrix}
=
\begin{bmatrix}
b_1 \\ b_2 \\ \vdots \\ \\ b_{n-1}
\end{bmatrix}
-
\begin{bmatrix}
Cy_1 \\ Cy_2 \\ \vdots \\ \\ Cy_{n-1}
\end{bmatrix},
\tag{14.17.2}
$$

or in shortened matrix notation as

$$Ay = b - Cy. \tag{14.17.3}$$

In this equation Cy is the vector of difference corrections, and A is a tridiagonal or band matrix of width three. To start the computation, Cy is not included because its values depend on y values, so far unknown. The difference correction also depends on h and is negligible for sufficiently small h. A suitable method of solution is one of successive approximation, such as

   1) Neglect Cy and solve

$$Ay^{(1)} = b \tag{14.17.4}$$

for a first approximation, $y^{(1)}$.

   2) Next we compute a correction $\Delta y^{(1)}$ by solving

$$A \, \Delta y^{(1)} = -Cy^{(1)}. \tag{14.17.5}$$

The boundary values of $\Delta y^{(1)}$ are of course zero, since $y^{(1)}$ already has its correct values at these points, and the terms $h^2 k_i$ have been included in the calculation of $y^{(1)}$. The right member of (14.17.5) contains only the difference correction, and the matrix on the left is identical with the coefficient matrix of (14.17.2).

   3) The process can be continued. If $C \, \Delta y^{(1)}$ is significant, we compute a further correction, $\Delta y^{(2)}$, by solving

$$A \, \Delta y^{(2)} = -C \, \Delta y^{(1)}, \tag{14.17.6}$$

and repeat until there is no further change. In practice, the cycle rarely needs to be performed more than twice.

   In order to calculate central differences near the ends of a range we need additional points outside of the range. We can calculate y_{n-1} and y_{n+2} from (14.15.6) by rewriting the difference equations as

$$(1 - \tfrac{1}{2}hf_n)y_{n-1} = (2 - h^2 g_n)y_n - (1 + \tfrac{1}{2}hf_n)y_{n+1} + h^2 k_n - Cy_n$$

and

$$(1 + \tfrac{1}{2}hf_{n+1})y_{n+2} = (2 - h^2 g_{n+1})y_{n+1} - (1 - \tfrac{1}{2}hf_n)y_n + h^2 k_{n+1} - Cy_{n+1}. \tag{14.17.7}$$

The terms in Cy are neglected in the first approximation and included in the others. The difference equation can be used as in (14.17.7) to extend the solution to other points at each end of the range in order to provide sufficient information for computing the central differences needed in Cy.

   By choosing h very small the difference corrections may be negligible, but the matrix A may be of such high order the desirable accuracy would be difficult to achieve. If h is taken too large, then the difference corrections may not converge or may converge too slowly to be practical. We usually choose h such that the number of linear equations to be solved is acceptable.

If either boundary condition involves the first derivative, a slightly different procedure is necessary. When the derivative is involved at the boundary x_0, the differential equation is satisfied at this point by using the equation

$$(1 - \tfrac{1}{2}hf_0)y_{-1} - (2 - h^2g_0)y_0 + (1 + \tfrac{1}{2}f_0)y_1 + Cy_0 = h^2k_0, \quad (14.17.8)$$

with boundary condition

$$y_0' + ay_0 = b. \quad (14.17.9)$$

We replace the boundary condition by its central difference equation

$$y_1 - y_{-1} + 2hay_0 + C_1y_0 = 2hb, \quad (14.17.10)$$

where C_1 is a new difference-correction operator

$$C_1 = 2(-\tfrac{1}{6}\mu\delta^3 + \tfrac{1}{30}\mu\delta^5 - \cdots),$$

and the first difference $\mu\delta y_0$ in the derivative formula has been replaced by $\tfrac{1}{2}(y_1 - y_{-1})$. Since y_{-1} is external to the range, we eliminate y_{-1} from (14.17.8) by the use of (14.17.10), and we obtain the equation

$$\{(1 - \tfrac{1}{2}hf_0)2ha - (2 - h^2g_0)\}y_0 + 2y_1$$
$$= h^2k_0 + 2hb(1 - \tfrac{1}{2}hf_0) - Cy_0 - (1 - \tfrac{1}{2}hf_0)C_1y_0. \quad (14.17.11)$$

This is the first of the new equations corresponding to (14.17.1); the second is obtained by moving the term in y_0 over to the left in the first equation of (14.17.1). The remaining equations are unchanged until the second boundary is reached. Here the procedure again depends on the boundary condition. If a first derivative is involved at that boundary, the new matrix will have order $n + 1$, corresponding to the $n + 1$ unknowns $y_0, y_1, \ldots, y_n$, and it will still be a band matrix. We calculate Cy and C_1y as before.

Example. Problems of boundary-value type occur frequently in vibration theory and often lead to linear homogeneous equations involving a parameter. The simplest example of this type is the equation

$$y'' + \lambda y = 0$$

with boundary conditions $y = 0$ at $x = 0$ and $x = 1$. This problem is known to have a nontrivial solution only if

$$\lambda = n^2\pi^2 \quad (n = 1, 2, \ldots)$$

when $y = \sin n\pi x$. The use of the finite-difference equations leads to a matrix of the form

$$[A - \lambda I]x = 0,$$

and the problem reduces to that of finding the eigenvalues and eigenvectors of the matrix A. The eigenvalues λ_i are the natural frequencies, and the associated eigenvectors $x^{(i)}$ are the modes of oscillation.

14.18 MATRIX FORM OF A SYSTEM OF SECOND-ORDER EQUATIONS

Assume the most general form of a system of second-order linear differential equations with constant coefficients:

$$a_{11}\ddot{q}_1(t) + \cdots + a_{1n}\ddot{q}_n(t) + b_{11}\dot{q}_1(t) + \cdots + b_{1n}\dot{q}_n(t) + c_{11}q_1(t) + \cdots + c_{1n}q_n(t) = f_1(t),$$
$$a_{21}\ddot{q}_1(t) + \cdots + a_{2n}\ddot{q}_n(t) + b_{21}\dot{q}_1(t) + \cdots + b_{2n}\dot{q}_n(t) + c_{21}q_1(t) + \cdots + c_{2n}q_n(t) = f_2(t),$$
$$\vdots \qquad\qquad (14.18.1)$$
$$a_{n1}\ddot{q}_1(t) + \cdots + a_{nn}\ddot{q}_n(t) + b_{n1}\dot{q}_1(t) + \cdots + b_{nn}\dot{q}_n(t) + c_{n1}q_1(t) + \cdots + c_{nn}q_n(t) = f_n(t)$$

We write this in matrix form as

$$
\begin{bmatrix} a_{11} & a_{12} & \cdots & a_{1n} \\ a_{21} & & \cdots & a_{2n} \\ \vdots & & & \vdots \\ a_{n1} & & \cdots & a_{nn} \end{bmatrix}
\begin{bmatrix} \ddot{q}_1(t) \\ \ddot{q}_2(t) \\ \vdots \\ \ddot{q}_n(t) \end{bmatrix}
+
\begin{bmatrix} b_{11} & b_{12} & \cdots & b_{1n} \\ b_{21} & & & \vdots \\ \vdots & & & \\ b_{n1} & & \cdots & b_{nn} \end{bmatrix}
\begin{bmatrix} \dot{q}_1(t) \\ \dot{q}_2(t) \\ \vdots \\ \dot{q}_n(t) \end{bmatrix}
$$

$$
+
\begin{bmatrix} c_{11} & c_{12} & \cdots & c_{1n} \\ c_{21} & & & \vdots \\ \vdots & & & \\ c_{n1} & & \cdots & c_{nn} \end{bmatrix}
\begin{bmatrix} q_1(t) \\ q_2(t) \\ \vdots \\ q_n(t) \end{bmatrix}
=
\begin{bmatrix} f_1(t) \\ f_2(t) \\ \vdots \\ f_n(t) \end{bmatrix},
\qquad (14.18.2)
$$

or as the simple matrix equation

$$A\ddot{q}(t) + B\dot{q}(t) + Cq(t) = f(t). \qquad (14.18.3)$$

We shall find this last equation a very useful and convenient form for working with systems of equations in some of the material to be covered in the remainder of this and the next chapter.

14.19 SECOND-ORDER REDUCTION

Since a second-order equation can be reduced to two first-order equations, an $n \times n$ system of second-order equations can be reduced to a $2n \times 2n$ system of first-order equations. The most convenient way to accomplish this is by matrix operations. We now consider again the second-order system of (14.18.3).

Let

$$\dot{q}(t) = u(t), \qquad (14.19.1)$$

then

$$H\dot{g}(t) + Kg(t) = r(t), \qquad (14.19.2)$$

where

$$H = \begin{bmatrix} A & 0 \\ 0 & I \end{bmatrix}, \qquad K = \begin{bmatrix} B & C \\ -I & 0 \end{bmatrix},$$

$$g(t) = \begin{bmatrix} u(t) \\ q(t) \end{bmatrix} = \begin{bmatrix} \dot{q}(t) \\ q(t) \end{bmatrix}, \qquad r(t) = \begin{bmatrix} f(t) \\ 0 \end{bmatrix}. \qquad (14.19.3)$$

Therefore,

$$\dot{g}(t) + H^{-1}Kg(t) = H^{-1}r(t) \tag{14.19.4}$$

or

$$\dot{g}(t) + Lg(t) = R(t), \tag{14.19.5}$$

where

$$L = H^{-1}K = \begin{bmatrix} A^{-1}B & A^{-1}C \\ -I & 0 \end{bmatrix} \quad \text{and} \quad R(t) = H^{-1}r(t) = \begin{bmatrix} A^{-1}f(t) \\ 0 \end{bmatrix}. \tag{14.19.6}$$

14.20 MATRIX EXPONENTIAL METHOD

We now discuss the matrix exponential method of solving a system of second-order linear differential equations with constant coefficients. Starting with the system as given in (14.17.3), we wish to find a solution analogous to the solution of a single equation, which involves the exponential. We define the matrix exponential by means of the infinite series

$$e^{At} = I + At + \frac{A^2 t^2}{2!} + \cdots + \frac{A^n t^n}{n!} + \cdots. \tag{14.20.1}$$

By the second-order reduction process, we transform our system of equations to the form (14.19.5), and we have

$$\dot{g}(t) + Lg(t) = R(t).$$

If we consider R as a series of slopes $\dot{R}$ and intercepts R_0, then

$$\dot{g}(t) + Lg(t) = \dot{R}t + R_0. \tag{14.20.2}$$

This matrix equation is then analogous to the single linear differential equation of the first order, where L and R are not functions of g. Using the usual method of solving such an equation, we find an integrating factor which is

$$e^{\int L \, dt} = e^{Lt}. \tag{14.20.3}$$

Multiplying by our integrating factor, we have

$$e^{Lt}\dot{g} + e^{Lt}Lg = e^{Lt}\dot{R}t + e^{Lt}R_0. \tag{14.20.4}$$

From (14.20.1) it can be seen that

$$\frac{d}{dt}(e^{Lt}) = e^{Lt}L. \tag{14.20.5}$$

We now integrate our equation, and

$$e^{Lt}g = \int (e^{Lt}\dot{R}t + e^{Lt}R_0) \, dt. \tag{14.20.6}$$

Integrating the right side by parts, we have

$$e^{Lt}g = \dot{R}te^{Lt}L^{-1} - \dot{R}e^{Lt}L^{-2} + R_0 e^{Lt}L^{-1} + C. \tag{14.20.7}$$

Again, the validity of the integration may be seen from (14.20.1). At t_0, we find that $g = g_0$ and

$$e^{Lt_0}g_0 = \dot{R}t_0 e^{Lt_0}L^{-1} - \dot{R}e^{Lt_0}L^{-2} + R_0 e^{Lt_0}L^{-1} + C. \qquad (14.20.8)$$

Thus

$$C = e^{Lt_0}g_0 - \dot{R}t_0 e^{Lt_0}L^{-1} + \dot{R}e^{Lt_0}L^{-2} - R_0 e^{Lt_0}L^{-1} \qquad (14.20.9)$$

and

$$g(t) = e^{L(t_0-t)}[g_0 + L^{-1}(L^{-1}\dot{R} - R_0 - \dot{R}t_0)] + L^{-1}[\dot{R}t - L^{-1}\dot{R} + R_0]. \qquad (14.20.10)$$

At $t = t_0 + \Delta t$, we have

$$g(t + \Delta t) = e^{-L\Delta t}[g(t_0) + L^{-1}(L^{-1}\dot{R} - R_0 + \dot{R}t_0)] + L^{-1}[L^{-1}\dot{R} - R_0 - \dot{R}t_0 + \dot{R}\Delta t]. \qquad (14.20.11)$$

The accuracy of the method depends on the condition of the matrices. This determines how accurately L, L^{-1}, A^{-1}, $\dot{R}$, and R_0 may be computed. The accuracy with which the forcing functions $f(t)$ are represented also affects the accuracy of the solution, as well as the size of Δt. For a stable system of equations, this method has proved to be a very fast method for solving on a computer.

For those interested in a more thorough study of this method, Varga [154] shows the relationship of the matrix exponential method with the Crank-Nicolson method and the Padé methods.

14.21 SURVEY OF NONLINEAR ORDINARY DIFFERENTIAL EQUATIONS

Linear differential equations have been given an exhaustive mathematical treatment. In the nonlinear case, it is only in recent years that men such as J. Schröder, L. Collatz, and S. V. Parter have made significant contributions.

Engineers and those interested in practical results have investigated a large number of very specific problems and obtained partial or approximate results by various special approaches, graphical methods, or even experimental means.

All of the popular numerical methods such as the Milne, Adams-Bashforth, Runge-Kutta methods, etc., are as applicable to nonlinear systems as to linear. In the former, more operations may be required and fewer shortcuts found, but this is only to be expected from the greater complexity of nonlinear systems.

The numerical schemes given in the first part of this chapter are well known. Perhaps not so well known is a technique recommended by Davis [Section 14.22(c)]. The method is called continuous analytic continuation, and Davis claims the following advantages for it. It is linearly iterative, i.e., the algorithm connecting successive steps does not increase in complexity with each step. It is applicable in the complex domain. It may be extended to any ordinary point of the complex plane not excluded by a natural bound. The error increases linearly, i.e., is nK after n steps where K is a constant. Some criticisms of the method are the fact that each approximation relies only on the previous point and uses no old data, which may lead to instability, and the fact that the given error estimate is a very crude bound. For examples of applications of this method see Davis [Section 14.22(c), pp. 254–266].

A technique often employed in the analytical solution of differential equations is to assume that the solution has the form of an infinite series with undetermined coefficients, such as a power series, a Fourier series, or a series of any complete family of orthogonal functions such as Bessel, Lagrange, Chebyshev, etc. Then the series is substituted into the differential equation and the coefficients of like terms are equated. When done by hand this is a tedious method, and, while one might design a program to do it on a computer, it nevertheless seems grossly inefficient.

Very little has been written on finite-difference methods and the subject of replacing nonlinear differential equations by difference equations. Cunningham [Section 14.22(b), pp. 230–234] discusses nonlinear difference equations. For nonlinear systems of difference equations the method of variation of parameters seems to be applicable.

Among nonlinear problems, there are certain classes for which a complete solution can be found, and other equations which have had such important applications that much is known about them. Some famous equations with analytic solutions include Bernoulli's equation, $dx/dt = f(t)x + g(t)x^\alpha$, Clairaut's equation, $x = t(dx/dt) + f(dx/dt)$, Chrystal's equation, $(dx/dt)^2 + At\,dx/dt + Bx + Ct^2 = 0$, and the generalized Riccati equation, $dx/dt + Q(t)x + R(t)x^2 = P(t)$. Problems from the calculus of variations often give rise to nonlinear problems. A particular problem of this type is the pursuit problem. For more on this problem see Davis [Section 14.22(c), pp. 113–127]. Incidentally, this problem lends itself well to graphical solutions. Mentioned in passing is another curious variational problem known as Plateau's problem. In general, the problem is to discover the shape of the minimal surface bounded by a given space curve. This problem is one in which experimental techniques have been applied. Other well-known problems are the various forms of the Duffing and Van der Pol equations which have been extensively discussed in the literature. For further references see Section 14.22 which contains books by Davis [c], Struble [h], Stoker [g], Minorsky [f], and Cunningham [b]. The latter three along with McLachlan [e], give numerous examples of electrical circuitry problems of a nonlinear character.

Much of the theoretical work on nonlinear systems has been exclusively pre-occupied with the study of stability. Indeed it is precisely the nonlinearity which makes this field of study interesting, as only the nonlinear equations exhibit much of that pathological behavior which excites the theoretical mathematician's interest. Historically, much of the interest in stability was generated by the notable successes of Poincaré and Bendixon in explaining the behavior of two-dimensional autonomous systems. Some theorems on stability of nonlinear systems are found in Coddington and Levinson [a], Struble [h], and Minorsky [f].

14.22 SUPPLEMENTARY REFERENCES

The following is a list of recommended references on nonlinear differential equations:

a) E. A. CODDINGTON and N. LEVINSON, *Theory of Ordinary Differential Equations,* McGraw-Hill, New York, 1955.

b) W. J. CUNNINGHAM, *Introduction to Nonlinear Analysis,* McGraw-Hill, New York, 1958.

c) H. T. DAVIS, "Introduction to Nonlinear Differential and Integral Equations," *U.S.A.E.C.,* 1961.

d) S. LEFSCHETZ, *Contributions to the Theory of Nonlinear Oscillations,* Princeton University Press, Princeton, Vol. 1, 1950, *Annals of Math. Studies,* No. 20; Vol. 2, **20,** 1952, No. 29; Vol. 3, 1956, No. 36; Vol. 4, 1958, No. 41.

e) N. W. McLACHLAN, *Ordinary Nonlinear Differential Equations in Engineering and Physical Sciences,* Oxford University Press, Oxford, 1950.

f) N. MINORSKY, *Introduction to Nonlinear Mechanics,* J. W. Edwards, Ann Arbor, 1947.

g) J. J. STOKER, *Nonlinear Vibrations in Mechanical and Electrical Systems,* Interscience, New York, 1950.

h) R. A. STRUBLE, *Nonlinear Differential Equations,* McGraw-Hill, New York, 1962.

EXERCISES

1. Distinguish between open-type and closed-type integration formulas.

2. What are the disadvantages of closed-type formulas?

3. Show geometrically the relationship between the Euler and Heun methods.

4. Solve by Heun's method: $y' = x^2 - y^2$, $y = 0$ at $x = 1$, $h = 0.1$, from $x = 1$ to $x = 2$.

5. Solve Exercise 4 using the Adams-Bashforth method.

6. Solve Exercise 4 using the Runge-Kutta fourth-order formulas.

7. Integrate $y'' - \frac{1}{2}y'^2 + y = 0$ from $y = 1$, $y' = 0$ to the point where $y' = 0$ again.

8. Integrate $x'' = x'y$, $y'' = xy'$, $x = y = 1$, $x' = y' = 1$ at $t = 0$.

9. Solve the differential equation $y' = x^2 + y^2 - 2$, $x = 0$, $y = 1$, using Heun's method for $x = 0(0.1).5$.

10. Solve Exercise 9 using a simple predictor-corrector method.

11. Solve the differential equation $y'' + \lambda xy = 0$ with boundary conditions $y(0) = 0$, $y(1) = 0$. Use $h = \frac{1}{4}$ and find the smallest eigenvalue λ.

12. Using $h = \frac{1}{4}$, find the smallest eigenvalue of the differential equation $xy'' + y' + \lambda xy = 0$ with boundary conditions $y(0) = y(1) = 0$.

13. Solve the system of differential equations $y' = xz + 1$, $z' = -xy$ with initial conditions $x = 0$, $y = 0$, $z = 1$ for $x = 0(0.1).5$.

14. Solve the differential equation $y'' + xy + \frac{1}{6}xy^3 = 0$ with initial conditions $y(0) = 0$, $y'(0) = 1$ for $x = 0(0.1).5$.

CHAPTER 15

TRANSFER FUNCTION COMPUTATIONS

15.1 INTRODUCTION

In Section 12.4 we defined the Laplace transform of the first derivative as

$$\mathcal{L}\{y'(t)\} = sy(s) - y(0), \tag{15.1.1}$$

and the transform of the second derivative as

$$\mathcal{L}\{y''(t)\} = s^2 y(s) - sy(0) - y'(0). \tag{15.1.2}$$

Also in Section 12.5, we discussed the method of finding the Laplace transform of a single ordinary differential equation with initial conditions. From the resulting auxiliary equation the transform function was obtained. Many problems related to mechanical systems or electrical systems lead to coupled systems of second-order linear ordinary differential equations with constant coefficients and known initial conditions. The most general form of such a system was given in (14.18.1) and expressed in (14.18.3) as the matrix equation

$$A\ddot{q}(t) + B\dot{q}(t) + Cq(t) = f(t). \tag{15.1.3}$$

We now concern ourselves with finding the Laplace transform of this system of differential equations and solving for the transform functions. If the system relates to mechanical or electrical systems involving vibrations or oscillations, the transform functions are called the transfer functions. As we shall see, these functions can be used to obtain the time response of the system or to do a frequency response analysis of the system.

15.2 MATRIX TRANSFORM EQUATION

We consider first the $n \times n$ system:

$$A\ddot{q}(t) + B\dot{q}(t) + Cq(t) = f(t).$$

Taking the Laplace transform of both sides, we obtain

$$As^2 q(s) - Asq(0) - A\dot{q}(0) + Bsq(s) - Bq(0) + Cq(s) = f(s) \tag{15.2.1}$$

or

$$[As^2 + Bs + C]q(s) = Asq(0) + [A\dot{q}(0) + Bq(0)] + f(s), \tag{15.2.2}$$

198

where the transfer function vector is

$$q(s) = \begin{bmatrix} q_1(s) \\ q_2(s) \\ \vdots \\ q_n(s) \end{bmatrix}, \tag{15.2.3}$$

the forcing transform vector is

$$f(s) = \begin{bmatrix} f_1(s) \\ f_2(s) \\ \vdots \\ f_n(s) \end{bmatrix}, \tag{15.2.4}$$

and the initial condition vectors are

$$q(0) = \begin{bmatrix} q_1(0) \\ q_2(0) \\ \vdots \\ q_n(0) \end{bmatrix} \quad \text{and} \quad \dot{q}(0) = \begin{bmatrix} \dot{q}_1(0) \\ \dot{q}_2(0) \\ \vdots \\ \dot{q}_n(0) \end{bmatrix}. \tag{15.2.5}$$

The transform equation (15.2.2) may be written as

$$[As^2 + Bs + C]q(s) = F(s), \tag{15.2.6}$$

where $F(s) = f(s)$, if $q(0) = \dot{q}(0) = 0$, that is, if the initial conditions are equal to zero.

If the system relates to mechanical oscillations, A is called the mass matrix, B is the damping matrix, and C is the spring matrix. In the analogy between mechanical and electrical oscillations, we substitute inductance for inertia, resistance for damping, reciprocal value of capacitance for elastic restraint, impressed electromotive force for the impressed mechanical force, and the q_i may be condenser charges Q_i, currents I_i, or voltages E_i. The matrix $[As^2 + Bs + C]$ is called the system matrix, and the roots s_i of

$$|As^2 + Bs + C| = 0 \tag{15.2.7}$$

are called the system roots.

Multiplying the transform equations (15.2.6) by the inverse of the system matrix, we obtain the transfer function vector

$$q(s) = [As^2 + Bs + C]^{-1}F(s). \tag{15.2.8}$$

The system matrix is, in general, an $n \times n$ matrix of elements which are quadratic in s. The inverse can be found by the adjoint method given in Chapter 7. That is, (15.2.8) can be written as

$$q(s) = \frac{[D_{ji}(s)]}{|As^2 + Bs + C|} F(s), \tag{15.2.9}$$

where $[D_{ji}(s)]$ is the transpose of the cofactor matrix of $[As^2 + Bs + C]$. In general, it is not convenient to use (15.2.9). However, it can be handled in a manner suitable for computer programming. If $F(s)$ is a column of zeros except for one entry, and a particular one of the transfer functions is desired, then only one cofactor of $[As^2 + Bs + C]$ is required.

Thus, if $q_i(s)$ is desired and $F(s)$ has a nonzero entry, $\overline{f}_k(s)$ in the kth row, then

$$q_i(s) = \frac{|D_{ki}(s)|}{|As^2 + Bs + C|}\overline{f}_k(s), \qquad (15.2.10)$$

where $|D_{ki}(s)|$ is the cofactor of $[As^2 + Bs + C]$ obtained by striking out the kth row and ith column.

If we use $\overline{f}_k(s) = 1$ for all $k = 1, 2, \ldots, n$ and $i = 1, 2, \ldots, n$, then the coefficient fractions T_{ij} can be computed for all arbitrary $F(s)$:

$$\begin{aligned}
q_1(s) &= T_{11}f_1(s) + T_{12}f_2(s) + \cdots + T_{1n}f_n(s) \\
q_2(s) &= T_{21}f_1(s) + T_{22}f_2(s) + \cdots + T_{2n}f_n(s) \\
&\vdots \\
q_n(s) &= T_{n1}f_1(s) + T_{n2}f_2(s) + \cdots + T_{nn}f_n(s).
\end{aligned} \qquad (15.2.11)$$

If the second-order reduction process has been applied to (15.1.3), as discussed in Section 14.19, we have the $2n \times 2n$ matrix equation

$$\dot{g}(t) + Lg(t) = R(t), \qquad (15.2.12)$$

where L and $R(t)$ are as defined in (14.19.6). Taking the Laplace transform we have

$$sg(s) - g(0) + Lg(s) = R(s)$$

or

$$[L + Is]g(s) = g(0) + R(s), \qquad (15.2.13)$$

where

$$g(s) = \begin{bmatrix} \dot{q}_1(s) \\ \vdots \\ \dot{q}_n(s) \\ q_1(s) \\ \vdots \\ q_n(s) \end{bmatrix}, \qquad R(s) = \begin{bmatrix} A^{-1}\begin{bmatrix} f_1(s) \\ \vdots \\ f_n(s) \end{bmatrix} \\ 0 \\ \vdots \\ 0 \end{bmatrix}, \qquad (15.2.14)$$

and the initial conditions are contained in

$$g(0) = \begin{bmatrix} \dot{q}_1(0) \\ \vdots \\ \dot{q}_n(0) \\ q_1(0) \\ \vdots \\ q_n(0) \end{bmatrix}. \qquad (15.2.15)$$

In this case note that the transfer function vector consists of the transforms of the n first derivatives $\dot{q}_i(s)$, as well as the n transfer function $q_i(s)$.

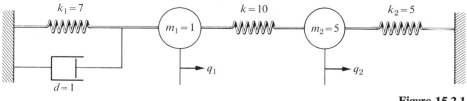

Figure 15.2.1

Example. Find the transfer functions for the simple mechanical system (Fig. 15.2.1) involving masses, springs, and a damper, with all initial conditions equal to zero and $f_1(t) = U'(t)$, that is, unit impulse, and $f_2(t) = 0$.

Solution. The equations of motion are

$$m_1\ddot{q}_1(t) + d\dot{q}_1(t) + (k + k_1)q_1(t) - kq_2(t) = f_1(t),$$
$$m_2\ddot{q}_2(t) - kq_1(t) + (k + k_2)q_2(t) = f_2(t). \tag{15.2.16}$$

This can be written as the matrix transform equation

$$[As^2 + Bs + C]q(s) = f(s), \tag{15.2.17}$$

where

$$A = \begin{bmatrix} 1 & 0 \\ 0 & 1 \end{bmatrix}, \quad B = \begin{bmatrix} 1 & 0 \\ 0 & 0 \end{bmatrix}, \quad C = \begin{bmatrix} 17 & -10 \\ -2 & 3 \end{bmatrix}, \tag{15.2.18}$$

and

$$f(s) = \begin{bmatrix} \mathcal{L}\{U'(t)\} \\ \mathcal{L}\{0\} \end{bmatrix} = \begin{bmatrix} 1 \\ 0 \end{bmatrix}. \tag{15.2.19}$$

Note that since the initial conditions are zero, the terms on the right-hand side of (15.2.2) containing $q(0)$ and $\dot{q}(0)$ are zero.

Therefore, the transform equation (15.2.17) is

$$\begin{bmatrix} s^2 + s + 17 & -10 \\ -2 & s^2 + 3 \end{bmatrix} \begin{bmatrix} q_1(s) \\ q_2(s) \end{bmatrix} = \begin{bmatrix} 1 \\ 0 \end{bmatrix}. \tag{15.2.20}$$

The inverse of the system matrix $[As^2 + Bs + C]$ is found to be

$$[As^2 + Bs + C]^{-1} = \frac{\begin{bmatrix} s^2 + 3 & 10 \\ 2 & s^2 + s + 17 \end{bmatrix}}{s^4 + s^3 + 20s^2 + 3s + 31}. \tag{15.2.21}$$

Multiplying both sides of (15.2.20) by this inverse, we have

$$\begin{bmatrix} q_1(s) \\ q_2(s) \end{bmatrix} = \frac{\begin{bmatrix} s^2 + 3 & 10 \\ 2 & s^2 + s + 17 \end{bmatrix} \begin{bmatrix} 1 \\ 0 \end{bmatrix}}{s^4 + s^3 + 20s^2 + 3s + 31} \tag{15.2.22}$$

$$= \frac{\begin{bmatrix} s^2 + 3 \\ 2 \end{bmatrix}}{s^4 + s^3 + 20s^2 + 3s + 31}. \tag{15.2.23}$$

Therefore,

$$q_1(s) = \frac{s^2 + 3}{s^4 + s^3 + 20s^2 + 3s + 31}, \qquad (15.2.24)$$

$$q_2(s) = \frac{2}{s^4 + s^3 + 20s^2 + 3s + 31}. \qquad (15.2.25)$$

15.3 TRANSFER FUNCTION ANALYSIS

Very often the scientist or engineer is interested in doing a transfer function analysis. This may involve any number of things. He may be interested in obtaining the time response from the transfer function. He may be interested in doing a frequency response analysis which may involve testing the transfer function to see if it is minimum phase or nonminimum phase, determination of stability of his system, calculation of gain and phase values for a specified range of frequencies, or obtaining Bode, Nichols, or root locus plots. He may also be interested in doing a root locus study. We shall proceed to discuss all of these topics with emphasis directed toward programming for a digital computer.

If the problem is one in electronics, the transfer functions of individual electronic components are often known, and the transfer function of a single loop, a combination of loops, or the entire system may be set up without starting with the basic differential equations of the system. However, if the transfer functions of individual components are not known, or if it is a problem in mechanical vibration or structural analysis, the basic differential equations are set up and the transfer functions are obtained as previously described.

15.4 TIME RESPONSE FROM TRANSFER FUNCTIONS

If $f(s) = P(s)/Q(s)$, then $f(t)$ is the inverse Laplace transform, that is,

$$f(t) = \mathcal{L}^{-1}\{f(s)\}.$$

In theory, if $P(s)$ and $Q(s)$ are polynomials, and the degree of $Q(s) >$ the degree of $P(s)$, this can be accomplished by resolving $P(s)/Q(s)$ into its partial fractions and finding the inverse Laplace transform of each fraction. In practice, this is accomplished by applying Cauchy's residue theorem, which is adaptable to a computer.

If the denominator $Q(s)$ is of degree n, then it will have n roots or zeros. The zeros of $Q(s)$ are called poles. Applying Cauchy's residue theorem one computes the residue at each pole. These residues are the numerators of the resolved partial fractions. The inverse transform of each fraction involves an appropriate power of e. The residue and inverse transform (time response function) may be found simultaneously.

The poles of $Q(s)$ may be distinct, repeated, or complex. The method of finding the residue and time response function has been discussed in detail in Sections 12.5 and 12.6. These sections should be reviewed at this time.

When we have a thorough understanding of these two sections, we see that if the transfer function is

$$y(s) = \frac{P(s)}{Q(s)},$$

and $Q(s)$ has a repeated root s_i of multiplicity m, p pairs of complex roots, and $n - m - 2p$ distinct roots, then the time response function is

$$
y(t) = \sum_{r=1}^{n-m-2p} \frac{e^{s_r t} P(s_r)}{Q'(s_r)} + \sum_{j=1}^{p} 2R_j e^{A_j t} \cos (B_j t \pm \theta_j)
$$
$$
+ \left\{ \frac{e^{st}}{(m-1)!} \left[t^{m-1} + \frac{(m-1)}{1!} t^{m-2} D + \cdots \right. \right.
$$
$$
\left. \left. + \frac{(m-1)(m-2)\cdots(m-r+1)}{(r-1)!} t^{m-r} D^{r-1} \right] F \right\}_{s=s_i},
$$

(15.4.1)

where all symbols are as defined in Section 12.6.

The above method is very adaptable to a high-speed computer. If $P(s)$ and $Q(s)$ are polynomials, the zeros of $Q(s)$ are found by using a polynomial root finder. A routine for finding the derivative of $Q(s)$ is incorporated in a routine for finding any order derivatives of $F(s)$, a rational fraction. Thus the method of finding the polynomial in t, corresponding to a repeated root, can be completely mechanized. The method of finding the term corresponding to any pair of complex roots is very easily mechanized.

Example. Find $y(t)$ for the following:

$$
y(s) = \frac{P(s)}{Q(s)} = \frac{3s^6 + 30s^5 + 125s^4 + 277s^3 + 342s^2 + 218s + 48}{s^7 + 11s^6 + 50s^5 + 122s^4 + 172s^3 + 136s^2 + 48s}
$$
$$
= \frac{3s^6 + 30s^5 + 125s^4 + 277s^3 + 342s^2 + 218s + 48}{s(s+3)(s+2)^3(s^2 + 2s + 2)}.
$$

Solution. The roots, or poles, of the denominator are $s = 0, -3, -2, -2, -2, -1 + i, -1 - i$. And we have

$$
\left. \frac{P(s)}{Q'(s)} \right]_{s=0} = 1, \qquad \text{therefore } y_1(t) = 1 \cdot e^{0t} = 1;
$$

$$
\left. \frac{P(s)}{Q'(s)} \right]_{s=-3} = 1, \qquad \text{therefore } y_2(t) = 1 \cdot e^{-3t} = e^{-3t};
$$

$$
\left. \frac{P(s)}{Q'(s)} \right]_{s=-1+i} = 0 - \tfrac{1}{2}i \qquad \text{and} \qquad \left. \frac{P(s)}{Q'(s)} \right]_{s=-1-i} = 0 + \tfrac{1}{2}i.
$$

Thus, $A_1 + B_1 i = -1 + i$ gives $C_1 - D_1 i = 0 - \tfrac{1}{2}i$. And we have

$$
R = \sqrt{C_1^2 + D_1^2} = \tfrac{1}{2}, \qquad \theta_1 = \arctan \frac{|D_1|}{|C_1|} = \arctan \frac{\tfrac{1}{2}}{0}.
$$

Since $C_1 = 0$, $\theta_1 = \pi/2$, therefore

$$y_3(t) = 2R_1 e^{A_1 t} \cos(|B_1|t - \theta_1)$$

$$= e^{-t} \cos\left(t - \frac{\pi}{2}\right),$$

$$F(s) = (s + 2)^3 \frac{P(s)}{Q(s)}, \qquad F(s)]_{s=-2} = 1,$$

$$DF(s)]_{s=-2} = 1, \qquad D^2 F(s)]_{s=-2} = 2,$$

and therefore

$$y_4(t) = \left\{\frac{e^{st}}{2!}[t^2 \cdot F + 2t \cdot DF + D^2 F]\right\}_{s=-2}$$

$$= \tfrac{1}{2} e^{-2t}(t^2 + 2t + 2).$$

Hence

$$y(t) = y_1(t) + y_2(t) + y_3(t) + y_4(t)$$

$$= 1 + e^{-3t} + e^{-t} \cos\left(t - \frac{\pi}{2}\right) + \tfrac{1}{2} e^{-2t}(t^2 + 2t + 2).$$

15.5 FREQUENCY RESPONSE FROM TRANSFER FUNCTIONS

Mechanical, structural, and electrical systems involving vibrations or frequencies lead to problems of great interest in frequency and stability analyses. Frequency analysts are often interested in more than just frequency-response computations. They may be interested in whether a transfer function is minimum phase or non-minimum phase, stability of an open loop or closed loop system, Bode plots or Nichols plots. They may be interested in computing the frequency response at certain selected values of the frequency, or at certain "preferred" values which were selected automatically through monitoring of the phase curve.

Preliminary to computing the frequency-response (phase-frequency curve and gain-frequency curve), we shall consider automatic monitoring, minimum-phase transfer functions, nonminimum-phase transfer functions, and stability.

15.6 AUTOMATIC MONITORING

The phase change from one frequency to the next is compared to a *maximum allowable* and a *minimum allowable* value, both being constants. If the phase change in the interval is within these *allowable* values, the computation of frequency response continues along the same *set* of frequency values. If the phase change is greater than the maximum allowable, the mesh is reduced by switching to the next finer set of frequency values.

The monitoring and switching (which tend to keep the phase change per interval constant) tend to keep the mesh size inversely proportional to phase slope, i.e., rate of change of phase with respect to log frequency.

Table 15.6.1

Extra coarse set (optional)	Coarse set	Medium set	Fine set	Extra fine set	Extra-extra fine set
⋮	⋮	⋮	⋮	⋮	⋮
10	10	10	10	10	10
		12	11	10.5	10.25
	14	14	12	11	10.5
		17	13	⋮	⋮
20	20	20	14		
		25	15		$\Delta\omega = 0.25$
	30	30	16	$\Delta\omega = 0.5$	⋮
		35	17	⋮	
		40	18		
50	50	50	19	19	
		60	20	19.5	19.5
	70	70	22.5	20	19.75
		85	25	21	20.0
100	100	100	27.5	22	20.5
		120	30	⋮	21
⋮	140	140	32.5		⋮
	⋮	170	35	$\Delta\omega = 1.0$	
		⋮	37.5	⋮	$\Delta\omega = 0.5$
			40		⋮
			42.5		
			45	48	
			47.5	49	49
			50	50	49.5
			55	52.5	50
			60	55	51
			65	⋮	52
			70		⋮
			75	$\Delta\omega = 2.5$	
			80	⋮	$\Delta\omega = 1.0$
			85		⋮
			90		
			95	95	98

    In practice frequency values should be short, natural, common (45 and 50 rather than 43 and 52) and logarithmically spaced. However, we cannot always have values which are short and common and logarithmically spaced. The following sets of values, however, have proved satisfactory in practice and a good compromise for the desirable features. (See Table 15.6.1.)

    Each of the six sets is infinitely long, like an endless logarithmic scale. The coarse set, for example, is 1.0×10^n, 1.4×10^n, 2.0×10^n, 3×10^n, 5×10^n, 7×10^n, etc., where n is the succession of integers $-1, 0, 1, 2, \ldots$

The medium set has a minimum of digits, is finer everywhere than the coarse set, has fairly common values, harmonizes well with the fine set, and is exceptionally smooth (very evenly spaced, that is, the percentage change from one value to the next is always between 14.3 and 25).

For monitoring purposes the maximum allowable parameter may be set to 12 degrees phase change per interval and the minimum allowable to one third the maximum allowable value. Practice has shown that these are optimum values, in general, that will give enough, but not many more than enough, frequency-response points to permit a good frequency-response curve to be drawn.

15.7 MINIMUM PHASE AND NONMINIMUM PHASE TRANSFER FUNCTIONS

For a minimum phase transfer function, the rate of change of the gain slope is approximately proportional to the phase slope. So, a rapid change in the gain characteristic is accompanied by a corresponding rapid change in the phase curve. By simply monitoring the phase and adjusting the frequency mesh as described above, enough points on the gain curve will be obtained to give a good plot of the sharp peaks and dips induced by low-damped quadratic factors.

Nonminimum phase functions are often the result of products of minimum phase and nonminimum phase factors (whether we know the factors or not). The phase-frequency characteristic of a minimum phase factor and that of a nonminimum phase factor can cancel each other partially or completely. The net rate of change of phase with frequency, then, is relatively small. The gain curve, however, may have rapid changes. Normal monitoring would not give enough points to draw a good gain curve. This can be taken care of, however, by restricting the frequency selection so that the coarsest mesh used is that of the fine set.

15.8 STABILITY

The frequency analyst sometimes needs to know the answer to the stability question—whether or not his system (or subsystem or unit) is stable. When the transfer function directly represents the system, the answer is straight-forward and easy to obtain. But when it is an open-loop transfer function, the answer for the system is more involved.

In practice, we can employ the comprehensive Nyquist criterion. Also, we may form the characteristic equation of the system and find its roots. However, certain difficulties are encountered in using a root-finder. Rather than either of these two methods a simple test can be used to answer the stability question and, at the same time, tell whether the transfer function is minimum phase or nonminimum phase. This test will be explained in the next section.

When is a system stable? Some consider it stable only if all its characteristic-equation roots (system roots or poles) are in the left half-plane. Others consider a system stable if no roots lie in the right half-plane. Others say that there may be one root or pole at the origin. Since a system may sometimes have poles at the origin but may not have any on the nonzero part of the imaginary axis, the best thing to do is class all poles at the origin with poles in the left half-plane. The engineer will then decide if there are too many poles at the origin.

A pole at the origin imparts ± 6 db/octave (decibels per octave) to the gain curve and $\pm 90°$ to the phase curve. Such mild contributions to the frequency response are easily handled by the normal monitoring. In the case of poles on the nonzero part of the imaginary axis, however, the net rate of change of the phase-frequency curve is relatively small or zero. The gain-frequency curve may be rapidly changing in some places. Therefore, the special frequency selection should be used.

15.9 THE STABILITY AND PHASENESS TEST

The Routh or Hurwitz criteria have been used for decades in stability determinations. However, theoreticians have discovered that there is redundancy in these tests and that simpler criteria are possible. A. T. Fuller presents a test that is similar to the Hurwitz test but involves only about half the work.

To ascertain stability, the test must be applied to the characteristic function. When the transfer function represents a (closed loop) system or unit, the characteristic function is simply the denominator D of the transfer function. The only other important possibility is an open-loop transfer function representing a complete loop or aggregate of complete loops. For an open-loop transfer function, the characteristic function is the sum of the transfer-function numerator and denominator $N + D$.

The Fuller test is presented here in a modified form to ascertain if all the zeros are in the left half-plane or at the origin. If the characteristic function is

$$a_n s^{n+k} + a_{n-1} s^{n+k-1} + \cdots + a_1 s^{1+k} + a_0 s^k = 0, \qquad a_0 \neq 0, \qquad (15.9.1)$$

where k (a positive integer or zero) is the lowest power of s appearing, k is the order of a pole at the origin. Dividing by s^k, or reducing the exponents of s by k, the polynomial becomes

$$a_n s^n + a_{n-1} s^{n-1} + \cdots + a_2 s^2 + a_1 s + a_0 = 0, \qquad a_0 \neq 0. \quad (15.9.2)$$

If a_n is not positive, it is made so by changing the signs of all the coefficients. Then, as the first step in the test, the coefficients are inspected. If

$$\left.\begin{array}{l} a_{n-1}, a_{n-3}, \ldots, \text{ or } a_0 \text{ is equal to or less than zero, for } n \text{ odd} \\ a_{n-1}, a_{n-3}, \ldots, a_1, \text{ or } a_0 \text{ is equal to or less than zero, for } n \text{ even} \end{array}\right\}, \quad (15.9.3)$$

then at least one root of the polynomial lies in the right half-plane or on the non-zero part of the imaginary axis, and no further testing is necessary.

If, however, all the coefficients are greater than zero, further testing is necessary, and this consists of evaluating one of the following sequences of determinants:

$$\begin{Bmatrix} H_2, H_4, H_6, \ldots \text{ if } n \text{ is odd} \\ H_3, H_5, H_7, \ldots \text{ if } n \text{ is even} \end{Bmatrix}, \tag{15.9.4}$$

where

$$H_2 = \begin{vmatrix} a_{n-1} & a_{n-3} \\ a_n & a_{n-2} \end{vmatrix}, \qquad H_3 = \begin{vmatrix} a_{n-1} & a_{n-3} & a_{n-5} \\ a_n & a_{n-2} & a_{n-4} \\ 0 & a_{n-1} & a_{n-3} \end{vmatrix},$$

$$H_4 = \begin{vmatrix} a_{n-1} & a_{n-3} & a_{n-5} & a_{n-7} \\ a_n & a_{n-2} & a_{n-4} & a_{n-6} \\ 0 & a_{n-1} & a_{n-3} & a_{n-5} \\ 0 & a_n & a_{n-2} & a_{n-4} \end{vmatrix},$$

and

$$H_n = \begin{vmatrix} a_{n-1} & a_{n-3} & a_{n-5} & a_{n-7} & \cdots \\ a_n & a_{n-2} & a_{n-4} & a_{n-6} & \cdots \\ 0 & a_{n-1} & a_{n-3} & a_{n-5} & \cdots \\ 0 & a_n & a_{n-2} & a_{n-4} & \cdots \\ 0 & 0 & a_{n-1} & a_{n-3} & \cdots \\ 0 & 0 & a_n & a_{n-2} & \cdots \\ \vdots & \vdots & \vdots & \vdots \end{vmatrix}.$$

If all of these alternate determinants are greater than zero, all zeros of the polynomial are in the left half-plane.

To ascertain transfer-function phaseness, the test must, in general, be applied to both the numerator and the denominator of the transfer function. If neither has zeros in the right half-plane or the nonzero part of the imaginary axis, the transfer function is considered minimum phase and normal monitoring is used. However, if either has zeros in the right half-plane or on the nonzero part of the imaginary axis, the transfer function is nonminimum phase and the special frequency selection is used.

15.10 FREQUENCY RESPONSE COMPUTATIONS

If $s = j\omega$ is substituted in the transfer function $T(s) = P(s)/Q(s)$, and simplified, one obtains the frequency response function in the form

$$T(\omega) = u(\omega) + jv(\omega). \tag{15.10.1}$$

For a particular value of the frequency ω_k in radians per second, one gets

$$T(\omega_k) = u(\omega_k) + jv(\omega_k) = A + jB. \tag{15.10.2}$$

The gain for this particular frequency is

$$\rho = \sqrt{A^2 + B^2}. \tag{15.10.3}$$

Of greater interest, however, is the gain expressed in decibels (db), defined as

$$\text{GAIN} = 20 \log_{10} \sqrt{A^2 + B^2}$$
$$= 10 \log_{10} (A^2 + B^2). \tag{15.10.4}$$

Corresponding to this gain for a particular ω_k is a phase angle theta, in degrees, where

$$\text{THETA} = 57.29577 \text{ arc } \tan \frac{B}{A}. \tag{15.10.5}$$

In order to get the correct value of theta one uses the following set of formulas:

$$\theta = 57.29577 \text{ arc } \tan \frac{|B|}{|A|}, \qquad 0 \le \theta \le 90°. \tag{15.10.6}$$

1) If A is $-$, and B is 0, THETA $= -180°$
   If A is $-$, and B is $-$, THETA $= \theta - 180°$
   If A is $-$, and B is $+$, THETA $= -180° - \theta$

2) If A is 0, and B is 0, Alarm because of indeterminate form
   If A is 0, and B is $-$, THETA $= -90°$
   If A is 0, and B is $+$, THETA $= -270°$

3) If A is $+$, and B is 0, THETA $= 0°$
   If A is $+$, and B is $-$, THETA $= -\theta$
   If A is $+$, and B is $+$, THETA $= \theta - 360°$

15.11 BODE PLOTS AND NICHOLS PLOTS

These plots are best explained in terms of standard K and E plotting paper.

a) *Bode plot.* These plots are made on K and E semilogarithmic paper 359-81LG, which has a 4-cycle logarithmic scale in one direction and a rectangular scale in the other direction. Both the phase curve and gain curve are plotted on the same sheet with phase above the gain. The plotting starting frequency PS, in practice, is generally one of the following values: 10^n, $n = -2, -1, 0, 1, \ldots$ The final frequency value is 10^{n+4}. For convenience of rectangular plotting, the phase and gain curves are plotted against the logarithm of the frequency. In order to account for the plot starting frequency PS, computing logarithms to the base 10, and scaling to orient the phase curve above the gain curve as related to the K and E 359-81LG paper, we use the following formulas:

1) GANE $= (\text{GAIN} + 100)(0.12700025 \times 10^{-2})$. To give the plotting origin at -100 db level, 100 is added to all the values of gain and we calculate

$$0.12700025 \times 10^{-2} = 0.01(\text{in. to cms})/(\text{units per in.})$$
$$= 0.01(2.540005)/(20).$$

The 0.01 eliminates the sign and decimal point.

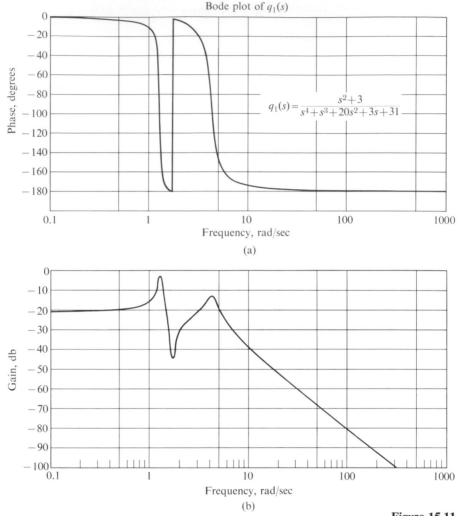

Bode plot of $q_1(s)$

$$q_1(s) = \frac{s^2+3}{s^4+s^3+20s^2+3s+31}$$

(a)

(b)

Figure 15.11.1

2) PHASE $=$ (THETA $+$ 560)(0.63500125 $\times$ 10^{-3}). The plotting origin is at -560 level, and

$$0.63500125 \times 10^{-3} = 0.01(2.540005)/(40).$$

3) OMEGA $=$ (0.43429448)[log$_e$ ω $-$ log$_e$ PS](6.35000125 $\times$ 10^{-2}). Thus

$$6.35000125 \times 10^{-2} = 0.01(2.540005)/(0.4).$$

Example. In the example of Section 15.2 two transfer functions, $q_1(s)$ and $q_2(s)$, were obtained (15.2.24 and 15.2.25). The Bode plot of $q_1(s)$ is shown in Fig. 15.11.1 and of $q_2(s)$ is shown in Fig. 15.11.2. The system roots (roots of

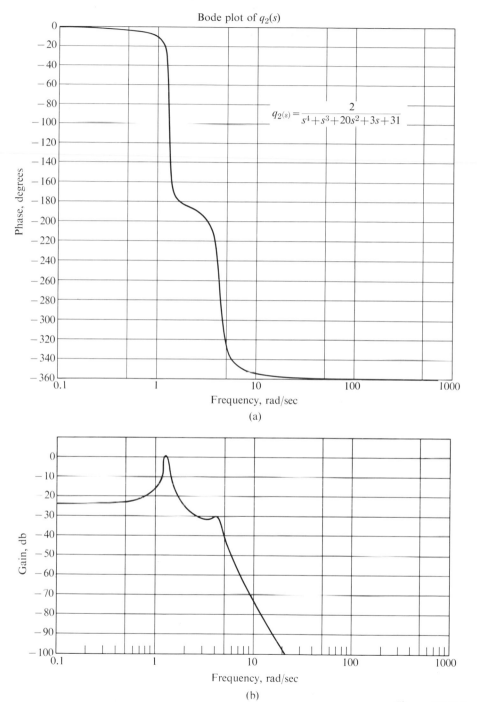

Bode plot of $q_2(s)$

$$q_{2(s)} = \frac{2}{s^4 + s^3 + 20s^2 + 3s + 31}$$

(a)

(b)

Figure 15.11.2

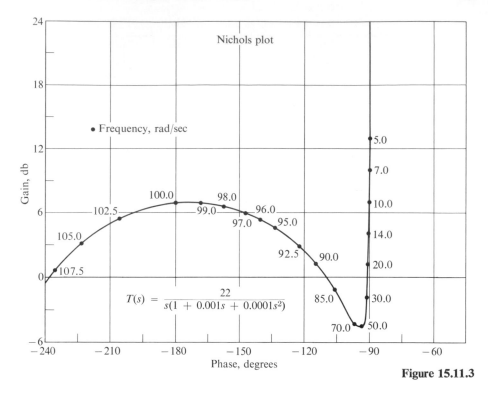

Figure 15.11.3

denominator) of $q_1(s)$ and $q_2(s)$ are

$$s = -0.0393 \pm i1.3036 \quad \text{and} \quad s = -0.46069 \pm i4.2444.$$

The influence of the system roots may be noticed as two peaks in the gain curve at the two frequencies, 1.3036 rad/sec and 4.2444 rad/sec. A pure imaginary root in the numerator of $q_1(s)$ gives a zero response (gain $= -\infty$ db) at a frequency of 1.7321 rad/sec.

b) *Nichols plot*. These plots are made on "6 by 6 to the inch" rectangular paper. Gain in decibels on a vertical axis is plotted against phase in degrees on a horizontal axis. Each point on the gain-phase curve is plotted and labeled with its corresponding value of frequency. Figure 15.11.3 is a Nichols plot for the transfer function

$$T(s) = \frac{22}{s(1 + 0.001s + 0.0001s^2)}.$$

15.12 STATIC AND ROOT LOCUS GAIN CONSTANTS

There are two constants which may be of interest to engineers. They are the root locus gain constant and the static gain constant.

If the transfer function is written in the form

$$T(s) = \frac{P(s)}{Q(s)} = \frac{a_m(s - s_{z1})(s - s_{z2}) \cdots (s - s_{zm})}{a_n(s - s_{p1})(s - s_{p2}) \cdots (s - s_{pn})}$$

$$= k \frac{(s - s_{z1})(s - s_{z2}) \cdots (s - s_{zm})}{(s - s_{p1})(s - s_{p2}) \cdots (s - s_{pn})}, \qquad (15.12.1)$$

then k is the root locus gain constant.

If the above form is further written as

$$T(s) = \frac{k\Pi_{i=1}^{m} s_{zi} \ (s/s_{z1} - 1)(s/s_{z2} - 1) \cdots (s/s_{zm} - 1)}{\Pi_{j=1}^{n} s_{pj} \ (s/s_{p1} - 1)(s/s_{p2} - 1) \cdots (s/s_{pn} - 1)}, \qquad (15.12.2)$$

then

$$k' = \frac{k\Pi_{i=1}^{m} s_{zi}}{\Pi_{j=1}^{n} s_{pj}} \qquad (15.12.3)$$

is the static gain constant.

15.13 THE ROOT LOCUS CURVE FROM TRANSFER FUNCTIONS

If a given transfer function is written in the modified form

$$\overline{T}(s) = \frac{s^m + \bar{a}_{m-1}s^{m-1} + \cdots + \bar{a}_0}{s^n + \bar{a}_{n-1}s^{n-1} + \cdots + a_0} = \frac{\overline{P}(s)}{\overline{Q}(s)}, \qquad (15.13.1)$$

the root locus equation is

$$\overline{Q}(s) + K\overline{P}(s) = 0, \qquad 0 \leq K \leq \infty. \qquad (15.13.2)$$

As the gain parameter K is assigned different values, each of the corresponding nth-degree polynomials is solved for its n roots. Each of the n roots will trace a locus. If any of the n branches of the root locus touches the imaginary axis, the system becomes unstable for that value of K.

In practice, there are two methods of choosing the values of K. An initial value K_0 and a maximum value $K_{\max}$ are designated. The intermediate values are chosen as spaced equally by using

$$K_i = K_0 + i \Delta K, \qquad i = 0, 1, 2, \ldots, \qquad (15.13.3)$$

or as spaced in an arithmetic progression by using

$$K_{i+1} = K_0 + 2^i \Delta K, \qquad i = 0, 1, 2, \ldots \qquad (15.13.4)$$

These intermediate values are used successively in the root locus equation until $K_{\max}$ is reached or until the system becomes unstable.

15.14 SUPPLEMENTARY REFERENCES

A more extensive treatment of transfer function analysis may be found in Karman and Biot [83], Scott [137], Timoshenko [148], Oldenburger [115], Duncan and Collar [38] and [39], Pipes [125], and

a) E. T. WHITTAKER, *Treatise on the Analytical Dynamics of Particles and Rigid Bodies*, Cambridge University Press, Cambridge, 1959.

b) G. S. BROWN and D. P. CAMPBELL, *Principles of Servomechanisms*, Wiley, New York, 1948.

c) A. T. FULLER, "Stability Criteria for Linear Systems . . . ," *Proc. Camb. Phil. Soc.* **53** (1957), 878–885.

EXERCISES

1. Find the transfer functions $q_1(s)$, $q_2(s)$, and $q_3(s)$, of the following system of differential equations:

$$\ddot{q}_1(t) + \ddot{q}_2(t) + \dot{q}_3(t) - q_2(t) = t^2,$$
$$\ddot{q}_2(t) - \ddot{q}_3(t) + \dot{q}_2(t) + q_1(t) = 1,$$
$$\ddot{q}_3(t) - \ddot{q}_1(t) + \dot{q}_1(t) + q_2(t) + q_3(t) = t,$$
$$q_1(0) = q_2(0) = q_3(0) = 0,$$
$$\dot{q}_1(0) = \dot{q}_2(0) = \dot{q}_3(0) = 0.$$

2. Find the time response function for the transfer function

$$T(s) = \frac{s^2 + 7s + 44}{s^3 + 8s^2 + 37s + 50}.$$

3. Find the time response function for the transfer function

$$T(s) = \frac{(5 + 2\sqrt{3})s^2 + (14 + 6\sqrt{3})s + (59 + 4\sqrt{3})}{s^3 + 5s^2 + 17s + 13}.$$

4. Find the time response function for the transfer function

$$T(s) = \frac{1}{s^3 + 2s^2 + 2s}.$$

5. Find the frequency response function, the expression for the gain, and the expression for the phase from the transfer function

$$T(s) = \frac{1}{s^3 + 2s^2 + 2s}.$$

CHAPTER 16

PARTIAL DIFFERENTIAL EQUATIONS

16.1 INTRODUCTION

A partial differential equation (PDE) is a relation among some of the derivatives of a function of more than one variable. A PDE may be classified according to the number of independent variables, the order of the highest derivative, the algebraic nature of the equation, and the type of auxiliary conditions which must be imposed to produce a well-posed problem. The order of a PDE is that of the highest ordered derivative appearing in the equation. A PDE is linear, quasilinear, or nonlinear according as the equation is linear in the dependent variable and its derivatives, linear in the highest ordered derivatives, or not linear in the highest ordered derivatives. A linear PDE may have constant coefficients.

Whether or not a problem is well posed is closely connected with the nature of certain surfaces, called characteristic surfaces, which are associated with the PDE. According to Hadamard [64] a problem is well posed if its solution exists, is unique, and depends continuously on the auxiliary conditions.

Any attempt to give a complete coverage of partial differential equations in one chapter would be presumptuous. One could spend an unlimited amount of time in the study of classical partial differential equations, analytical methods of solution, and stability and convergence criteria. The amount of material found in the literature is voluminous. This chapter gives only the briefest introduction to well-posed problems and the classification of partial differential equations with most of the emphasis on finite difference methods and the numerical solution of the various classes.

16.2 EXAMPLES OF WELL-POSED PROBLEMS

Some problems from classical physics which are well posed are

a) *Dirichlet's problem* for Laplace's equation. The deflection of a circular membrane is this type of problem. The PDE and its associated conditions are

$$\frac{\partial^2 u}{\partial x^2} + \frac{\partial^2 u}{\partial y^2} = 0, \qquad x^2 + y^2 < 1 \qquad (16.2.1)$$

with

$$u = f(x, y), \qquad x^2 + y^2 = 1. \qquad (16.2.2)$$

We write the PDE in (16.2.1) as

$$u_{xx} + u_{yy} = 0, \qquad x^2 + y^2 < 1, \qquad (16.2.3)$$

which is a more compact and convenient form.

b) *Cauchy's problem*, or an initial-value problem, for the wave equation. The problem of elastic vibrations of a long rod is one of this type. The PDE and the associated initial conditions are

$$u_{xx} - u_{yy} = 0 \qquad \text{for } t > 0 \qquad (16.2.4)$$

and

$$u(x, 0) = f(x), \qquad u_t(x, 0) = g(x). \qquad (16.2.5)$$

c) *Initial-value problem* for the diffusion equation. Temperature distribution in a long rod is an example of this. The PDE and associated initial conditions are

$$u_t - u_{xx} = 0 \qquad \text{for } t > 0 \qquad (16.2.6)$$

and

$$u(x, 0) = f(x). \qquad (16.2.7)$$

16.3 CLASSIFICATION OF PARTIAL DIFFERENTIAL EQUATIONS

We now consider the fundamental classification of quasilinear PDE of the second order in two independent variables into parabolic, elliptic, and hyperbolic types. The general equation has the form

$$a \frac{\partial^2 u}{\partial x^2} + b \frac{\partial^2 u}{\partial x \, \partial y} + c \frac{\partial^2 u}{\partial y^2} = d, \qquad (16.3.1)$$

where a, b, c, and d are functions of u, $\partial u/\partial x$, $\partial u/\partial y$, x, and y, but are not functions of the second derivatives.

We adopt the standard notation with

$$p = \frac{\partial u}{\partial x}, \qquad q = \frac{\partial u}{\partial y}, \qquad r = \frac{\partial^2 u}{\partial x^2},$$
$$s = \frac{\partial^2 u}{\partial x \, \partial y}, \qquad t = \frac{\partial^2 u}{\partial y^2}. \qquad (16.3.2)$$

Then Eq. (16.3.1) becomes

$$ar + bs + ct = d. \qquad (16.3.3)$$

Assume that we are given a curve in the (x, y)-plane and values of u, p, and q at all points on that curve. Assume also that these satisfy the relation

$$du = \frac{\partial u}{\partial x} dx + \frac{\partial u}{\partial y} dy = p \, dx + q \, dy \qquad (16.3.4)$$

along the curve. Otherwise, p and q could not be derivatives of u. Assuming the values of u, p, and q on the curve, together with the requirement that u satisfy the differential equation, we determine r, s, and t on the curve. We must have

$$dp = r\,dx + s\,dy \tag{16.3.5}$$

and

$$dq = s\,dx + t\,dy. \tag{16.3.6}$$

Equations (16.3.3), (16.3.5), and (16.3.6) form a set of three linear equations in the three unknowns r, s, and t. In general, there exists one solution, so that unique values of the second derivatives are determined at each point of the curve. If the determinant of the coefficients of r, s, and t vanishes at any point, that is, if

$$\begin{vmatrix} a & b & c \\ dx & dy & 0 \\ 0 & dx & dy \end{vmatrix} = 0, \tag{16.3.7}$$

then the system of linear equations has no solution for that point. Expanding the above determinant, we have

$$a(dy)^2 - b\,dx\,dy + c(dx)^2 = 0, \tag{16.3.8}$$

which is a quadratic equation in dy/dx. For a point (x, y) associated with the given values of u, p, and q, then, according as b^2 is greater than, equal to, or less than $4ac$, there will be two directions for which (16.3.8) is satisfied, one direction or no possible direction respectively.

If we have a region in the (x, y)-plane in which u, p, and q are defined, and if $b^2 > 4ac$ at each point in that region, then the differential equation is said to be hyperbolic in that region. Similarly, if $b^2 = 4ac$ throughout the region, the equation is said to be parabolic, and if $b^2 < 4ac$, the equation is said to be elliptic.

It is important to observe that the class to which the equation belongs may be dependent upon the solution. For example, the equation

$$\frac{\partial^2 u}{\partial x^2} + u\frac{\partial^2 u}{\partial y^2} = 0 \tag{16.3.9}$$

is elliptic in any region over which the solution u is positive, and hyperbolic in any region over which the solution is negative. If the equation is linear, that is, if a, b, and c are functions of x and y or constants only, then for a given region in the (x, y)-plane, the class of the differential equation is independent of the solution and can be determined in advance. For example, the equation

$$(1 + x^2)\frac{\partial u^2}{\partial x^2} + (1 + y^2)\frac{\partial^2 u}{\partial y^2} = 0 \tag{16.3.10}$$

is always elliptic, and the equation

$$\frac{\partial^2 u}{\partial x^2} + (1 - x^2 - y^2)\frac{\partial^2 u}{\partial y^2} = 0 \tag{16.3.11}$$

is elliptic inside the unit circle and hyperbolic outside.

16.4 FINITE DIFFERENCE METHODS, CONVERGENCE, AND STABILITY

As in the case of ordinary differential equations, the basis of the finite difference method is the replacement of all derivatives in the differential problem by finite difference quotients to obtain a finite difference problem which approximates the solution of the differential problem at a finite set of grid points of a mesh. The difference problem is said to be a consistent approximation of the differential problem if the difference quotients converge to the corresponding derivatives, as the mesh is refined, for every function having continuous derivatives of sufficiently high order.

We can obtain some notion of how well a difference equation approximates a differential equation by replacing the independent variables in the difference equation by a Taylor expansion about a mesh point, subtracting the differential equation from the difference equation, and examining the remainder. For a consistent approximation, the remainder must vanish as the mesh is refined.

Let u be the exact solution of a well-posed differential problem, $\bar{u}$ the exact solution of a consistent difference problem, and u^* the numerical solution of the difference problem. The truncation, or discretization, error is

$$e_d = u - \bar{u}. \tag{16.4.1}$$

The roundoff error, or departure, is

$$e_r = \bar{u} - u^*. \tag{16.4.2}$$

The total error is then

$$e = u - u^* = e_d + e_r. \tag{16.4.3}$$

The solution of the difference problem is said to converge to the solution of the differential problem if $e_d \to 0$ as the mesh is appropriately refined.

The difference problem is said to be stable, subject to appropriate mesh restrictions, if e_r does not grow too rapidly as the mesh is refined. Since, generally, e_d tends to decrease and e_r to increase as the mesh is refined, it is natural to expect a mesh refinement to exist which minimizes the total error.

In PDE the question of stability usually arises when one coordinate direction, such as time, is somehow different from the remaining directions, such as space. This situation is usually associated with the presence of characteristic curves or surfaces, and is generally not encountered in dealing with elliptic equations. Elliptic equations generally describe stationary phenomena, that is, partial derivatives with respect to time do not occur.

Typical problems for parabolic and hyperbolic equations are the initial-value or the mixed initial-value and boundary-value problems. The finite difference equations consistent with these problems are generally solved by a marching technique, that is, having the solution for all space mesh points at a given time level, one proceeds to obtain the solution for all space mesh points at the next time level, etc. As a passing note, computer storage requirements are not likely to be as severe for these problems, as for equal dimensioned boundary-value problems for elliptic equations.

Difference equations are explicit if the solution at each time level is expressed in terms of the solution at preceding time levels only; otherwise, the difference equations are implicit. Implicit equations are generally stable since the instability in the direction of increasing time is balanced out by the stability in the direction of decreasing time.

We may summarize the general notion of stability with the following comments. A difference equation is weakly stable if the departure resulting from an error, such as roundoff, introduced at a single mesh point does not grow too rapidly. A difference equation is strongly stable if the cumulative departure caused by all errors does not grow too rapidly. Suppose, as a computation proceeds, an error is introduced at each mesh point. Let b be a bound on the magnitude of these errors and let h be the mesh size. A difference equation is called stable if the cumulative departure goes to zero with b and does not grow faster than some power of h^{-1} as h goes to zero.

The departure may grow exponentially, for instance, in time, as a consequence of the solution's exhibiting a similar growth. This probably should not be, but sometimes is, interpreted as instability. Consider, for example, the differential problem,

$$\dot{u} = u, \qquad u(0) = 1,$$

with solution $u = e^t$. The departure for the difference approximation,

$$\bar{u}(t + h) - \bar{u}(t) = -h\bar{u}(t), \qquad \bar{u}(0) = 1,$$

is bounded by

$$\frac{b}{h}[e^t(1 + h) - 1],$$

and so the relative departure is small as long as b/h is small.

A type of instability frequently results when the difference equation is of higher order than the differential equation. Often it is not as serious as the type of instability caused by errors introduced at each mesh point, but it can be disastrous. For example, for the differential problem

$$\dot{u} = -u, \qquad u(0) = u_0,$$

the departure of the approximating difference problem,

$$\bar{u}(t + h) - 2\bar{u}(t) + \bar{u}(t - h) = h^2\bar{u}(t), \qquad \bar{u}(0) = u_0, \qquad \bar{u}(h) = u(h) + b,$$

due to the single error at $t = h$ is approximately

$$\frac{b}{2}[e^{-t} - (-1)^{t/h}e^t].$$

Lax and Richtmyer call a difference equation stable if the solution $\bar{u}(x, t)$ corresponding to an initial function $f(x)$ satisfies a boundedness relation of the form

$$|\bar{u}(x, t)| \leqq M(t)|f(x)|, \qquad 0 \leqq t \leqq T,$$

where M is independent of h. This condition is considerably stronger than that when errors are introduced at each mesh point. It is, in fact, equivalent to convergence.

16.5 NUMERICAL SOLUTION OF PARABOLIC EQUATIONS

We may write a general linear second-order equation of the parabolic class as

$$L[u(x, t)] \equiv u_t - a(x, t)u_{xx} - 2b(x, t)u_x + c(x, t)u = d(x, t), \quad (16.5.1)$$

where $a(x, t) > 0$, subject to the initial condition

$$u(x, 0) = f(x), \qquad 0 < x < L, \tag{16.5.2}$$

and the boundary conditions

$$u(0, t) = g_0(t), \qquad u(L, t) = g_1(t), \qquad t > 0. \tag{16.5.3}$$

The problem is to determine u in the region

$$R[0 \leq x \leq L; 0 \leq t \leq T]. \tag{16.5.4}$$

This problem has a unique solution.

We shall consider the same problem but with the simpler equation

$$L[u(x, t)] \equiv u_t - a(x, t)u_{xx} = d(x, t). \tag{16.5.5}$$

The central ideas can still be illustrated. The statement and proof of the main tool, the maximum principle, is somewhat simplified. This equation differs from the heat conduction equation, $u_t - u_{xx} = 0$, only slightly. The right-hand side $d(x, t)$ may be thought of as a heat source. It will be useful in establishing convergence. The coefficient of u_{xx}, $a(x, t)$, may be thought of as expressing an inhomogeneity in space and time of the thermal properties of the material. The slight complication introduced by taking this coefficient other than 1 is justified, as it illustrates a use of the hypothesis $a > 0$.

On R we place a net (grid, lattice, mesh)

$$R_{hk}[x_j = jh, j = 0(1)(L/h); t_n = nk, n = 0(1)(T/k)], \tag{16.5.6}$$

and use the conventional notation,

$$f(x_j, t_n) \equiv f_j^n. \tag{16.5.7}$$

We extend the definition of functions defined only on net points by linear interpolation

$$f(x_j, t_n + \theta k) \equiv f_j^{n+\theta} \equiv \theta f_j^{n+1} + (1 - \theta)f_j^n, \qquad 0 \leq \theta \leq 1. \tag{16.5.8}$$

By Taylor's formula

$$u_t(x_j, t_n + \theta k) = (1/k)(u_j^{n+1} - u_j^n) + \tau_t, \tag{16.5.9}$$

where

$$\tau_t = \frac{1 - 2\theta}{2} k\bar{u}_{tt} + \frac{1 - 3\theta + 3\theta^2}{6} k^2 \bar{u}_{ttt}. \tag{16.5.10}$$

Also,

$$u_{xx}(x_j, t_n + \theta k) = (1/h^2)(u_{j+1}^{n+\theta} - 2u_j^{n+\theta} + u_{j-1}^{n+\theta}) + \tau_{xx}, \tag{16.5.11}$$

where

$$\tau_{xx} = \frac{h^2}{12}\left[\bar{u}_{xxxx} + \frac{\theta(1 - \theta)}{2} k^2 \bar{u}_{xxxxtt}\right]. \tag{16.5.12}$$

The calculations are elementary but rather tedious. Therefore, we do only the first:

$$u(x_j, t_{n+1}) = u(x_j, t_n + \theta k) + u_t(x_j, t_n + \theta k)(1 - \theta)k$$

$$+ u_{tt}(x_j, t_n + \theta k)\frac{(1 - \theta)^2 k^2}{2!} + \bar{u}_{ttt}\frac{(1 - \theta)^3 k^3}{3!}, \tag{16.5.13}$$

and

$$u(x_j, t_n) = u(x_j, t_n + \theta k) - u_t(x_j, t_n + \theta k)\theta k$$

$$+ u_{tt}(x_j, t_n + \theta k)\frac{\theta^2 k^2}{2!} - u_{ttt}^*\frac{\theta^3 k^3}{3!}. \tag{16.5.14}$$

Subtracting the second equation from the first and dividing by k, we have

$$\frac{u(x_j, t_{n+1}) - u(x_j, t_n)}{k} = u_t(x_j, t_n + \theta k) + \tau_t, \tag{16.5.15}$$

where

$$\tau_t = k\left[\frac{(1 - \theta)^2}{2!} - \frac{\theta^2}{2!}\right]u_{tt}(x_j, t_n + \theta k)$$

$$+ k^2\left[\frac{(1 - \theta)^3}{3!}\bar{u}_{ttt} + \frac{\theta^3}{3!}u_{ttt}^*\right]$$

or

$$\tau_k = k\frac{1 - 2\theta}{2}u_{tt} + \frac{1 - 3\theta + 3\theta^2}{6}k^2\bar{u}_{ttt}, \tag{16.5.16}$$

since $[(1 - \theta)^3/3!]\bar{u}_{ttt} + (\theta^3/3!)u_{ttt}^*$ lies between $[(1 - 3\theta + 3\theta^2)/6]\bar{u}_{ttt}$ and $[(1 - 3\theta + 3\theta^2)/6]u_{ttt}^*$.

We now define a finite difference operator on R_{hk}. If we write

$$kL_{h,k}[v(x_j, t_n + \theta k)] \equiv v_j^{n+1} - v_j^n$$

$$- \lambda a_j^{n+\theta}(v_{j+1}^{n+\theta} - 2v_j^{n+\theta} + v_{j-1}^{n+\theta}) = k\, d_j^{n+\theta}, \tag{16.5.17}$$

where

$$\lambda = \frac{k}{h^2}, \tag{16.5.18}$$

the operator $L_{h,k}$ is obtained by replacing the derivatives in L by the finite difference approximations obtained above.

We observe that the truncation error,

$$L[u] - L_{h,k}[u] = \tau_t - a\tau_{xx} = 0(k) + 0(h^2),\tag{16.5.19}$$

vanishes as $k \to 0$, $h \to 0$. The operator $L_{h,k}$ is, therefore, a consistent approximation to the operator L. We also observe that the truncation error becomes

$$0(k^2) + 0(h^2)\tag{16.5.20}$$

for the so-called Crank-Nicholson [24] approximation which results from taking

$$\theta = \tfrac{1}{2}.\tag{16.5.21}$$

The difference equations

$$L_{h,k}[v_j^{n+\theta}] = k\,d_j^{n+\theta}\tag{16.5.22}$$

are explicit if $\theta = 0$, as they are immediately solved for v_j^{n+1}. Any choice of $\theta \neq 0$ yields an implicit system of equations for v_j^{n+1} of the general form

$$\alpha_j v_{j-1}^{n+1} + \beta_j v_j^{n+1} + \gamma_j v_{j+1}^{n+1} = S_j^n,\tag{16.5.23}$$

where S_j^n involves only known or previously computed quantities. The finite difference problem is completed by replacing the boundary and initial conditions by

$$v_j^0 = f(x_j), \qquad v_0^n = g(t_n), \qquad v_{L/h}^n = g_1(t_n).\tag{16.5.24}$$

The equations can be written in the matrix form

$$Av = s,\tag{16.5.25}$$

where A is of tridiagonal form or band matrix of width 3. The system of linear equations which constitutes the finite difference problem has a unique solution as a direct consequence of the maximum principle.

16.6 THE MAXIMUM PRINCIPLE

For every net $R_{h,k}$ such that

$$(1 - \theta)\lambda \leq 1/2a,\tag{16.6.1}$$

we have

$$\max_j |v_j^n| \leq \max_{\substack{j \\ 0 \leq t \leq t_n}} [|g_0(t)|, |g_1(t)|, |f(x_j)|] + t_n \max_{\substack{j \\ 0 \leq t \leq t_n}} |d(x_j, t)|.\tag{16.6.2}$$

To show this, let

$$V(t_n) \equiv \max_j |v_j^n|, \quad G(t_n) = \max_{0 \leq t \leq t_n} [|g_0(t)|, |g_1(t)|],$$

$$D(t_n) = \max_{\substack{j \\ 0 \leq t \leq t_n}} |d(x_j, t)|.\tag{16.6.3}$$

For $j = 1(1)(L/h) - 1$, the difference equation is written

$$(1 + 2\lambda a_j^{n+\theta}\theta)v_j^{n+1} = v_j^n + \lambda a_j^{n+\theta}\theta[v_{j+1}^{n+1} + v_{j-1}^{n+1}] + k\,d_j^{n+1}.\tag{16.6.4}$$

Now, since $(1 - \theta)\lambda \leq 1/2a$, $a > 0$, we have

$$V(t_{n+1}) \leq V(t_n) + kD(t_{n+1}), \tag{16.6.5}$$

or, for $j = 0(1)L/h$, and reducing n by 1 for convenience, we have

$$V(t_n) \leq \max [G(t_n), V(t_{n-1})] + kD(t_n). \tag{16.6.6}$$

The maximum principle follows, by n applications of this formula. For example, taking $n = 2$, we have

$$V(t_2) \leq \max [G(t_2), V(t_1)] + kD(t_2). \tag{16.6.7}$$

Also,

$$V(t_1) \leq \max [G(t_1), V(t_0)] + kD(t_1). \tag{16.6.8}$$

Therefore,

$$V(t_2) \leq \max [G(t_2), V(t_0)] + 2kD(t_2), \tag{16.6.9}$$

and so,

$$V(t_2) \leq \max_{\substack{j \\ 0 \leq t \leq t_2}} [|g_0(t)|, |g_1(t)|, |f(x_j)|] + t_2 \max_{\substack{j \\ 0 < t \leq t_2}} |d(x_j, t)|. \tag{16.6.10}$$

The maximum principle shows that the only solution for a net satisfying

$$g_0(t) \equiv g_1(t) \equiv f(x_j) \equiv d(x_j, t) = 0 \tag{16.6.11}$$

is $v_j^n \equiv 0$. The fundamental theorem on linear systems then implies that the inhomogeneous equations have a unique solution.

16.7 CONVERGENCE AND STABILITY

The discretization error is

$$e_j^n = u(x_j, t_n) - v_j^n. \tag{16.7.1}$$

The solution of the finite difference problem is said to converge to the solution of the differential problem if

$$\lim_{h,k \to 0} |e_j^n| = 0. \tag{16.7.2}$$

Now,

$$0 = L[u(x_j, t_n + \theta k)] - L_{h,k}[v_j^{n+\theta}]$$
$$= L[u(x_j, t_n + \theta k)] - L_{h,k}[u_j^{n+\theta}] + L_{h,k}[u_j^{n+\theta}] - L_{h,k}[v_j^{n+\theta}], \tag{16.7.3}$$

and so

$$L_{h,k}[e_j^{n+\theta}] = -\tau_j^{n+\theta}, \tag{16.7.4}$$

where

$$\tau_j^{n+\theta} = \tau_t - a\tau_{xx} \tag{16.7.5}$$

is the truncation error.

Thus, by the maximum principle,

$$|e_j^n| \leq t_n \max_{j,n} |\tau_j^{n+\theta}|, \tag{16.7.6}$$

and the convergence is assured.

Stability in the sense of Lax and Richtmyer also follows from the maximum principle. Take

$$M(t) = 1 + \frac{t|d|}{|f|}.$$ (16.7.7)

Convergence and stability here are equivalent. The hypothesis of the maximum principle is automatically satisfied for $\theta = 1$.

Introducing a roundoff error $\rho_j^{n+\theta}$ in each equation, we obtain a bound on the total error by replacing

$$\max_{j,n} |\tau_j^{n+\theta}|$$ (16.7.8)

by

$$\max_{j,n} (|\rho_j^{n+\theta}| + |\tau_j^{n+\theta}|).$$ (16.7.9)

Thus there is usually little advantage to be gained by taking the truncation error much smaller than the roundoff error.

16.8 NUMERICAL SOLUTION OF ELLIPTIC EQUATIONS

We will consider the differential problem of finding a function u which satisfies the linear second-order differential equation of elliptic type

$$L[u] \equiv au_{xx} + 2bu_{xy} + cu_{yy} + du_x + eu_y + fu = g$$ (16.8.1)

in the region R, and the linear boundary condition

$$u = \gamma$$ (16.8.2)

on the boundary B of R.

We use the following abbreviations for the points of a rectangular net and their separations as shown in Fig. 16.8.1.

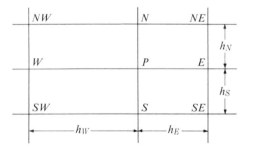

Figure 16.8.1

Let I_x, I_y, and I_{xy} denote the interval $W - E$, the interval $S - N$, and the rectangle $SW - SE - NE - NW$ respectively. Let $M_k(I)$ denote the least-upper bound of all derivatives of u of order k on I. All derivatives appearing in a given statement are assumed continuous on I. We shall now proceed to present some useful formulas for replacement of derivatives by finite differences.

a) $u_x(P) = \dfrac{h_W h_E^{-1}[u(E) - u(P)] + h_E h_W^{-1}[u(P) - u(W)]}{h_W + h_E} + R_x(P),$ (16.8.3)

where $|R_x(P)| \leq \frac{1}{6}h^2 M_3(I_x),\ h = \max(h_W, h_E)$. If $h_W = h_E$, then

$$u_x(P) = \frac{u(E) - u(W)}{2h} + R_x(P).$$ (16.8.4)

b) $u_{xx}(P) = \dfrac{h_E^{-1}[u(E) - u(P)] - h_W^{-1}[u(P) - u(W)]}{(h_W + h_E)/2} + R_{xx}(P),$ (16.8.5)

where

$$|R_{xx}(P)| \leq \tfrac{1}{3}hM_3(I_x) + \tfrac{1}{12}h^2 M_4(I_x), \qquad h = \max(h_W, h_E). \quad (16.8.6)$$

If $h_W = h_E$, then

$$u_{xx}(P) = \frac{u(W) - 2u(P) + u(E)}{h^2} + R'_{xx}(P),$$ (16.8.7)

where $|R'_{xx}(P)| \leq \frac{1}{12}h^2 M_4(I_x),\ h = h_W = h_E$.

c) $u_{xy}(P) = \dfrac{u(NE) - u(NW) + u(SW) - u(SE)}{4h^2} + R_{xy}(P),$ (16.8.8)

where $|R_{xy}(P)| \leq \frac{1}{3}h^2 M_4(I_{xy}),\ h = h_W = h_E = h_N = h_S$.

The advantage of using a square net is evident from the simplified form of the formulas obtained. Similar formulas are also obtained for u_y and u_{yy}.

Replacing the various derivatives in $L[u]$ by the above finite difference approximations yields a consistent difference operator

$$L_h[v(P)] \equiv h^2 \sum_Q A(P, Q)v(Q), \quad Q = P,\ N,\ E,\ NE,\ \text{etc.,}$$ (16.8.9)

where

$$
\begin{aligned}
A(P, P) &= -2a - 2c + fh^2, & A(P, NE) &= \tfrac{1}{2}b, \\
A(P, E) &= a - \tfrac{1}{2}hd, & A(P, NW) &= -\tfrac{1}{2}b, \\
A(P, W) &= a - \tfrac{1}{2}hd, & A(P, SW) &= \tfrac{1}{2}b, \\
A(P, N) &= c + \tfrac{1}{2}he, & A(P, SE) &= -\tfrac{1}{2}b, \\
A(P, S) &= c - \tfrac{1}{2}he.
\end{aligned}
$$

If all Q lie in R or on B, then P is called an interior net point and

$$L_n[v(P)] = g(P)$$ (16.8.10)

is called a body equation. The truncation error is $0(h^2)$ for any four-times continuously differentiable function in I_{xy}.

16.9 BOUNDARY EQUATIONS FOR ELLIPTIC PROBLEMS

If all net points lie either in R or on B, there will be no special boundary equations. However, if Q is a point of B, it is sometimes worthwhile to take $v(Q)$ equal to the average of u in the vicinty of Q.

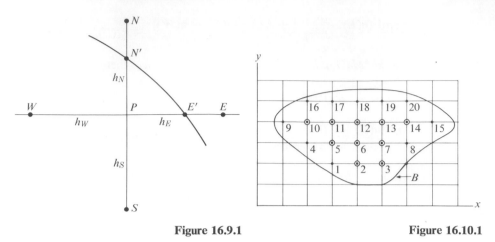

Figure 16.9.1   **Figure 16.10.1**

On the other hand, consider the situation illustrated by Fig. 16.9.1. Here we have taken $b = 0$ in order to simplify L_h to the so-called five-point star point pattern. We could use the approximations given in Section 16.8 with appropriate point spacings, $h_W = h_S = h$, h_E, h_N. This, however, has an adverse effect on the truncation error. A better procedure would seem to be to use a special boundary equation with truncation error $0(h^2)$. Such an equation is provided by linear interpolation,

$$v(P) = \frac{hu(N') + h_N v(S)}{h + h_N},\tag{16.9.1}$$

or the more symmetric formula

$$v(P) = \frac{1}{2}\left[\frac{hu(N') + h_N v(S)}{h + h_N} + \frac{hu(E') + h_E v(W)}{h + h_E}\right].\tag{16.9.2}$$

16.10 MATRIX FORM OF THE FINITE DIFFERENCE PROBLEM

In order to illustrate how the finite difference problem is put into matrix form, we consider Fig. 16.10.1. Here a square net has been placed over the region R to obtain R_h, the set of all modal points in R. The set R_h contains 20 points (generally this number will be considerably larger). Next, some ordering is placed on the points. The ordering indicated in the figure is not only a natural choice, but is also consistent (a property of orderings we will discuss in connection with the properties of A). The points of R_h we now designate by P_i, $i = 1(1)20$.

Now assume $b = 0$ so that the basic point pattern is the five-point star. In the figure there are 10 circled points each of which has the property that all points of the point pattern lie in R or on B. These points are called interior net points. The remaining 10 points are called boundary net points. The set R_k is called connected because it cannot be divided into two nonempty sets such that neither set contains a point whose point pattern involves points of the other set.

For each interior net point we can write a body equation, and for each boundary net point we can write a boundary equation. Thus with each point there is associated an equation. It will be useful to think of these equations as being ordered by the point ordering. We write this system of equations as the single matrix equation

$$Av = B, \tag{16.10.1}$$

where A is a known square matrix of order N, and v is the column vector

$$v = \begin{bmatrix} v_1 \\ v_2 \\ \vdots \\ v_N \end{bmatrix}, \qquad v_i = v(P_i). \tag{16.10.2}$$

Here N is the number of points in R_h (20 in the figure), and B is a known column vector. Two properties of A are: (1) N becomes large as the net is refined, and (2) A is sparse, that is, it contains a large number of zeros. These properties generally recommend the use of indirect, iterative, methods over direct (e.g., Gauss elimination) methods for solving the matrix equation. We now consider some other important properties of A.

The system of difference equations $Av = B$ was formed in such a way that

a) A has diagonal dominance (Section 8.10) and is of positive type if $b = 0$, $f/a \leqq 0$, h small.

b) A is not reducible if R_h is connected.

c) A is symmetric, that is, $a_{ij} = a_{ji}$, only if a, b, c are constant and $d = e = 0$. That A has diagonal dominance if $b = 0$ is shown as follows. With like interchanges of rows and columns, A can be put in matrix tridiagonal form, that is, if there exist a permutation matrix P such that

$$PAP^t = \begin{bmatrix} D_1 & F_1 & \cdots & & 0 \\ E_1 & D_2 & F_2 & \cdots & 0 \\ \vdots & & & & \vdots \\ 0 & & \cdots & & D_m \end{bmatrix}, \tag{16.10.3}$$

where the D_i are square diagonal matrices. Let S_j, $j = 1(1)m$, denote the set of elements v_i of v, corresponding to D_j. The elements v_i and v_j are said to be coupled if either $a_{ij} \neq 0$ or $a_{ji} \neq 0$. An order of solving the equations $Av = B$, iteratively, is consistent with the matrix tridiagonal representation of A if, for $j = 2, 3, \ldots, m$ within each cycle of the iteration, each component v_i of S_{j-1} is computed before any component of S_j with which v_i is coupled. An order of solving the equations (ordering of equations) is consistent if there is a tridiagonal representation of A with which it is consistent. Referring to Fig. 16.10.1, take the S_j as the sets of v_i

on the same net diagonal. That is,

$$S_1 = (v_1, v_4, v_9), \qquad S_2 = (v_2, v_5, v_{10}), \qquad S_3 = (v_3, v_6, v_{11}, v_{16}),$$
$$S_4 = (v_7, v_{12}, v_{17}), \qquad S_5 = (v_8, v_{13}, v_{18}), \qquad S_6 = (v_{14}, v_{19}),$$
$$S_7 = (v_{15}, v_{20}). \tag{16.10.4}$$

Observing that the five-point star pattern leaves the v's of each S uncoupled, it is clear that the corresponding D's yield a matrix tridiagonal representation of A, and that the ordering chosen is consistent.

16.11 ITERATIVE SOLUTION OF $Av = B$ FOR ELLIPTIC EQUATIONS

In Section 8.10 we found that the most general linear iteration which leaves the solution $v = A^{-1}B$ invariant is

$$v^{(k)} = H_k v^{(k-1)} + M_k B, \tag{16.11.1}$$

where $H_k + M_k A = I$. We shall consider only stationary iterations, that is, $H_k = H$ and $M_k = M$ are considered independent of k.

Since the error

$$E^{(k)} = v^{(k)} - A^{-1}B \tag{16.11.2}$$

satisfies the iteration

$$E^{(k)} = HE^{(k-1)}, \tag{16.11.3}$$

the iteration will generally converge for an initial error $E^{(0)}$ if and only if $H^{(k)} X \to 0$ for arbitrary X, or equivalently, if and only if the spectral radius, $\bar{\lambda}$ (maximum of the absolute values of the eigenvalues of H) is less than 1. The rate of convergence is defined to be

$$r = -\log \bar{\lambda}. \tag{16.11.4}$$

Roughly speaking, r is the asymptotic average number of "base e digits" by which the error is decreased per iterative step.

In several of the better known iterative methods one writes

$$A = E + D + F, \tag{16.11.5}$$

where E contains the below diagonal elements, D contains the diagonal elements, and F contains the above diagonal elements. All other elements of E, D, and F are zero. We then write the method of simultaneous displacements as

$$Ev^{(k-1)} + Dv^{(k)} + Fv^{(k-1)} = B. \tag{16.11.6}$$

The method of successive displacements, such as the Gauss-Seidel method (Section 8.10), is written

$$Ev^{(k)} + Dv^{(k)} + Fv^{(k-1)} = B. \tag{16.11.7}$$

For these two methods

$$H = -D^{-1}(E + F), \qquad M = D^{-1}, \tag{16.11.8}$$

and

$$H = -(D + E)^{-1}F, \qquad M = (D + E)^{-1} \tag{16.11.9}$$

respectively. If A has diagonal dominance, is of positive type, and is not reducible, both methods converge for all initial vectors $v^{(0)}$. If A is symmetric with positive diagonal elements, then the Gauss-Seidel method converges for all initial vectors $v^{(0)}$, if and only if A is positive definite (Section 7.8).

The rate of convergence of the Gauss-Seidel procedure can sometimes be greatly increased by the method of successive over relaxation. By arguments based on a maximum principle, the discretization error is $0(h^2)$, while the roundoff error (assuming the iteration has converged) is $0(h^{-2})$.

16.12 NUMERICAL SOLUTION OF HYPERBOLIC EQUATIONS

In order to illustrate the relationship between a hyperbolic equation of second order and a system of first-order equations, we start with the problem

$$L \equiv au_{xx} + 2bu_{xy} + cu_{yy} = 0,$$
$$u(x, 0) = \overline{f}(x), \qquad u_y(x, 0) = g(x).$$

(16.12.1)

The second-order equation is hyperbolic when $b^2 - ac > 0$. If a, b, and c do not depend on u, u_{xx}, u_{xy}, and u_{yy}, this problem can be replaced by the equivalent problem

$$L_1 \equiv av_x + bw_x + bv_y + cv_y = 0,$$
$$L_2 \equiv v_y - w_x = 0,$$

(16.12.2)

with

$$v(x, 0) = d\overline{f}(x)/dx = f(x), \quad w(x, 0) = g(x).$$

That is,

$$v = u_x \qquad \text{and} \qquad w = u_y.$$

(16.12.3)

We shall consider the second problem.

Let

$$L = \lambda_1 L_1 + \lambda_2 L_2$$

$$= \lambda_1 a \left[v_x + \frac{\lambda_1 b + \lambda_2}{\lambda_1 a} v_y \right] + (\lambda_1 b - \lambda_2) \left[w_x + \frac{\lambda_1 c}{\lambda_1 b - \lambda_2} w_y \right].$$

(16.12.4)

Along a curve

$$C: y = y(x),$$

(16.12.5)

v and w can be considered as functions of x, and so

$$\frac{d}{dx} v[x, y(x)] = v_x + \frac{dy}{dx} v_y,$$

(16.12.6)

and

$$\frac{d}{dx} w[x, y(x)] = w_x + \frac{dy}{dx} w_y.$$

(16.12.7)

We thus seek those characteristic curves, if any, such that

$$\frac{\lambda_1 b + \lambda_2}{\lambda_1 a} = \frac{\lambda_1 c}{\lambda_1 b - \lambda_2} = \frac{dy}{dx}. \tag{16.12.8}$$

In order for such curves to exist

$$\lambda_1^2(b^2 - ac) = \lambda_2^2. \tag{16.12.9}$$

There are two such curves, C_+ and C_-, through each point (hyperbolic system) when $b^2 - ac > 0$. On C_+ we have

$$dy = \eta_+ \, dx, \qquad dv + \left(\frac{2b}{a} - \eta_+\right) dw = 0, \tag{16.12.10}$$

while on C_- we have

$$dy = \eta_- \, dx, \qquad dv + \left(\frac{2b}{a} - \eta_-\right) dw = 0, \tag{16.12.11}$$

where

$$\eta_+ = \frac{b + \sqrt{b^2 - ac}}{a} \qquad \text{and} \qquad \eta_- = \frac{b - \sqrt{b^2 - ac}}{a}. \tag{16.12.12}$$

16.13 METHOD OF CHARACTERISTICS

In Fig. 16.13.1 suppose v and w are known along the x axis between 1 and 4. Our problem can then be solved in the roughly triangular shaped region 1–4–10 by the method of characteristics. We will illustrate the method by obtaining the point 5 from the points 1 and 2. In like manner the point 6 can be obtained from 2 and 3, point 7 from 3 and 4, point 8 from 5 and 6, point 9 from 6 and 7, and finally, point 10 from 8 and 9.

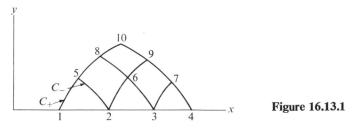

Figure 16.13.1

The method of characteristics consists of integrating the characteristic equations. The simple approximation

$$\int_{x_0}^{x_1} f(s) \, ds = f(x_0)(x_1 - x_0) + \frac{(x_1 - x_0)^2}{2} f'(\xi) \tag{16.13.1}$$

yields

$$y_5 - y_1 = (\eta_+)_1(x_5 - x_1),$$

$$(v_5 - v_1) + \left(\frac{2b}{a} - \eta_+\right)_1 (w_5 - w_1) = 0, \tag{16.13.2}$$

on C_+ and yields

$$y_5 - y_2 = (\eta_-)_2(x_5 - x_2),$$

$$(v_5 - v_2) + \left(\frac{2b}{a} - \eta_-\right)_2 (w_5 - w_2) = 0. \tag{16.13.3}$$

on C_-. These four equations are then solved for the four unknowns x_5, y_5, v_5, and w_5.

16.14 FINITE DIFFERENCE METHOD FOR HYPERBOLIC EQUATIONS

The method of finite differences can also be used for hyperbolic equations. Care must be taken, however, that the net used does not contradict the characteristic structure of the differential equation. Consider, for example, the equation

$$u_{tt} = u_{xx}, \tag{16.14.1}$$

whose characteristics are lines with slope ± 1. The difference equation

$$v_j^{n+1} = 2v_j^n - v_j^{n-1} + \lambda^2[v_{j+1}^n - 2v_j^n + v_j^{n-1}], \tag{16.14.2}$$

where

$$\lambda = \frac{k}{h} \tag{16.14.3}$$

is a consistent approximation whose characteristics are lines with slope $\pm \lambda$. In case $\lambda > 1$, there are infinitely many initial value problems such that the solution of the difference problem does not converge to the solution of the differential problem.

16.15 SUPPLEMENTARY REFERENCES

Only the briefest introduction on the numerical solution of partial differential equations has been presented here. There are many excellent references that go extensively into the subject and answer many of the questions left unanswered here. Some suggested references for further study are Collatz [20], Courant and Hilbert [21], Courant, Friedrichs, and Levy [22], Courant and Lax [23], Crank and Nicholson [24], Eddy [40], Forsythe and Rosenbloom [44], Forsythe and Wasow [45], Fox [52], Hadamard [64], Kantorovich and Krylov [82], Miller [104], Milne [106], Obrien, Hyman, and Kaplan [114], Petrovsky [122], and Richtmyer [130].

CHAPTER 17

HARMONIC ANALYSIS

17.1 INTRODUCTION

Pythagoras, about 600 B.C., is credited with the discovery of the acoustical importance of a fundamental vibration and its overtones. Euler and Lagrange, in the eighteenth century, recognized the mathematical significance of analyzing a periodic function in terms of functions of the type $\sin kx$ and $\cos kx$, where k is an integer. It was Fourier's discovery in 1822 that removed previous restrictions, i.e., that a harmonic analysis did not have to be limited to functions which were continuous and could be differentiated any number of times. Fourier gave the harmonic analysis of functions which had a finite number of discontinuities in the given fundamental interval. This fundamental interval, generally normalized to the range from $-\pi$ to $+\pi$, is all that is needed for the definition of the function $y = f(x)$. Periodicity of the function is not necessary and is of concern only if we leave the fundamental interval. In fact, the theory of harmonic analysis need not leave the fundamental range. Another important discovery of Fourier was the Fourier integral by which he generalized the theory of harmonic analysis to an infinite interval which ranges from $-\infty$ to $+\infty$, without requiring any periodicity. Later, Dirichlet presented some conditions such that the arbitrary function of Fourier had to satisfy these conditions in order to be represented by a harmonic series. These conditions are sufficient for the convergence of the series, but not always necessary. The Dirichlet conditions are:

a) $f(x)$ is defined at every point of the interval $-\pi \leqq x \leqq \pi$.
b) $f(x)$ is everywhere single valued, finite, and sectionally continuous; $f(x)$ can have only a finite number of discontinuities, and two consecutive discontinuities must be separated by a finite interval.
c) $f(x)$ is of bounded variation, that is, $f(x)$ cannot have an infinite number of maxima and minima in the given interval.

A function meeting these conditions can be expanded into a convergent infinite series of the form discussed in Sections 5.10 and 5.11. This is the Fourier approximation.

At a point of discontinuity, $x = a$, $f(a)$ is defined as the arithmetic mean of the two limiting ordinates. That is,

$$f(a) = \tfrac{1}{2}[f(a_+) + f(a_-)]. \tag{17.1.1}$$

This is the value to which the infinite Fourier series converges at the fixed point $x = a$.

17.2 THE FOURIER SERIES

Pure analysis is generally centered around the convergence and properties of the Fourier series. Practical analysis is centered effectively around the representation of a large class of functions by a relatively small number of harmonic components. The Fourier series belongs to that class of functions which gives a uniformly good approximation of a given function $f(x)$ in a finite interval. It does this in the least-squares sense as discussed and illustrated in Chapter 5. We also recall that the functions of the Fourier series form an orthogonal set. A good example of Fourier expansion is provided by the square wave, defined as

$$
\begin{aligned}
f(-x) &= -f(x), \\
f(x) &= \tfrac{1}{2}, \quad 0 < x < \pi, \\
f(0) &= f(\pi) = 0.
\end{aligned}
\tag{17.2.1}
$$

The corresponding Fourier series is

$$
f(x) \sim \frac{2}{\pi}\left(\sin x + \frac{\sin 3x}{3} + \frac{\sin 5x}{5} + \cdots\right).
\tag{17.2.2}
$$

This series converges at every point of the interval $(-\pi, \pi)$ to $f(x)$, but the convergence is slow. Note the similarity of this function with the unit-step function $U(t - a)$, as illustrated in Section 12.8(a).

　　The derivative of (17.2.1) is often called the delta function, and is denoted by $\delta(x)$. It is not a legitimate function, since the original function cannot be differentiated at the point $x = 0$. It is, however, the limit of a legitimate function and is useful for many analytical purposes. We define this function as zero everywhere, except between the limits $\pm\tfrac{1}{2}\epsilon$, where ϵ tends toward zero. At $x = 0$ the function goes to infinity in such a way that the area under the function is 1. In physical interpretation the delta function represents a pulse of intensity 1, applied during a time interval ϵ around the point $x = 0$, when ϵ converges to zero. Note the similarity of this function with the unit impulse $U'(t - a)$, as illustrated in Section 12.8(c).

17.3 HARMONIC ANALYSIS OF EQUIDISTANT DATA

A periodic function of period $2l$ is given in the range $(-l, l)$ by observing it at the $2n + 1$ equidistant points

$$
x_\alpha = \alpha(l/n), \quad \alpha = -n, \ldots, n.
\tag{17.3.1}
$$

This function can be analyzed by fitting a Fourier series of the form given in (5.11.18) and using the functions

$$
\cos\frac{k\pi}{l}x, \quad \sin\frac{k\pi}{l}x.
\tag{17.3.2}
$$

In many problems of applied analysis the function is not periodic in itself but is defined in a given interval of x such as from $x = 0$ to $x = l$. The Fourier expansion may be used as a means of interpolating the given data by giving an analytical expression for the entire function $f(x)$, observed or tabulated in a discrete set of equidistant points only. Such an analytical expression may be of importance for evaluating $f(x)$ at points which lie between the data points. Of greater value, however, may be its operational value. It is also of importance that the trigonometric series have good convergence. This requires that the function and its first derivative return to the same values at each end of the given interval. Since this condition is not always satisfied at the two ends of the given interval, we cannot choose the given interval as the full period of a harmonic analysis. If we choose the interval $(0, l)$ as the half period and define $f(x)$ as an even function in the negative half, that is, $f(-x) = f(x)$, we avoid the discontinuity of the function at the two endpoints $\pm l$ of the interval. However, $f'(l) = -f'(l)$, and we generally have a discontinuity in the first derivative. We obtain better convergence by substracting a linear function $a + bx$ from the given $f(x)$, and operating with a function

$$g(x) = f(x) - (a + bx), \qquad (17.3.3)$$

which vanishes at the two endpoints $x = 0$ and $x = l$. If we reflect this $g(x)$ as an odd function $g(-x) = -g(x)$, and consider $2l$ as the full period of harmonic analysis, we have continuity of function and first derivative at the two endpoints of the period, since

$$g(-l) = g(l) = 0 \qquad \text{and} \qquad g'(-l) = g'(l). \qquad (17.3.4)$$

Fitting a Fourier series according to Section 5.11, we can expand $g(x)$ into a pure sine series of the form

$$g(x) \sim \sum b_m \sin \frac{m\pi}{l} x. \qquad (17.3.5)$$

17.4 CHEBYSHEV APPROXIMATION

The disadvantage of the trigonometric approximation for equidistant data is that $f(x)$ is generally not periodic, and is made periodic by definition. The best we can hope for is continuity of the function and its first derivative at each end of the period. Discontinuities in the higher derivatives usually make the resulting series relatively slowly convergent. This slow convergence may be avoided by using the Chebyshev polynomials. The Chebyshev approximation is essentially a modified form of the Fourier series, and was discussed in Section 5.12.

17.5 THE FOURIER INTEGRAL

The Fourier integral has become one of the most powerful tools of mathematical analysis. It is particularly fundamental in problems pertaining to the input-output relation of electric networks. Fourier found that decomposition of arbitrary functions into harmonic components remains possible even if the range of the function $f(x)$ extends on both sides to infinity.

The Fourier series analyzes a function of a definite finite range in terms of sine and cosine functions of given frequencies. The function may be truly periodic, or it may exist in a finite interval $(-l, l)$ only, and we force periodicity on it to obtain a Fourier approximation. In the latter case, periodicity is employed as a mathematical artifice only.

We start with the function $y = f(x)$, defined in the range from $-l$ to $+l$, which satisfies the Dirichlet conditions. Let us now use the complex form of the Fourier series

$$f(x) = \sum_{k=-\infty}^{\infty} c_k e^{ik\pi x/l},$$

where

$$c_k = \frac{1}{2l} \int_{-l}^{l} f(x) e^{ik\pi x/l} \, dx. \tag{17.5.1}$$

The usual real form arises if we put $c_k = \frac{1}{2}(a_k - ib_k)$ and $c_{-k} = \frac{1}{2}(a_k + ib_k)$ and combine the terms of the subscripts k and $-k$.

Although the function $f(x)$ is originally given in the range $\pm l$ only, we now enlarge the range to $\pm L$. Outside the original range we define $f(x)$ as zero.

The new function $y = f(x)$, defined in the enlarged range, is expanded into a Fourier series

$$f(x) = \sum_{k=-\infty}^{\infty} c_k e^{ik\pi x/L}$$

with

$$c_k = \frac{1}{2L} \int_{-l}^{l} f(x) e^{ik\pi x/L} \, dx. \tag{17.5.2}$$

The new series analyzes the function $f(x)$ in entirely new frequencies and new coefficients, but it approaches the same $f(x)$ for any x between $\pm l$, and approaches zero outside that range up to $\pm L$.

If a sine or cosine function is written in the form $\sin 2\pi \mu t$, cosine $2\pi \mu t$, then μ, the number of vibrations per second, is called the frequency of the harmonic vibrations. The harmonic functions associated with (17.5.1) are written as

$$\cos \frac{2\pi kx}{2l} + i \sin \frac{2\pi kx}{2l}. \tag{17.5.3}$$

Hence the frequencies present are

$$\mu_1 = \frac{1}{2l}, \mu_2 = \frac{2}{2l}, \ldots, \mu_k = \frac{k}{2l}, \ldots, \tag{17.5.4}$$

The corresponding frequencies for (17.5.2) are

$$\mu_1 = \frac{1}{2L}, \mu_2 = \frac{2}{2L}, \ldots, \mu_k = \frac{k}{2L}, \ldots. \tag{17.5.5}$$

If L is twice as large as l, the fundamental frequency becomes one-half of the

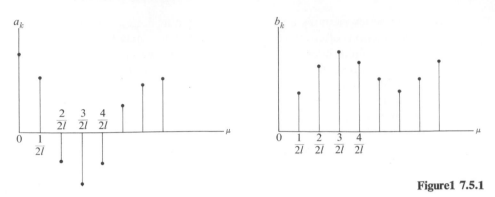

Figure1 7.5.1

previous fundamental frequency. Thus, the harmonics 1, 2, 3, 4 of the first analysis now become the harmonics 2, 4, 6, 8, and our complete analysis contains twice as many frequencies. Plotting the real and imaginary parts of c_k separately against frequency for our first analysis, we obtain a graph similar to Fig. 17.5.1.

We now consider our second analysis. We get more lines, since more frequencies are present. Rewriting the integral in (18.5.2) as

$$c_k = \frac{1}{2L} \int_{-l}^{l} f(x) e^{ik\pi x/L} \, dx = \frac{C_k}{2L}, \tag{17.5.6}$$

we do not need to change the amplitudes C_k as we make L larger and larger. All we have to do is fill in more lines. Let us define the following function of the continuous variable μ,

$$F(\mu) = \int_{-l}^{l} f(x) e^{-2\pi i \mu x} \, dx. \tag{17.5.7}$$

This function contains all possible harmonic components of $f(x)$, no matter how small or how large L may be. That is,

$$C_k = F(k/2L). \tag{17.5.8}$$

Our previous graph is now replaced by Fig. 17.5.2. Regardless of how irregular $f(x)$ may be, the new function $F(\mu)$ is always a continuous and analytic function of μ and is called the Fourier transform of the original function $f(x)$.

Let us now consider what happens as L increases to infinity. The lines we must fill in get denser and denser. In the limit, all frequencies are equally represented. The previous line spectrum changes in the limit to a continuous spectrum. The function now gives the total distribution of the harmonic amplitudes of $f(x)$.

Defining the function

$$G(\mu) = F(\mu) e^{2\pi i \mu x}, \tag{17.5.9}$$

we can then write (18.5.2) as

$$f(x) = \frac{1}{2L} \sum_{k=-\infty}^{\infty} G\left(\frac{k}{2L}\right). \tag{17.5.10}$$

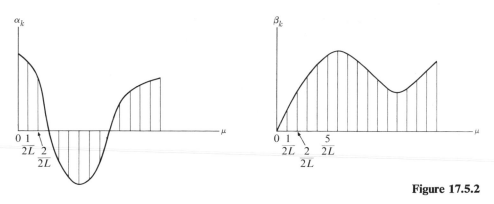

Figure 17.5.2

Putting $1/2L = \epsilon$, we have

$$f(x) = \epsilon \sum_{k=-\infty}^{\infty} G(k\epsilon). \tag{17.5.11}$$

As L becomes larger, the ordinates of $G(\mu)$ which are involved in the Fourier sum become denser. Now, as L increases to infinity, ϵ tends to zero. By the fundamental theorem of integral calculus the limit of this sum is the total area under the function $y = G(\mu)$. Therefore,

$$f(x) = \int_{-\infty}^{\infty} G(\mu) \, d\mu = \int_{-\infty}^{\infty} F(\mu)e^{2\pi i\mu x} \, d\mu. \tag{17.5.12}$$

This is the Fourier integral. While the Fourier transform $F(\mu)$ resolves the given $f(x)$ into its harmonic components, the Fourier integral synthesizes these harmonic components to the original function.

The Fourier transform as given in Eq. (17.5.7) has the limits $-l$ and $+l$. This is only because we assumed $f(x)$ was given between $\pm l$ and was zero outside of that interval. If we define $f(x)$ in an arbitrarily large interval, and gradually approach infinity, we obtain, in the limit,

$$F(\mu) = \int_{-\infty}^{\infty} f(x)e^{-2\pi i\mu x} \, dx. \tag{17.5.13}$$

In practical applications it is often more advantageous to introduce the angular frequency, $\omega = 2\pi\mu$, instead of the ordinary frequency μ. Then, the formulas of harmonic analysis and synthesis become

$$F(\omega) = \int_{-\infty}^{\infty} f(x)e^{-i\omega x} \, dx, \tag{17.5.14}$$

and

$$f(x) = \frac{1}{2\pi} \int_{-\infty}^{\infty} F(\omega)e^{i\omega x} \, d\omega. \tag{17.5.15}$$

In summary we note again that the Fourier series gives a discrete spectrum and the Fourier integral gives a continuous spectrum.

17.6 APPLICATIONS OF FOURIER TRANSFORM

The Fourier transform is one of the most important tools of applied analysis. It has wide applications in electric network problems as well as many other problems of physics and engineering. The situation may involve an electronic component, a servomechanism which responds to a given command, or a differential equation in which the right side is the input and the solution is the output. In all these situations we have two functions, the input $f(t)$ and the output $g(t)$. The given physical mechanism determines the relation between these two functions. We say that this relation is of the communications type if the following conditions exist:

a) The relation is linear if $f(t)$ is changed into $\alpha f(t)$ and, correspondingly, $g(t)$ is changed into $\alpha g(t)$.

b) If $f(t)$ is periodic, written in the complex form,

$$f(t) = e^{i\omega t}, \tag{17.6.1}$$

then $g(t)$ reproduces this function with only a factor of proportionality,

$$g(t) = \phi(\omega)e^{i\omega t}. \tag{17.6.2}$$

The factor $\phi(\omega)$ is generally complex and can thus be expressed in the form

$$\phi(\omega) = A(\omega) + iB(\omega). \tag{17.6.3}$$

The factor $\phi(\omega)$ is called the frequency response function (see Chapter 15). If the input is a strictly periodic function of definite frequency and constant amplitude, the output is likewise a periodic function of the same frequency but modified amplitude and modified phase. These are the so-called gain and phase characteristics discussed in Chapter 15.

Another interesting problem associated with harmonic analysis is filter analysis. One may be interested in a "low-pass" filter which would absorb all frequencies beyond a certain cutoff frequency but would let through all frequencies below that cutoff. A "band-pass," fixed, or adaptive filter may be of interest. Filter analysis and digital filtering will be discussed in detail in Chapter 19.

17.7 SUPPLEMENTARY REFERENCES

Recommended for a more extensive study of some of the topics discussed in this chapter are Carslaw [16], Thompson [147], Widder [159], and the following.

a) V. BUSH, *Operational Circuit Analysis*, Wiley, New York, 1929.

b) R. V. CHURCHILL, *Fourier Series and Boundary Value Problems*, McGraw-Hill, New York, 1941.

c) P. FRANKLIN, *Fourier Methods*, McGraw-Hill, New York, 1949.

d) E. A. GUILLEMIN, *Mathematics of Circuit Analysis*, Wiley, New York, 1949.

e) N. WIENER, *The Fourier Integral and its Applications*, Cambridge University Press, Cambridge, 1933.

CHAPTER 18

SPECIAL FUNCTIONS AND INTEGRALS

18.1 INTRODUCTION

Problems in mathematical physics frequently involve certain special functions and integrals such as Bessel functions, sine and cosine integrals, the exponential integrals, and Fourier transform integrals. For some of these, storage of extensive tables in a computer may be inefficient or prohibitive. Therefore, it is desirable to be able to compute their values with a reliable degree of accuracy. Special consideration has to be given to the numerical methods used to accomplish this. This chapter concerns itself with these numerical methods, particularly oriented to computation on a high-speed digital computer.

18.2 BESSEL FUNCTIONS

We wish to compute $J_\nu(z)$, $J_{\nu\pm1}(z)$, $\ldots$, $J_{\nu\pm N}(z)$, and $Y_\nu(z)$, $Y_{\nu\pm1}(z)$, $\ldots$, $Y_{\nu\pm N}(z)$, where $z = x + iy$ and $\nu = \alpha + i\beta$. We first select some integer larger than the largest order desired. One possible choice is to take the greater of $|z| + 20 = \sqrt{x^2 + y^2} + 20$ and $|N| + 10$. Then, if this number is even, we add 1 to it and set it equal to k.

Set $J_{k+2} = 0$ and $J_{k+1} = 10^{-37}$. From the recursive relationship

$$J_{\nu-1}(z) = (2\nu/z)J_\nu(z) - J_{\nu+1}(z), \tag{18.2.1}$$

we compute J_k, J_{k-1}, $\ldots$, J_2, J_1. We then compute the sum

$$J_1 + (\nu + 2)J_3 + \sum_{n=2}^{k} \frac{(\nu + 2n)(\nu + n - 1)(\nu + n - 2)\cdots(\nu + 1)}{n!} J_{2n+1}, \tag{18.2.2}$$

and multiply this by

$$\left(\frac{2}{z}\right)^\nu \Gamma(\nu + 1). \tag{18.2.3}$$

We compute $\Gamma(\nu + 1)$ from the relationship

$$\ln \Gamma(\nu) = -\nu + (\nu - \tfrac{1}{2}) \ln (\nu) + \ln (\sqrt{2\pi}) + J, \tag{18.2.4}$$

where J is given as a continued fraction (see Wall [155], p. 364, Formula 93.9).

In $\nu = \alpha + i\beta$, if $\alpha < 2$, then the recursive relation

$$\ln \Gamma(\nu) = \ln \Gamma(\nu + 1) - \ln (\nu) \tag{18.2.5}$$

is used.

Watson (Section 18.5a) gives Gegenbauer's formula as

$$\sum_{n=0}^{\infty} \frac{(\nu + 2n)\Gamma(\nu + n)}{n!} \left(\frac{2}{z}\right)^{\nu} J_{\nu+2n}(z) = 1. \tag{18.2.6}$$

Thus, for some factor F, we have

$$F\left(\frac{2}{z}\right)^{\nu} \Gamma(\nu + 1)\Bigg[J_1 + (\nu + 2)J_3$$

$$+ \sum_{n=2}^{k} \frac{(\nu + 2n)(\nu + n - 1)(\nu + n - 2)\cdots(\nu + 1)}{n!} J_{2n+1}\Bigg] = 1. \tag{18.2.7}$$

If we solve for F, and then multiply each J_i by F, then

$$J_1 = J_{\nu}(z), J_2 = J_{\nu+1}(z), \ldots, J_k = J_{\nu+k-1}(z).$$

In order to compute $Y_{\nu}(z), \ldots, Y_{\nu\pm N}(z)$, we need $Y_{\nu}(z)$ and $Y_{\nu+1}(z)$ for starting values in the recursive relationship we shall use. To compute $Y_{\nu}(z)$ we need $J_{-\nu}(z)$. Erdelyi, Magnus, Oberhettinger, and Tricomi (Section 18.5b) give the following formula:

$$\left(\frac{az}{2}\right)^{\mu-\nu} J_{\nu}(az)\Gamma(\nu + 1)$$

$$= \sum_{n=0}^{\infty} \frac{{}_2F_1(-n, \mu + n; \nu + 1; a^2)\Gamma(\mu + n)(\mu + 2n)J_{\mu+2n}(z)}{n!}. \tag{18.2.8}$$

Setting $\nu = -\mu$, $a = 1$, and noting that

$${}_2F_1(-n, n + b; c; 1) = \frac{(-1)^n(b - c + 1)_n}{(c)_n}, \tag{18.2.9}$$

where

$$(a)_0 = 1, \quad (a)_k = a(a + 1)\cdots(a + k - 1) = \frac{\Gamma(a + k)}{\Gamma(a)}, \tag{18.2.10}$$

we have

$$\left(\frac{z}{2}\right)^{2\mu} J_{-\mu}(z)\Gamma(-\mu + 1)$$

$$= \sum_{n=0}^{\infty} \frac{(-1)^n\Gamma(2\mu + n)\Gamma(-\mu + 1)\Gamma(\mu + n)(\mu + 2n)J_{\mu+2n}(z)}{\Gamma(2\mu)\Gamma(-\mu + 1 + n)n!}. \tag{18.2.11}$$

After a considerable amount of algebraic manipulation, and using the relationships

$$\Gamma(\nu)\Gamma(1 - \nu) = \pi \csc \pi\nu \tag{18.2.12}$$

and

$$Y_\nu(z) = \frac{J_\nu(z)\cos \pi\nu - J_{-\nu}(z)}{\sin \pi\nu},$$ (18.2.13)

we obtain

$$Y_\nu(z) = J_\nu(z)\left\{\cot \pi\nu - \frac{1}{\pi\nu}\left[\left(\frac{2}{z}\right)^\nu \Gamma(\nu + 1)\right]^2\right\} + \frac{2}{\pi}\left[\left(\frac{2}{z}\right)^\nu \Gamma(\nu + 1)\right]^2 S,$$ (18.2.14)

where

$$S = \left(\frac{\nu + 2}{1 - \nu}\right)J_{\nu+2}(z) - \frac{(2\nu + 1)(\nu + 1)(\nu + 4)}{(1 - \nu)(2 - \nu)2!}J_{\nu+4}(z)$$

$$+ \frac{(2\nu + 1)(2\nu + 2)(\nu + 1)(\nu + 2)(\nu + 6)}{(1 - \nu)(2 - \nu)(3 - \nu)3!}J_{\nu+6}(z)$$ (18.2.15)

$$- \frac{(2\nu + 1)(2\nu + 2)(2\nu + 3)(\nu + 1)(\nu + 2)(\nu + 3)(\nu + 8)}{(1 - \nu)(2 - \nu)(3 - \nu)(4 - \nu)4!}J_{\nu+8}(z)$$

$$+ \cdots.$$

This formula cannot be used for $\nu = 0$. In this case, S is computed as usual, but we use the special formula

$$Y_0(z) = \frac{2}{\pi}(\ln z - 0.1159315157)J_0(z) + \frac{2}{\pi}S.$$ (18.2.16)

Luke (Section 18.5c) gives this formula as

$$Y_0(z) = \frac{2}{\pi}\ln\left(\frac{z}{2} + \gamma\right)J_0(z) - \frac{4}{\pi}\sum_{k=1}^{\infty}\frac{(-1)^k J_{2k}(z)}{k},$$ (18.2.17)

where $\gamma = 0.577215664901533$, Euler's constant.

Then, $Y_{\nu+1}(z)$ is computed from the relationship

$$Y_\nu(z)J_{\nu+1}(z) - J_\nu(z)Y_{\nu+1}(z) - \frac{2}{\pi z},$$ (18.2.18)

Finally, if $N > 0$, we compute $Y_{\nu+2}(z)$, $Y_{\nu+3}(z)$, ..., $Y_{\nu+N}(z)$ from

$$J_\mu(z)Y_{\mu-1}(z) - Y_\mu(z)J_{\mu-1}(z) = \frac{2}{\pi z},$$ (18.2.19)

and, if $N < 0$, we compute $J_{\nu-1}(z)$, $J_{\nu-2}(z)$, $J_{\nu-3}(z)$, ..., $J_{\nu-N}(z)$, $Y_{\nu-1}(z)$, $Y_{\nu-2}(z)$, ..., $Y_{\nu-N}(z)$ from

$$J_\nu(z) = \frac{2(\nu + 1)}{z}J_{\nu+1}(z) - J_{\nu+2}(z)$$

and

$$Y_\nu(z) = \frac{2(\nu + 1)}{z}Y_{\nu+1}(z) - Y_{\nu+2}(z).$$ (18.2.20)

18.3 SINE, COSINE, AND EXPONENTIAL INTEGRALS

These integrals, which occur frequently in mathematical physics, are defined as follows:

a) *Sine integral:*

$$Si(x) = \int_0^x \frac{\sin t}{t}\, dt. \tag{18.3.1}$$

b) *Cosine integral:*

$$Ci(x) = \int_\infty^x \frac{\cos t}{t}\, dt. \tag{18.3.2}$$

c) *Exponential integrals:*

$$Ei(x) = \int_{-\infty}^x \frac{e^t}{t}\, dt, \tag{18.3.3}$$

$$-Ei(-x) = \int_x^\infty \frac{e^{-t}}{t}\, dt. \tag{18.3.4}$$

These functions have been tabulated extensively in Works Project Administration (W.P.A.) tables (Section 18.5d). For purposes of computations we use the following series expansions:

$$Si(x) = T_1(x) - T_3(x) + T_5(x) - T_7(x) + \cdots, \tag{18.3.5}$$
$$Ci(x) = \gamma + \ln x - T_2(x) + T_4(x) - T_6(x) + \cdots, \tag{18.3.6}$$
$$Ei(x) = \gamma + \ln x + T_1(x) + T_2(x) + T_3(x) + \cdots, \tag{18.3.7}$$
$$-Ei(-x) = -\gamma - \ln x + T_1(x) - T_2(x) + T_3(x) - \cdots. \tag{18.3.8}$$

In the above formulas the logarithm is to the base e, $\gamma = 0.577215665$, and

$$T_n(x) = \frac{x^n}{n \cdot n!}. \tag{18.3.9}$$

For any argument x, the number of terms to be taken is such that the last term used is equal to or less than 1 in the thirteenth place, that is, 1×10^{-13}. This criterion, used in preparation of the W.P.A. tables, has proved to be satisfactory in practice. For $Ei(-x)$, x must be less than 6 to obtain the same accuracy given by the other functions.

18.4 NUMERICAL INTEGRATION OF FOURIER TRANSFORM INTEGRALS

In applied problems we must often evaluate numerically integrals of the form

$$S(x) = \int_0^\infty \phi(k) \sin kx\, dk \tag{18.4.1}$$

and

$$C(x) = \int_0^\infty \psi(k) \cos kx\, dk. \tag{18.4.2}$$

At times, $\psi(k)$ and $\phi(k)$ may be given by a closed expression which is too complicated to permit a sufficiently accurate analytic evaluation of the integral for the entire range of the parameter x. In other cases $\phi(k)$ and $\psi(k)$ may be available only in numerical form.

The conventional methods of numerical integration, such as Simpson's rule, are not suitable for evaluation of the given integrals when x is large. There are two reasons for difficulty with standard methods. First, when x is large, there is a rapid oscillation of the trigonometric function, and the integrand cannot be accurately approximated by a polynomial unless undesirably small intervals of integration are chosen. Second, strong cancellation between the contributions to the integral from regions where the trigonometric function is positive and regions where it is negative tends to increase the error.

Hurwitz and Zweifel (Section 18.5e) present a method which tends to overcome many of the difficulties associated with standard methods. A summary of the Hurwitz and Zweifel method is now given.

Let

$$S(x) = \frac{\pi}{x} \sum_{n=0}^{\infty} S_n(x), \tag{18.4.3}$$

where

$$S_n(x) = (-1)^n \sum_{j=1}^{N} \frac{w_j^{(N)}}{\cos \pi y_j^{(N)}} \left\{ \phi\left(\frac{\pi}{x}\left[y_j^{(N)} + n + \frac{1}{2}\right]\right) + \phi\left(\frac{\pi}{x}\left[-y_j^{(N)} + n + \frac{1}{2}\right]\right) \right\}, \tag{18.4.4}$$

and let

$$C(x) = \frac{\pi}{x} \left[\frac{1}{2} C_0(x) + \sum_{n=1}^{\infty} C_n(x) \right], \tag{18.4.5}$$

where

$$C_n(x) = (-1)^n \sum_{j=1}^{N} \frac{w_j^{(N)}}{\cos \pi u_j^{(N)}} \left\{ \psi\left(\frac{\pi}{x}[u_j^{(N)} + n]\right) + \psi\left(\frac{\pi}{x}[-u_j^{(N)} + n]\right) \right\}. \tag{18.4.6}$$

The values for $y_j^{(N)}$ and $u_j^{(N)}$ are given by

$$y_j^{(N)} = \frac{2j - 1}{2(2N + 1)},$$

$$u_j^{(N)} = \frac{2j - 1}{2(2N + 1)}, \quad j = 1, 2, \ldots, N. \tag{18.4.7}$$

We find the $w_j^{(N)}$ by solving the following system of N linear equations in N unknowns:

$$\frac{1}{\sqrt{\pi}} \frac{\Gamma(\lambda + \frac{1}{2})}{\Gamma(\lambda + 1)} = 2 \sum_{j=1}^{N} \cos^{2\lambda - 2}(\pi y_j^{(N)}) w_j^{(N)}, \quad \lambda = 1, 2, \ldots, N. \tag{18.4.8}$$

In order to sum the series we use the following technique:

1) Form the sequence of partial sums

$$\beta_n = \sum_{\alpha=0}^{n} S_\alpha(x) \tag{18.4.9}$$

so that

$$S(x) = \frac{\pi}{x} \lim_{n \to \infty} \beta_n. \tag{18.4.10}$$

2) The limit of the sequence $\beta_0, \beta_1, \beta_2, \ldots, \beta_n, \ldots$ is then found by the averaging technique:

$$\begin{aligned}
a_1^{(n)} &= \tfrac{1}{2}(\beta_n + \beta_{n+1}), \\
a_2^{(n)} &= \tfrac{1}{2}(a_1^{(n)} + a_1^{(n+1)}), \\
a_3^{(n)} &= \tfrac{1}{2}(a_2^{(n)} + a_2^{(n+1)}), \\
&\;\;\vdots
\end{aligned} \tag{18.4.11}$$

and

$$\lim_{n \to \infty} \beta_n = \lim_{j \to \infty} a_j. \tag{18.4.12}$$

We stop the process when

$$a_j^{(n)} \cong a_{j+1}^{(n)}, \tag{18.4.13}$$

and thus

$$S(x) \cong \frac{\pi}{x} a_{j+1}^{(n)}. \tag{18.4.14}$$

The technique for computing $C(x)$ is exactly the same. This summation procedure is useful because the series of a's converges much more rapidly than the original series.

The values of ϕ and ψ are found by interpolating in the given list of data points.

18.5 SUPPLEMENTARY REFERENCES

The following are recommended references for the material covered in this chapter.

a) C. N. WATSON, *A Treatise on the Theory of Bessel Functions*, Cambridge University Press, Cambridge (1944), p. 138.

b) A. ERDÉLYI, W. MAGNUS, F. OBERHETTINGER, and F. G. TRICOMI, *Higher Transcendental Functions*, Vol. 2, McGraw-Hill, New York (1953), p. 64.

c) Y. L. LUKE, *Integrals of Bessel Functions*, McGraw-Hill, New York, 1962.

d) *Tables of Sine, Cosine and Exponential Integrals*, Vol. I, Vol. II, Federal Works Agency, Works Project Administration 1940.

e) H. HURWITZ and P. F. ZWEIFEL, "Numerical Quadrature of Fourier Transform Integrals," *MTAC*, **10**, No. 55 (July 1956) pp. 140–149.

CHAPTER 19

SAMPLED DATA AND DIGITAL FILTERING

19.1 INTRODUCTION

The trend of the past few decades has been toward dynamical systems that operate with variables which are in the form of a sequence of numbers. The advent of guided missiles, satellites, and space research has given impetus to this. These variables are generally quantized in amplitude and are available only at specified instants of time, which are usually equally spaced. The major difference between analog and discrete systems lies in the fact that analog, or continuous, systems have variables which are known at all instants of time, whereas discrete systems have variables which are known only at sampling instants. The latter is known as a sampled-data system.

In a dynamical or an electronic system, independent variables are usually referred to as inputs, and the dependent variables are outputs. Certain input functions may be called forcing functions. Also, a system may consist of a number of components linked together in various ways. The output from one component may be used as input to another component.

In a sampled-data system the sampling frequency must be related to the characteristics of the function being sampled, lest important information be lost in the sampling process. If the sampling frequency is well chosen relative to the characteristics of the function being sampled, only negligible information is lost in the sampling process.

19.2 SAMPLED DATA AND THE CARDINAL FUNCTION

Let $x(t)$ be a real function of time. For any fixed increment $h = \Delta t$ of time, the sequence

$$x_n = x(nh) \tag{19.2.1}$$

is called a sampling of the function $x(t)$. The cardinal function (see Section 3.12a) for this sampling is

$$C(t) = \sum_{n=-\infty}^{\infty} x_n \frac{\sin\left[(\pi t/h) - n\right]}{(\pi t/h) - n}. \tag{19.2.2}$$

245

The following statements may be made concerning the convergence of the series defining $C(t)$ (see Section 3.12h):

a) If $C(t)$ converges for any value of t not of the form nh, then it is uniformly convergent in any finite region of the complex t-plane, and $C(t)$ is an integral function.

b) The series $C(t)$ converges if and only if the series

$$\sum_{n=1}^{\infty} (-1)^{n+1} \frac{x_n - x_{-n}}{n}$$

converges.

c) If $\sum_{n=-\infty}^{\infty} x_n^2$ converges, then $C(t)$ converges absolutely.

When the cardinal function converges, it has the following properties (Section 3.12a):

d) $C(n) = x_n$.

e) $C(t)$ contains no frequencies higher than the sampling frequency $1/2h$.

f) $C(t)$ is analytic and has no singularities in the finite complex t-plane.

g) $C(t)$ is the only function with the properties of (d), (e), and (f).

We are thus led to the result that if $x(t)$ is an analytic function with no singularities in the finite part of the plane, $x(t)$ has no frequency components greater than $f = 1/2h$, and the cardinal function converges, then $C(t) = x(t)$. That is, the function $x(t)$ can be completely reconstructed from the sample points x_n. This result of Whittaker's (Section 3.12a) is called the Nyquist sampling theorem.

19.3 FOLDING FREQUENCY AND SAMPLING LEVEL NOISE

Consider any frequency $\phi = m/h \pm f$, where $f < 1/h$ and m is an integer, and let

$$x(t) = \sin 2\pi\phi t. \tag{19.3.1}$$

Then

$$x_n = \sin 2\pi \left(\frac{m}{h} \pm f\right) nh = \sin (2\pi mn \pm 2\pi fnh) = \pm \sin 2\pi fnh. \tag{19.3.2}$$

Therefore, $\sin 2\pi\phi t$ gives exactly the same set of sample points that $\pm \sin 2\pi ft$ does, and we say that the frequency ϕ is folded, or aliased, into the frequency f.

In many practical applications, the sampling values $x_n = x(nh)$ of the function $x(t)$ are obtained by analog-to-digital conversion to a fixed number of bits (binary digits), and are, therefore, subject to a truncation error ϵ_n. This means that one actually can only use the numbers $x_n + \epsilon_n$ for computation rather than the true values x_n. The sample-and-hold circuits common to most converters also contribute to the sampling error in most cases.

Let us assume that $\epsilon_n = \rho_n \epsilon$, where ϵ is the quantum of digitization, and ρ_n is a random variable with rectangular distribution on either the interval $(0, 1)$ or $(-\frac{1}{2}, \frac{1}{2})$.

It might appear at first that this sampling noise ϵ_n is all at high frequency and can be filtered out without affecting low frequency data. Unfortunately, as a consideration of the autocorrelation function shows, the resultant noise has a flat spectrum over the whole frequency range 0 to $1/2h$, and can be eliminated only by narrow-banding (providing the nature of the signal permits).

19.4 DIGITAL FILTERS

The remainder of this chapter is based on the extensive work of R. P. Rich and H. Shaw (Section 19.8a) on the discrete analogs for continuous filters. The substitution rule (Section 19.5) furnishes a practical and systematic method for simulating continuous linear systems on a digital computer. In particular, many analog data-processing techniques, such as the direct determination of power spectra, can be carried out with greater versatility on a digital computer by simulating analog equipment. A related application is the generation of a correlated noise sequence by passing a white noise sequence through a digital filter with a specified transfer function.

The transient responses of filters related by the substitution rule agree exactly at those points where the discrete filter output is defined, i.e., at the sample points. Thus, the discrete filter, corresponding to a stable continuous filter, is stable. Steady state responses agree at sample points up to terms of second order in frequency in cycles per sample point for a sufficiently high sampling rate.

19.5 SUBSTITUTION RULE

Consider the differential equation

$$p(\mathbf{D})\phi(t) = \alpha q(\mathbf{D})I(t), \tag{19.5.1}$$

where $\mathbf{D}$ is the differential operator $\mathbf{D}f(t) = df/dt$, and p and q are polynomials of degrees k and k', respectively, each with a leading coefficient of unity. The function I is a known function of time and is the filter input.

Let the roots of $p(z)$ be ρ_j, $j = 1, 2, \ldots, k$, and the roots of $q(z)$ be ρ'_j, $j = 1, 2, \ldots, k'$. Then

$$p(\mathbf{D}) = \prod_{j=1}^{k} (\mathbf{D} - \rho_j) \tag{19.5.2}$$

and

$$q(\mathbf{D}) = \prod_{j=1}^{k'} (\mathbf{D} - \rho'_j). \tag{19.5.3}$$

Construct the polynomials

$$p^*(\mathbf{E}) = \prod_{j=1}^{k} (\mathbf{E} - e^{\rho_j h}) \tag{19.5.4}$$

and

$$q^*(\mathbf{E}) = \prod_{j=1}^{k'} (\mathbf{E} - e^{\rho'_j h}), \tag{19.5.5}$$

where $\mathbf{E}$ is the shifting operator, $\mathbf{E}f(t) = f(t + h)$, and h is the sampling interval, i.e., the time between sample points.

The substitution rule yields the difference equation

$$p^*(\mathbf{E})\phi_n^* = \alpha(h\mathbf{E}^{1/2})^{k-k'}q^*(\mathbf{E})I_n, \tag{19.5.6}$$

where the subscript notation has the usual meaning, $f_n = f(nh)$. A recurrence formula suitable for computation is obtained by expanding $p^*(\mathbf{E})$ and $q^*(\mathbf{E})$. We should note that the coefficients of the recurrence formula are real if the coefficients of p and q are real.

Summarizing, we

a) express $p(\mathbf{D})$ and $q(\mathbf{D})$ as products of linear factors,

b) replace $\mathbf{D}$ by $\mathbf{E}$ (symbolically, $e^{h\mathbf{D}}$),

c) replace each root ρ by $e^{h\rho}$,

d) replace α by $\alpha(h\mathbf{E}^{1/2})^{k-k'}$, and

e) expand the result.

All steps except (c) are suggested by an exact relationship, computationally useful in itself, between the linear homogeneous differential equation and difference equations with constant coefficients. Step (c) is suggested by comparing the frequency response functions, that is, the ratio of input to steady state output, where input is $e^{i\omega t}$ for (19.5.1) and (19.5.6). The multiplier $h^{k-k'}$ of α is the proper gain adjustment which reflects the net integration multiplicity. The other multiplier $\mathbf{E}^{(k-k')/2}$ is the proper phase adjustment which adds $(k - k')/2$ to all input subscripts. This phase adjustment amounts to central approximation and yields accuracy up to terms of second order in ωh.

19.6 TRANSIENT RESPONSE

Consider the homogeneous differential equation of kth order with constant coefficients,

$$p(\mathbf{D})\phi(t) \equiv \phi^{(k)} + A_{k-1}\phi^{(k-1)} + \cdots + A_0\phi = 0, \tag{19.6.1}$$

whose auxiliary equation is

$$Z^k + A_{k-1}Z^{k-1} + \cdots + A_0 = 0. \tag{19.6.2}$$

Let $r_1, r_2, \ldots, r_\nu$ be the distinct roots of the auxiliary equation, where r_i has multiplicity μ_i. Then the complete solution of (19.6.2) is

$$\phi(t) = \sum_{i=1}^{\nu} B_i e^{r_i t}, \tag{19.6.3}$$

where

$$B_i = C_{i,0} + C_{i,1}t + \cdots + C_{i,\mu_i-1}t^{\mu_i-1}, \tag{19.6.4}$$

and the $C_{i,j}$ are arbitrary constants determined by the side conditions of the problem (Section 19.8c).

Now consider the homogeneous linear difference equation of kth order with constant coefficients

$$p^*(E)\phi^*_{n-k} \equiv \phi^*_n + A^*_{k-1}\phi^*_{n-1} + \cdots + A^*_0\phi^*_{n-k} = 0, \qquad (19.6.5)$$

whose auxiliary equation is

$$Z^k + A^*_{k-1}Z^{k-1} + \cdots + A^*_0 = 0. \qquad (19.6.6)$$

The distinct roots of the auxiliary equation are $s_1 = e^{r_1 h}$, $s_2 = e^{r_2 h}, \ldots,$ $s_\nu = e^{r_\nu h}$, where s_i has multiplicity μ_i. Then the complete solution of (19.6.5) is

$$\phi^*_n = \sum_{i=1}^\nu B^*_i s^n_i = \sum_{i=1}^\nu B^*_i e^{r_i(nh)}, \qquad (19.6.7)$$

where

$$B^*_i = C^*_{i,0} + C^*_{i,1}(nh) + \cdots + C^*_{i,\mu_i - 1}(nh)^{\mu_i - 1}, \qquad (19.6.8)$$

and the $C^*_{i,j}$ are arbitrary constants determined by the side conditions of the problem (Section 19.8d).

It follows from Eqs. (19.6.3) and (19.6.7) that if $\phi^*_n = \phi(nh)$ for any k integral values of n, then $\phi^*_n = \phi(nh)$ for all integral values of n. The substitution rule is exact for homogeneous equations.

This exact rule furnishes a convenient method for generating the values of linear combinations of exponentials, sinusoids, and damped sinusoids at equally spaced arguments on a digital computer. Some care must be taken, however, if the homogeneous differential equation (of which the linear combination is a solution) is not stable. Otherwise, significant roundoff errors may accumulate from repeated applications of the corresponding recurrence formula.

19.7 EXAMPLE OF A DISCRETE ANALOG FOR A CONTINUOUS FILTER

In Section 15.2 we found the transfer functions of a simple mechanical system involving masses, springs, and damping. One of the transfer functions as given in (15.2.24) was

$$q_1(s) = \frac{\phi(s)}{I(s)} = \frac{s^2 + 3}{s^4 + s^3 + 20s^2 + 3s + 31}.$$

The Bode plot of this was given in Fig. 15.11.1.

Since the initial conditions were zero, the differential equation of the above transfer function is

$$\frac{d^4\phi}{dt^4} + \frac{d^3\phi}{dt^3} + 20\frac{d^2\phi}{dt^2} + 3\frac{d\phi}{dt} + 31\phi = \frac{d^2I}{dt^2} + 3I.$$

In the following example, the method of Section 19.5 is applied to obtain the discrete analog. The plots of the continuous filter and its discrete analog are shown in Fig. 19.7.1. This may be compared with Fig. 15.11.1.

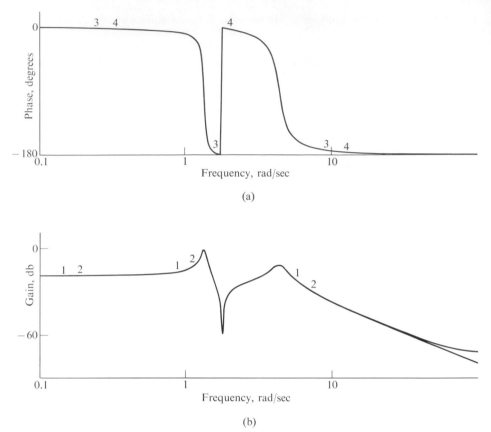

Figure 19.7.1

Example. Consider the differential equation

$$\frac{d^4\phi}{dt^4} + \frac{d^3\phi}{dt^3} + 20\frac{d^2\phi}{dt^2} + \frac{d\phi}{dt} + 31\phi = \frac{d^2I}{dt^2} + 3I,$$

which can be written as

$$\prod_{j=1}^{4}(\mathbf{D} - \rho_j)\phi(t) = \prod_{j=1}^{2}(\mathbf{D} - \rho_j')I(t),$$

where

$$\rho_1 = -0.039307967 + 1.3035528i,$$
$$\rho_2 = -0.039307967 - 1.3035528i,$$
$$\rho_3 = -0.46069203 + 4.2443530i,$$
$$\rho_4 = -0.46069203 - 4.2443530i,$$
$$\rho_1' = 1.7320508i,$$
$$\rho_2' = -1.7320508i.$$

Solution. The substitution rule yields

$$\prod_{j=1}^{4} (\mathbf{E} - e^{\rho_j h})\phi_n^* = h^2 \mathbf{E} \prod_{j=1}^{2} (\mathbf{E} - e^{\rho_j' h})I_n,$$

which can be written as the recurrence formula

$$\phi_{n+4}^* = -[A_3\phi_{n+3}^* + A_2\phi_{n+2}^* + A_1\phi_{n+1}^* + A_0\phi_n^*]$$
$$+ [A_3'I_{n+3} + A_2'I_{n+2} + A_1'I_{n+1}],$$

where, for $h = \pi/100$ sec,

$$A_3 = -3.9496211, \qquad A_2 = 5.8684357,$$
$$A_1 = -3.8878574, \qquad A_0 = 0.96907243,$$
$$A_3' = 0.98696044 \times 10^{-3}, \qquad A_2' = -1.9709993 \times 10^{-3},$$
$$A_1' = 0.98696044 \times 10^{-3}.$$

The gain curves, $G(\omega) = |F(\omega)|$ and $G^*(\omega) = |F^*(\omega)|$, are labeled 1 and 2, respectively (see Fig. 19.7.1). These two curves overlap so as to be indistinguishable (except near the folding frequency, $\omega = 100$ rad/sec). Since the slope of $G^*(\omega)$ must vanish at the folding frequency, such departure of the gain curves is inherent in sampling. The phase curves,

$$P(\omega) = \tan^{-1}\left|\frac{\text{Im } F(\omega)}{\text{Re } F(\omega)}\right| \quad \text{and} \quad P^*(\omega) = \tan^{-1}\left[\frac{\text{Im } F^*(\omega)}{\text{Re } F^*(\omega)}\right],$$

are labeled 3 and 4, respectively, in Fig. 19.7.1. These two curves overlap so as to be indistinguishable.

19.8 SUPPLEMENTARY REFERENCES

While we have discussed only linear filters with constant coefficients, Rich and Shaw (b) have used the substitution rule to construct an optimum adaptive second-order filter to track a sinusoid in the presence of white noise. In this application, the filter coefficients depend on a short-time mean and standard deviation of the zero crossings of the filter output. The references referred to are:

a) H. SHAW, "Discrete Analogues for Continuous Filters," *Journal for the Association of Computing Machinery*, 1966.

b) R. P. RICH, and H. SHAW, "An Application of Digital Filtering," *Applied Physics Laboratory Technical Digest*, **4**, 3 (1965) pp. 13–18.

c) A. COHEN, *Differential Equations*, D. C. Heath, Boston, 1933, p. 103.

d) G. BOOLE, *Calculus of Finite Differences*, Stechert, 1931, p. 208.

CHAPTER 20

NUMERICAL SOLUTION OF INTEGRAL EQUATIONS

20.1 INTRODUCTION

The theory concerning integral equations is generally well developed and classical. In practice there are two approaches to solving integral equation problems. The first is an analytic approach employing series, transforms, and the like, which by its nature yields only special results. The second approach employs numerical methods. The latter are of great interest, but, unfortunately, are not developed very completely at the present time. Only a few basic numerical methods are known, and little has been done to determine error bounds and rate of convergence.

In general, let $I = [a, b]$ denote a bounded interval on the real line. The principal types of equations are:

1) The Volterra equation of the first kind,

$$\int_a^x K(x, y)f(y)\, dy = g(x), \qquad a \leqq x \leqq b; \tag{20.1.1}$$

2) The Volterra equation of the second kind,

$$f(x) + \lambda \int_a^x K(x, y)f(y)\, dy = g(x), \qquad a \leqq x \leqq b; \tag{20.1.2}$$

3) The Fredholm equation of the first kind,

$$\int_I K(x, y)f(y)\, dy = g(x), \qquad a \leqq x \leqq b; \tag{20.1.3}$$

4) The Fredholm equation of the second kind,

$$f(x) + \lambda \int_I K(x, y)f(y)\, dy = g(x), \qquad a \leqq x \leqq b; \tag{20.1.4}$$

5) The Fredholm equation of the third kind,

$$\lambda \int_I K(x, y)f(y)\, dy = f(x), \qquad a \leqq x \leqq b. \tag{20.1.5}$$

In the above, g, the influence function, and K, the kernel, are given complex-valued functions; λ is a complex parameter, and f is the unknown function to be found.

Under very weak assumptions on the kernel and influence function, a Volterra equation of the second kind always has a unique solution given by the Neumann series,

$$\sum_{k=0}^{\infty} \lambda^k K_{k+1} g, \qquad\qquad (20.1.6)$$

and a Volterra equation of the first kind with sufficiently smooth kernel can be converted to an equation of the second kind.

The theory of Fredholm equations of the first kind for general kernels is very difficult. However, equations of the first kind, which arise in practice, frequently have a weighted Green's function as kernel, where the Green's function is symmetric. Examples of this special case can be found in the literature.

The theory of the general singular integral equation of the so-called Cauchy type can be reduced to the theory of Fredholm equations which is already known. Numerical methods are not suitable for singular integral equations, and so, before attempting to solve an equation numerically, singularities must be removed.

The remainder of this chapter will be devoted to numerical solutions of Fredholm integral equations of the second and third kinds.

20.2 THE FREDHOLM EQUATION OF THE SECOND KIND

An equation in the form of (20.1.4) is said to be a Fredholm linear integral equation of the second kind. It is linear since the unknown function f appears to no higher power than one. The equation is said to be nonsingular when both limits of integration are finite and the kernal $K(x, y)$ is well defined on $[a, b]$. We shall consider only linear nonsingular equations. The kernel $K(x, y)$, the influence function $g(x)$, the limits a, b, and the parameter λ are all known. We wish to find the unknown function f so that (20.1.4) is satisfied for all values of y in the closed interval $a \leqq y \leqq b$.

20.3 METHOD OF SOLUTION

Divide the interval $[a, b]$ into n equal intervals, each of length h:

$$h = \frac{b - a}{n}. \qquad\qquad (20.3.1)$$

Call the left and right endpoints of these intervals mesh points. Any such mesh point can be written as

$$Y_i = X_i = a + (i - 1)\frac{(b - a)}{n}, \qquad i = 1, 2, \ldots, n + 1. \quad (20.3.2)$$

Replace the definite integral $\int_a^b k(x, y) f(y) \, dy$ by the Gregory integration formula. This formula, applied to an arbitrary definite integral $\int_a^b H(t) \, dt$, gives the following:

$$\int_a^b H(t) \, dt = h[\tfrac{1}{2} H(t_1) + H(t_2) + \cdots + H(t_n) + \tfrac{1}{2} H(t_{n+1}) + c], \quad (20.3.3)$$

where h and n are defined as above and there are a total of $n + 1$ mesh points in the interval from a to b. The term c, to be defined later, is the correction term involving finite differences.

Applying Gregory's integration formula to Fredholm's equation, we have for some fixed point ξ:

$$f(\xi) + \lambda[h\{\tfrac{1}{2}k(\xi, x_1)f(x_1) + k(\xi, x_2)f(x_2) + \cdots$$
$$+ k(\xi, x_n)f(x_n) + \tfrac{1}{2}k(\xi, x_{n+1})f(x_{n+1}) + c(\xi)\}] = g(\xi).$$

In the integration formula, ξ may be assigned any value for which the kernel is defined. However, due to the appearance of $f(\xi)$ in the equation, it is convenient to choose the ξ's to be mesh points of $[a, b]$. The reason for the choice is clear when one notes that for any ξ the function f assumes the same $n + 1$ mesh values. Letting ξ vary over all mesh points, we obtain a set of linear algebraic equations involving our unknown f at the $n + 1$ mesh points. Thus

$$f(x_1) + \lambda h\{\tfrac{1}{2}k(x_1, x_1)f(x_1) + \cdots + \tfrac{1}{2}k(x_1, x_{n+1})f(x_{n+1})\} = g(x_1) - \lambda hc(x_1),$$
$$f(x_2) + \lambda h\{\tfrac{1}{2}k(x_2, x_1)f(x_1) + \cdots + \tfrac{1}{2}k(x_2, x_{n+1})f(x_{n+1})\} = g(x_2) - \lambda hc(x_2),$$
$$\vdots$$
$$f(x_{n+1}) + \lambda h\{\tfrac{1}{2}k(x_{n+1}, x_1)f(x_1) + \cdots + \tfrac{1}{2}k(x_{n+1}, x_{n+1})f(x_{n+1})\} = g(x_{n+1}) - \lambda hc(x_{n+1}),$$

(20.3.4)

or

$$AF = G - \lambda hC, \tag{20.3.5}$$

where

$$F = \begin{pmatrix} f(x_1) \\ f(x_2) \\ \vdots \\ f(x_{n+1}) \end{pmatrix}, \qquad G = \begin{pmatrix} g(x_1) \\ g(x_2) \\ \vdots \\ g(x_{n+1}) \end{pmatrix}, \qquad C = \begin{pmatrix} c(x_1) \\ c(x_2) \\ \vdots \\ c(x_{n+1}) \end{pmatrix},$$

and

$$A = \begin{pmatrix} 1 + \dfrac{\lambda h}{2} k(x_1, x_1) & + \lambda h k(x_1, x_2) \cdots & + \dfrac{\lambda h}{2} k(x_1, x_{n+1}) \\ + \dfrac{\lambda h}{2} k(x_2, x_1) & 1 + \lambda h k(x_2, x_2) \cdots & \vdots \\ \vdots & & \\ + \dfrac{\lambda h}{2} k(x_{n+1}, x_1) & \cdots & 1 + \dfrac{\lambda h}{2} k(x_{n+1}, x_{n+1}) \end{pmatrix}.$$

We can easily calculate A and G because they are composed of known quantities.

The general expression for the correction term c is

$$c = -[\tfrac{1}{12}\nabla + \tfrac{1}{24}\nabla^2 + \tfrac{19}{720}\nabla^3 + \cdots]H(t_{n+1})$$
$$+ [\tfrac{1}{12}\Delta - \tfrac{1}{24}\Delta^2 + \tfrac{19}{720}\Delta^3 + \cdots]H(t_1), \tag{20.3.6}$$

where ∇, Δ are the finite difference operators defined as follows: The first backward difference of a function H at a given point t is

$$\nabla H(t) = H(t) - H(t - h), \tag{20.3.7}$$

and the first forward difference is

$$\Delta H(t) = H(t + h) - H(t). \tag{20.3.8}$$

Likewise higher-order differences are given by

$$\nabla^r H(t) = \nabla^{r-1} H(t) - \nabla^{r-1} H(t - h), \tag{20.3.9}$$

$$\Delta^r H(t) = \Delta^{r-1} H(t + h) - \Delta^{r-1} H(t). \tag{20.3.10}$$

Applying (20.3.6) to the function for which we wish to form differences, namely $k(x_i, x_j)f(x_j)$, we have

$$c(x_i) = -[\tfrac{1}{12}\nabla + \tfrac{1}{24}\nabla^2 + \cdots]k(x_i, x_{n+1})f(x_{n+1})$$
$$+ [\tfrac{1}{12}\Delta - \tfrac{1}{24}\Delta^2 + \cdots]k(x_i, x_1)f(x_1).$$

For each i, $i = 1, 2, \ldots, n + 1$, the backward differences of the function $k(x_i, x_j)f(x_j)$ at the mesh point x_{n+1}, that is, $j = n + 1$ are

$$\nabla[k(x_i, x_{n+1})f(x_{n+1})] = k(x_i, x_{n+1})f(x_{n+1}) - k(x_i, x_{n+1} - h)f(x_{n+1} - h),$$
$$\nabla^r[k(x_i, x_{n+1})f(x_{n+1})] = \nabla^{r-1}[k(x_i, x_{n+1})f(x_{n+1})]$$
$$- \nabla^{r-1}[k(x_i, x_{n+1} - h)f(x_{n+1} - h)].$$

The forward differences of the function $k(x_i, x_j)f(x_j)$ at mesh point x_1 are

$$\Delta[k(x_i, x_1)f(x_1)] = k(x_i, x_1 + h)f(x_1 + h) - k(x_i, x_1)f(x_1),$$
$$\Delta^r[k(x_i, x_1)f(x_1)] = \Delta^{r-1}[k(x_i, x_1 + h)]f(x_1 + h)] - \Delta^{r-1}[k(x_i, x_1)f(x_1)].$$

For machine purposes it is more convenient to write c as a function of backward differences only. Thus

$$c = \{\tfrac{1}{12}\nabla H(t_2) - \tfrac{1}{24}\nabla^2 H(t_3) + \tfrac{19}{720}\nabla^3 H(t_4) - \tfrac{3}{160}\nabla^4 H(t_5) + \cdots\}$$
$$- \{\tfrac{1}{12}\nabla H(t_{n+1}) + \tfrac{1}{24}\nabla^2 H(t_{n+1}) + \tfrac{19}{720}\nabla^3 H(t_{n+1}) + \cdots\}.$$

It is easy to see that the two forms for c are equivalent since

$$\Delta H(t_1) = \nabla H(t_2),$$
$$\Delta^2 H(t_1) = \nabla^2 H(t_3),$$
$$\vdots$$
$$\Delta^p H(t_1) = \nabla^p H(t_{p+1}).$$

The coefficients $\{+\tfrac{1}{12}, -\tfrac{1}{24}, +\tfrac{19}{720}, \cdots\} = \{G_1, G_2, \ldots\}$, known as the Gregory coefficients, are generated by the following recurrence relation. Let $G_0 = 0$, $n = 1, 2, 3, \ldots$. Then

$$G_n = \frac{G_{n-1}}{2} - \frac{G_{n-2}}{3} + \frac{G_{n-3}}{4} + \cdots + (-1)^{n+1}\frac{G_0}{n+1}$$
$$+ (-1)^{n+1}\frac{n}{2(n+1)(n+2)}$$

or

$$G_n = \sum_{i=1}^{n} (-1)^{n+1}\frac{G_{n-i}}{i+1} + (-1)^{n+1}\frac{n}{2(n+1)(n+2)}. \tag{20.3.11}$$

This recurrence relation was formulated from the equation

$$\frac{1}{\log(1+x)} = \sum_{i=1}^{\infty} A_i X_i,$$

where

$$A_1 = 1,$$
$$A_2 = \tfrac{1}{2},$$
$$A_3 = -\tfrac{1}{12},$$
$$A_4 = +\tfrac{1}{24}.$$

20.4 DIFFERENCE CORRECTION TECHNIQUE

The natural question which now arises is how many differences does c involve? For any set of $P+1$ numbers, a maximum of P differences can be taken. If the set of $P+1$ values is obtained from a polynomial for equally spaced mesh points, then successive differences of these numbers give rise to a finite difference table in which some order of difference is a constant. By the *fundamental theorem of difference calculus* the nth difference of an nth-degree polynomial is a constant and the $n+1$ difference is zero. (This assumes that computational errors are negligible.) If the function is not a polynomial, successive differences will decrease in magnitude, and they will approach, but not necessarily attain, a constant value for some order of difference. When carried past this minimum term, differences begin to increase due to the introduction of random signs. Once the differences begin to grow in magnitude, they cease to have meaning. Differences taken of random numbers begin to grow immediately, unless by chance the random numbers represent the values of a reasonably well-behaved function.

We form differences of the function $k(x_i, x_j)f(x_j)$, which is rarely a polynomial in practice. Experimentally it is difficult to determine which column in the difference table is the column of constant terms, since a column may never be reached in which all elements are the same to even one decimal place. For our purposes this is not crucial, because we need only detect the vicinity of this column of constant terms. A good test to determine when the difference table should be truncated is the following: If $|\Delta^{p+1} - \nabla^{p+1}| > |\Delta^p - \nabla^p|$, then a sufficient number of differences have been taken, and we include in $c(x_i)$ all differences up through the Pth difference. Note that the general expression for c involves the values $f(x_{n+1})$ and $f(x_1)$.

20.5 APPROXIMATION AND CORRECTION

Our problem has now been reduced to solving a set of $n+1$ linear nonhomogeneous equations in $n+1$ unknowns. This system (20.3.4) has a unique solution if and only if the coefficient matrix A is nonsingular.

The first approximation, F_1 to f, is obtained by setting $c(x_i) = 0$, $i = 1, 2, \ldots, n+1$ and solving the resulting system $AF_1 = G$ (A, G, known) for the column F_1, where F_1 is the value of f at the $n + 1$ mesh points:

$$F_1 = \begin{pmatrix} f_1(x_1) \\ f_1(x_2) \\ \vdots \\ f_1(x_{n+1}) \end{pmatrix}.$$

All corrections to F_1 are obtained by use of the difference correction technique.

The first correction to F_1, call it F_2, is the result of solving $AF_2 = C_1$ for F_2. The matrix A is the same as before and C_1 uses $f_1(x_{n+1})$ and $f_1(x_1)$ for each x_i. Thus we have

$$C_1 = \begin{pmatrix} c_1(x_1) \\ c_1(x_2) \\ \vdots \\ c_1(x_{n+1}) \end{pmatrix},$$

$$c_1(x_1) = -[\tfrac{1}{12}\nabla + \tfrac{1}{24}\nabla^2 + \cdots]k(x_1, x_{n+1})f_1(x_{n+1})$$
$$+[\tfrac{1}{12}\nabla - \cdots]k(x_1, x_1)f_1(x_1),$$

$$c_1(x_{n+1}) = -[\tfrac{1}{12}\nabla + \cdots]k(x_{n+1}, x_{n+1})f_1(x_{n+1})$$
$$+[\tfrac{1}{12}\nabla - \cdots]k(x_{n+1}, x_1)f_1(x_1).$$

Likewise, once F_2 is found, the values $f_2(x_{n+1})$ and $f_2(x_1)$ are used in computing C_2. The second correction to F_1 is the result of solving $AF_3 = C_2$ for F_3. The final F is $F = F_1 + F_2 + F_3 + \cdots$. In the calculation of the final F,

$$F = \sum_{q=1}^{k} F_q,$$

iteration is continued until further corrections are small. A correction F_q,

$$F_q = \begin{pmatrix} f_q(x_1) \\ f_q(x_2) \\ \vdots \\ f_q(x_{n+1}) \end{pmatrix},$$

is considered to be negligible if $Z < 10^{-8}$, where

$$Z = \frac{\sum_{i=1}^{n+1} |f_q(x_i)|}{\sum_{i=1}^{n+1} |F(x_i)|},$$

and F is the final F summed up to the approximation in question. No more than two corrections were necessary on test examples solved. (That is, $F = F_1 + F_2 + F_3$.)

It should be noted that the complete answer to the integral equation is a function f. Our numerical answer is the value of f at the chosen mesh points.

This numerical answer does not, by itself, give any information regarding values of f at points other than those tabulated. As might be expected, smaller mesh sizes (i.e., greater number of points) give greater accuracy.

In the examples tried, fifty mesh points gave no less than seven decimals of accuracy, while ten points gave no less than three.

Example.

$$f(x) - \tfrac{1}{2} \int_0^1 xyf(y)\, dy = \frac{5x}{6}. \quad \text{Answer: } f(x) = x.$$

$$g(x) = \frac{5x}{6}, \; a = 0, \; b = 1, \; k(x, y) = xy, \; \lambda = -\tfrac{1}{2}.$$

Solution. Let $N = 11$, then $h = (1 - 0)/10$ length of each interval.

Applying Gregory's integration formula for some fixed mesh point x_i, we have

$$f(x_i) + (-\tfrac{1}{2})(\tfrac{1}{10})[\tfrac{1}{2}(x_i x_1)f(x_1) + (x_i x_2)f(x_2) + \cdots$$
$$+ (x_i x_{10})f(x_{10}) + \tfrac{1}{2}(x_i x_{11})f(x_{11}) + c(x_i)] = 5x_i/6.$$

Let i take on all possible values $i = 1, 2, \ldots, 11$. We obtain our set of 11 algebraic equations:

$$f(x_1) + (-\tfrac{1}{2})(\tfrac{1}{10})[\tfrac{1}{2}x_1 x_1 f(x_1) + x_1 x_2 f(x_2) + \cdots + x_1 x_{10}f(x_{10}) + \tfrac{1}{2}x_1 x_{11}f(x_{11}) + c(x_1)] = 5x_1/6,$$
$$f(x_2) + (-\tfrac{1}{2})(\tfrac{1}{10})[\tfrac{1}{2}x_2 x_1 f(x_1) + x_2 x_2 f(x_2) + \cdots + x_2 x_{10}f(x_{10}) + \tfrac{1}{2}x_2 x_{11}f(x_{11}) + c(x_2)] = 5x_2/6,$$
$$\vdots$$
$$f(x_{11}) + (-\tfrac{1}{2})(\tfrac{1}{10})[\tfrac{1}{2}x_{11} x_1 f(x_1) + x_{11} x_2 f(x_2) + \cdots + x_{11} x_{10}f(x_{10}) + \tfrac{1}{2}x_{11} x_{11}f(x_{11}) + c(x_{11})] = 5x_{11}/6.$$

Writing the set of algebraic equations in matrix form, we have

$$AF = G - (\tfrac{1}{2})(\tfrac{1}{10})C,$$

where

$$A = \begin{pmatrix}
1 - \dfrac{\frac{1}{2}(1/10)x_1 x_1}{2} & -\tfrac{1}{2}(1/10)x_1 x_2 & \cdots & \dfrac{-\frac{1}{2}(1/10)x_1 x_{11}}{2} \\
\dfrac{-\frac{1}{2}(1/10)x_2 x_1}{2} & 1 - \tfrac{1}{2}(1/10)x_2 x_2 & \cdots & \dfrac{-\frac{1}{2}(1/10)x_2 x_{11}}{2} \\
\vdots & & & \vdots \\
\dfrac{-\frac{1}{2}(1/10)x_{11} x_1}{2} & -\tfrac{1}{2}(1/10)x_{11} x_2 & \cdots & 1 - \dfrac{\frac{1}{2}(1/10)x_{11} x_{11}}{2}
\end{pmatrix},$$

$$G = \begin{pmatrix} \dfrac{5x_1}{6} \\ \dfrac{5x_2}{6} \\ \vdots \\ \dfrac{5x_{11}}{6} \end{pmatrix}$$
(the elements of A and G are known since the mesh points are known),

and

$$F = \begin{pmatrix} f(x_1) \\ f(x_2) \\ \vdots \\ f(x_{11}) \end{pmatrix} \qquad (F \text{ is to be found}).$$

Solve $AF_1 = G$ for F_1 to obtain an approximation to the final f:

$$F_1 = \begin{pmatrix} 0.0 \\ 0.100 & 100 & 09 \\ 0.200 & 200 & 19 \\ 0.300 & 300 & 29 \\ 0.400 & 400 & 39 \\ 0.500 & 500 & 49 \\ 0.600 & 600 & 59 \\ 0.700 & 700 & 69 \\ 0.800 & 800 & 79 \\ 0.900 & 900 & 88 \\ 0.100 & 100 & 09 & \times 10 \end{pmatrix}$$

The first approximation is good to 3 decimals of true answer. Using F_1, calculate C_1:

$$C_1 = \begin{pmatrix} c_1(x_1) \\ c_1(x_2) \\ \vdots \\ c_1(x_{11}) \end{pmatrix},$$

$$c_1(x_{10}) = \tfrac{1}{12}\{-\nabla[x_{10}x_{11}f_1(x_{11})] + \nabla[x_{10}x_2 f_1(x_2)]\}$$
$$+ \tfrac{1}{24}\{\ \nabla^2[x_{10}x_{11}f_1(x_{11})] - \nabla^2[x_{10}x_3 f_1(x_3)]\} + \cdots.$$

Consider $c_1(x_{10}) = \tfrac{1}{12}[\text{term 1}] + \tfrac{1}{24}[\text{term 2}] + \cdots$ We stop adding differences into $c_1(x_{10})$ when the absolute value of term $j + 1$ times its associated Gregory coefficient is larger than the absolute value of term j times its Gregory coefficient. Since we eventually wish to form $-\lambda h C$, it is convenient to calculate $-\lambda h c_1(x_i)$.

Table 20.5.1 lists differences which were computed to evaluate $-\lambda h c_1(x_{10})$. From the table, all components of $-\lambda h c_1(x_{10})$ may be read off. For example,

$$\nabla\ [-\lambda h k(x_{10}, x_2)f_1(x_2)] \ = 0.450\ 450\ 42 \times 10^{-3},$$
$$\nabla^2[-\lambda h k(x_{10}, x_3)f_1(x_3)] \ = 0.900\ 900\ 84 \times 10^{-3},$$
$$\nabla\ [-\lambda h k(x_{10}, x_{11})f_1(x_{11})] = 0.855\ 855\ 87 \times 10^{-2},$$
$$\nabla^2[-\lambda h k(x_{10}, x_{11})f_1(x_{11})] = 0.900\ 902\ 32 \times 10^{-3}.$$

In this example, the function for which we are taking differences is a polynomial of degree 2, hence third-order differences are essentially zero. The column

Table 20.5.1

Differences of the function $-\lambda hk(x_{10}, x_i)f(x_i)$, $i = 1, 2, \ldots, 11$

				∇
$x_1 = 0$	$-\lambda hk(x_{10}, x_1)f_1(x_1)$	$=$	0.0	
$x_2 = \frac{1}{10}$	$-\lambda hk(x_{10}, x_2)f_1(x_2)$	$=$	$+0.450\ 450\ 42 \times 10^{-3}$	$0.450\ 450\ 42 \times 10^{-3}$
$x_3 = \frac{2}{10}$	$-\lambda hk(x_{10}, x_3)f_1(x_3)$	$=$	$+0.180\ 180\ 17 \times 10^{-2}$	$0.135\ 135\ 12 \times 10^{-2}$
$x_4 = \frac{3}{10}$	$-\lambda hk(x_{10}, x_4)f_1(x_4)$	$=$	$+0.405\ 405\ 38 \times 10^{-2}$	$0.225\ 225\ 21 \times 10^{-2}$
$x_5 = \frac{4}{10}$	$-\lambda hk(x_{10}, x_5)f_1(x_5)$	$=$	$+0.720\ 720\ 68 \times 10^{-2}$	$0.315\ 315\ 30 \times 10^{-2}$
$x_6 = \frac{5}{10}$	$-\lambda hk(x_{10}, x_6)f_1(x_6)$	$=$	$+0.112\ 612\ 61 \times 10^{-1}$	$0.405\ 405\ 39 \times 10^{-2}$
$x_7 = \frac{6}{10}$	$-\lambda hk(x_{10}, x_7)f_1(x_7)$	$=$	$+0.162\ 162\ 15 \times 10^{-1}$	$0.495\ 495\ 45 \times 10^{-3}$
$x_8 = \frac{7}{10}$	$-\lambda hk(x_{10}, x_8)f_1(x_8)$	$=$	$+0.220\ 720\ 71 \times 10^{-1}$	$0.585\ 585\ 57 \times 10^{-2}$
$x_9 = \frac{8}{10}$	$-\lambda hk(x_{10}, x_9)f_1(x_9)$	$=$	$+0.288\ 288\ 27 \times 10^{-1}$	$0.675\ 756\ 67 \times 10^{-2}$
$x_{10} = \frac{9}{10}$	$-\lambda hk(x_{10}, x_{10})f_1(x_{10})$	$=$	$+0.364\ 864\ 84 \times 10^{-1}$	$0.765\ 765\ 64 \times 10^{-2}$
$x_{11} = \frac{10}{10}$	$-\lambda hk(x_{10}, x_{11})f_1(x_{11})$	$=$	$+0.450\ 450\ 43 \times 10^{-1}$	$0.855\ 855\ 87 \times 10^{-2}$

∇^2	∇^3	∇^4
$0.900\ 900\ 84 \times 10^{-3}$		
	$-0.727\ 595\ 76 \times 10^{-1}$	
$0.900\ 900\ 83 \times 10^{-3}$		$0.654\ 836\ 19 \times 10^{-10}$
	$0.582\ 076\ 61 \times 10^{-10}$	
$0.900\ 900\ 83 \times 10^{-3}$		$-0.291\ 038\ 30 \times 10^{-10}$
	$0.291\ 030\ 30 \times 10^{-10}$	
$0.900\ 900\ 92 \times 10^{-3}$		$-0.378\ 349\ 80 \times 10^{-9}$
	$-0.349\ 245\ 97 \times 10^{-9}$	
$0.900\ 900\ 57 \times 10^{-3}$		$0.104\ 773\ 79 \times 10^{-8}$
	$0.698\ 491\ 93 \times 10^{-9}$	
$0.900\ 091\ 27 \times 10^{-3}$		$-0.104\ 773\ 79 \times 10^{-8}$
	$-0.349\ 245\ 97 \times 10^{-9}$	
$0.900\ 900\ 92 \times 10^{-3}$		$-0.814\ 907\ 25 \times 10^{-9}$
	$-0.116\ 415\ 32 \times 10^{-8}$	
$0.900\ 899\ 75 \times 10^{-3}$		$0.372\ 529\ 03 \times 10^{-8}$
	$0.256\ 113\ 71 \times 10^{-8}$	
$0.900\ 902\ 32 \times 10^{-3}$		

of second differences is easily seen to be constant. Since 11 mesh points are used, it is possible to form 10 differences; however, our test stops us from taking more than 3 differences. If 50 mesh points had been used, 49 differences could have been formed. But, due to rounding error, higher-order differences, when they are included in $c_1(x_{10})$, are harmful. For 50 points, the 48 differences have magnitudes in the neighborhood of 10^{10}.

In order to compute $c_1(x_1)$, we form a table of differences of the function $-\lambda h k(x_1, x_i) f(x_i)$. The same thing would be done to compute $c_1(x_2), c_1(x_3), \ldots, c_1(x_{11})$. Thus

$$-\lambda h C_1 = \begin{pmatrix} 0 \\ -0.834\ 167\ 64 \times 10^{-4} \\ -0.166\ 833\ 53 \times 10^{-3} \\ -0.250\ 250\ 30 \times 10^{-3} \\ -0.333\ 667\ 05 \times 10^{-3} \\ -0.417\ 083\ 80 \times 10^{-3} \\ -0.500\ 500\ 60 \times 10^{-3} \\ -0.583\ 917\ 28 \times 10^{-3} \\ -0.667\ 334\ 12 \times 10^{-3} \\ -0.750\ 750\ 88 \times 10^{-3} \\ -0.834\ 167\ 60 \times 10^{-3} \end{pmatrix}.$$

The first correction to F_1 is obtained by solving

$$AF_2 = C_1 \text{ for } F_2.$$

Here A and C_1 are known. We form

$$F_2 = \begin{pmatrix} 0 \\ -0.100\ 200\ 31 \times 10^{-3} \\ -0.200\ 400\ 63 \times 10^{-3} \\ -0.300\ 600\ 96 \times 10^{-3} \\ -0.400\ 801\ 26 \times 10^{-3} \\ -0.501\ 001\ 56 \times 10^{-3} \\ -0.601\ 201\ 93 \times 10^{-3} \\ -0.701\ 402\ 15 \times 10^{-3} \\ -0.801\ 602\ 54 \times 10^{-3} \\ -0.901\ 802\ 85 \times 10^{-3} \\ -0.100\ 200\ 31 \times 10^{-3} \end{pmatrix} \quad \text{and} \quad F_1 + F_2 = \begin{pmatrix} 0 \\ 0.999\ 998\ 97 \times 10^{-1} \\ 0.199\ 999\ 79 \\ 0.299\ 999\ 69 \\ 0.399\ 999\ 59 \\ 0.499\ 999\ 49 \\ 0.599\ 999\ 39 \\ 0.699\ 999\ 29 \\ 0.799\ 999\ 18 \\ 0.899\ 999\ 07 \\ 0.999\ 998\ 98 \end{pmatrix}.$$

If a second correction F_3 to F_1 is necessary, then the values of F_2 are used to compute C_2 in exactly the same manner that F_1 was used to evaluate C_1.

In this example, final $F = F_1 + F_2 + F_3$ since further corrections are negligible. By negligible we mean that

$$\frac{\sum_{i=1}^{11} |F_4(x_i)|}{\sum_{i=1}^{11} |F_1(x_i) + F_2(x_i) + F_3(x_i)|} < 10^{-8},$$

and the final machine and true answers are as follows:

$$
\begin{array}{cc}
\text{Machine Answer} & \text{True Answer} \\
\begin{pmatrix}
0 \\
0.999\ 999\ 91 \times 10^{-1} \\
0.199\ 999\ 99 \\
0.299\ 999\ 99 \\
0.399\ 999\ 98 \\
0.499\ 999\ 99 \\
0.599\ 999\ 99 \\
0.699\ 999\ 99 \\
0.799\ 999\ 98 \\
0.899\ 999\ 98 \\
0.999\ 899\ 98
\end{pmatrix}
, &
\begin{pmatrix}
0 \\
0.100\ 000\ 00 \\
0.200\ 000\ 00 \\
0.300\ 000\ 00 \\
0.400\ 000\ 00 \\
0.500\ 000\ 00 \\
0.600\ 000\ 00 \\
0.700\ 000\ 00 \\
0.800\ 000\ 00 \\
0.900\ 000\ 00 \\
0.100\ 000\ 00 \times 10^{+1}
\end{pmatrix}
\end{array}.
$$

20.6 THE FREDHOLM EQUATION OF THE THIRD KIND

Fredholm's integral equation of the third kind is essentially an eigenvalue problem in which we must calculate both the eigenvalues and their associated eigenfunctions. By replacing the definite integral with Gregory's integration formula, the integral equation is reduced to a standard eigenvalue matrix equation, $BF = \xi F$. The form of Fredholm's linear nonsingular integral equation of the third kind is given by (20.1.5). The limits of integration are finite and real. The kernel $K(x, y)$, which is also real, is well behaved on $[a, b]$. The unknown function f appears to no higher power than one.

Solutions of (20.1.5) exist only for discrete values of λ. The problem is to find one or more eigenvalues (that is, λ's) and the associated eigenfunctions f. Note that the eigenvalues for an integral equation are defined with the parameter λ on the left side of the equation. Values of λ, real or complex, are computed, but eigenvectors are computed for only the real λ.

20.7 METHOD OF SOLUTION

Divide the interval $[a, b]$ into n equally spaced intervals, each of length h:

$$
h = \frac{b - a}{n}. \tag{20.7.1}
$$

Replace the definite integral $\int_a^b K(x, y)f(y)\, dy$ by Gregory's integration formula. We thus obtain the following set of linear algebraic equations involving the unknown f at the $n + 1$ mesh points:

$$
\frac{k(x_1, x_1)}{2} f(x_1) + k(x_1, x_2)f(x_2) + \cdots + k(x_1, x_n)f(x_n) + \frac{k(x_1, x_{n+1})f(x_{n+1})}{2} + c(x_1) = \frac{1}{\lambda h} f(x_1),
$$

$$
\frac{k(x_2, x_1)}{2} f(x_1) + k(x_2, x_2)f(x_2) + \cdots + k(x_2, x_n) + \frac{k(x_2, x_{n+1})f(x_{n+1})}{2} + c(x_2) = \frac{1}{\lambda h} f(x_2),
$$

$$
\vdots \tag{20.7.2}
$$

$$
\frac{k(x_{n+1}, x_1)f(x_1)}{2} + k(x_{n+1}, x_2)f(x_2) + \cdots + k(x_{n+1}, x_n)f(x_n) + \frac{k(x_{n+1}, x_{n+1})f(x_{n+1})}{2} + c(x_{n+1}) = \frac{1}{\lambda h} f(x_{n+1}).
$$

Rewriting (20.7.2) in matrix form, we have

$$AF + c = \frac{1}{\lambda h} F, \tag{20.7.3}$$

where A, F, and c are

$$F = \begin{pmatrix} f(x_1) \\ f(x_2) \\ \vdots \\ f(x_{n+1}) \end{pmatrix} \quad (F \text{ is to be found}),$$

$$A = \begin{pmatrix} \dfrac{k(x_1, x_1)}{2} & k(x_1, x_2) & \cdots & k(x_1, x_n) & \dfrac{k(x_1, x_{n+1})}{2} \\[2ex] \dfrac{k(x_2, x_1)}{2} & k(x_2, x_2) & \cdots & k(x_2, x_n) & \dfrac{k(x_2, x_{n+1})}{2} \\[2ex] \vdots & & & & \\[1ex] \dfrac{k(x_{n+1}, x_1)}{2} & k(x_{n+1}, x_2) & \cdots & k(x_{n+1}, x_n) & \dfrac{k(x_{n+1}, x_{n+1})}{2} \end{pmatrix},$$

$$c = \begin{pmatrix} c(x_1) \\ c(x_2) \\ \vdots \\ c(x_{n+1}) \end{pmatrix} \quad [c(x_i) \text{ is the correction term in Gregory's integration formula}],$$

and

$$c(x_i) = -[\tfrac{1}{12}\nabla + \tfrac{1}{24}\nabla^2 + \cdots]k(x_i, x_{n+1})f(x_{n+1}) + [\tfrac{1}{12}\Delta - \tfrac{1}{24}\Delta^2$$
$$+ \cdots]k(x_i, x_1)f(x_1), \quad i = 1, 2, \ldots, n+1. \tag{20.7.4}$$

Note that (20.7.3) closely resembles the form of the standard matrix eigenvalue problem $BF = \xi F$, where F is the eigenvector and ξ is the eigenvalue. If matrix c could be rewritten as a square matrix C, times a column matrix F, then (20.7.3) would reduce to the standard eigenform. That is, if $c = CF$, then

$$AF + c = AF + CF = (A + C)F = (1/\lambda h)F.$$

Once the order of the last significant difference is known, then $c(x_i)$ becomes nothing more than a linear combination of the f's. That is, for any fixed i,

$$c(x_i) = a_{i,1}f(x_1) + a_{i,2}f(x_2) + a_{i,3}f(x_3) + \cdots + a_{i,n+1}f(x_{n+1}),$$

where $\{a_{i,1}, a_{i,2}, \ldots, a_{i,n+1}\}$ is the set of known constants resulting from the expansion of $c(x_i)$. The f's are still unknown. Hence

$$c(x_i) = (a_{i,1}, a_{i,2}, \ldots, a_{i,n+1}) \begin{pmatrix} f(x_1) \\ f(x_2) \\ \vdots \\ f(x_{n+1}) \end{pmatrix},$$

and

$$c = \begin{pmatrix} a_{1,1} & a_{1,2} & \cdots & a_{1,n+1} \\ a_{2,1} & a_{2,2} & \cdots & a_{2,n+1} \\ \vdots & & & \vdots \\ a_{n+1,1} & a_{n+1,2} & \cdots & a_{n+1,n+1} \end{pmatrix} \underbrace{\begin{pmatrix} f(x_1) \\ f(x_2) \\ \vdots \\ f(x_{n+1}) \end{pmatrix}}_{F} = CF.$$

$$\underbrace{\qquad\qquad\qquad\qquad\qquad\qquad}_{C}$$

Formation of matrix C readily follows by keeping in mind three distinct operations.

1) Each difference in (20.7.4) (that is, ∇, ∇^2, ∇^3, ...) must be written explicitly as a linear combination of the f's.

2) The order of the last significant difference must be decided upon prior to the expansion of C.

3) The expanded differences must be multiplied by the corresponding Gregory coefficient and combined in the order specified by (20.7.4).

The general form for C is

$$C = \begin{pmatrix} ak(x_1, x_1) & bk(x_1, x_2) & \cdots & zk(x_1, x_N) \\ ak(x_2, x_1) & bk(x_2, x_2) & \cdots & zk(x_2, x_N) \\ \vdots & & & \vdots \\ ak(x_N, x_1) & bk(x_N, x_2) & \cdots & zk(x_N, x_N) \end{pmatrix},$$

where $a, b, \ldots, z$ are constants which result from the expansion of $c(x_i)$.

For example, if four mesh points are chosen and if it is found that there are only two significant differences, then the correction term for x_1 is

$$c(x_1) = -[\tfrac{1}{12}\nabla + \tfrac{1}{24}\nabla^2]k(x_1, x_4) + [\tfrac{1}{12}\Delta - \tfrac{1}{24}\Delta^2]k(x_1, x_1)f(x_1),$$
$$c(x_1) = \alpha k(x_1, x_1)f(x_1) + \beta k(x_1, x_2)f(x_2) + \gamma k(x_1, x_3)f(x_3) + \eta k(x_1, x_4)f(x_4),$$

where

$$\alpha = [+\tfrac{1}{12}(-1) - \tfrac{1}{24}(+1)],$$
$$\beta = [-\tfrac{1}{24}(+1) + \tfrac{1}{12}(+1) - \tfrac{1}{24}(-2)],$$
$$\gamma = [-\tfrac{1}{12}(-1) - \tfrac{1}{24}(-2) - \tfrac{1}{24}(+1)],$$
$$\eta = [-\tfrac{1}{12}(+1) - \tfrac{1}{24}(+1)].$$

Thus

$$\begin{pmatrix} \alpha k(x_1, x_1) & \beta k(x_1, x_2) & \gamma k(x_1, x_3) & \eta k(x_1, x_4) \\ \alpha k(x_2, x_1) & \beta k(x_2, x_2) & \gamma k(x_2, x_3) & \eta k(x_2, x_4) \\ \alpha k(x_3, x_1) & \beta k(x_3, x_2) & \gamma k(x_3, x_3) & \eta k(x_3, x_4) \\ \alpha k(x_4, x_1) & \beta k(x_4, x_2) & \gamma k(x_4, x_3) & \eta k(x_4, x_4) \end{pmatrix} = C.$$

It is possible for each mesh point to have a different number of significant differences. In practice, however, the order of significant difference varies little from one mesh point to another. The number of differences which are significant for three chosen mesh points are computed, namely the second mesh point, next to the last, and center or near center. The average of these three numbers is assumed to be the highest order difference which is significant for all mesh points.

The test for whether or not a difference of $k(x_i, x_j)$ adds significantly to the expansion of $c(x_i)$ is the following: if $|\Delta^{P+1} - \nabla^{P+1}| \geq |\Delta^P - \nabla^P|$, then all differences up through the Pth are included.

20.8 COMPUTING THE EIGENVALUES

We now have

$$\left((A + C) - \frac{1}{\lambda h} I\right) F = 0, \tag{20.8.1}$$

which we wish to solve for the eigenvalues. By definition the determinant

$$\left|(A + C) - \frac{1}{\lambda h} I\right|$$

is a polynomial of degree $n + 1$ in $1/\lambda h$, called the characteristic polynomial of $A + C$. The equation $|(A + C) - (1/\lambda h)I| = 0$ is called the characteristic equation of $A + C$, and the $n + 1$ roots of this equation are called the eigenvalues of $A + C$. Each eigenvalue of $A + C$ is of the form $1/\lambda h$, while an eigenvalue of the integral equation is of the form λ.

Since $n + 1$ mesh points always produce $n + 1$ eigenvalues of $A + C$, we see that our numerical method of integration has introduced eigenvalues of the matrix equation which are extraneous to the integral equation. Thus, from the set $\{1/\lambda_i h, i = 1, 2, \ldots, n + 1\}$ of eigenvalues of $A + C$, we must choose the values which give us nonzero, finite, real λ's. Only these values of λ produce a solution to (20.1.5). To within single precision, the following method determines which roots of the characteristic equation of $A + C$ produce valid λ's.

a) Select the maximum element from the set of values

$$K = \left\{\left|\frac{1}{\lambda_j h}\right|^2 = |a_j + ib_j|^2 = a_j^2 + b_j^2, \qquad j = 1, 2, \ldots, n + 1\right\}$$

$$= \{k_1, k_2, \ldots, k_{n+1}\};$$

call it $K_{\max}$.

b) If, for any j, the ratio $k_j/K_{\max}$ is $\leq 10^{-14}$, then assume the eigenvalue $1/\lambda_j h$ from which k_j was formed as zero; if the ratio is $> 10^{-14}$, then consider $1/\lambda_j h$ to be nonzero.

c) If the imaginary part of any nonzero $1/\lambda h$ is $\leq 10^{-8}$, then $1/\lambda h$ is taken to be a real number, otherwise $1/\lambda h$ is assumed to be complex. Real nonzero values of $1/\lambda h$ produce valid λ's.

20.9 COMPUTING THE EIGENVECTORS

The eigenfunctions associated with our integral equation (20.1.5) are approximated by the eigenvectors associated with the matrix equation (20.8.1). For each value of $1/\lambda h$ from (20.8.1), there exists an associated eigenvector, unique to within a nonzero scalar multiple; however, we compute only the eigenvectors which are associated with the nonzero, real $1/\lambda h$'s. The computation of these eigenvectors is accomplished by a method of triangular decomposition combined with back substitution. The vectors are normalized by putting the last nonzero component equal to the integer 1.

A lower-triangular matrix is one in which all elements above the principal diagonal are zero. An upper-triangular matrix is one in which all elements below the principal diagonal are zero. We decompose $\big((A + C) - (1/\lambda h)I\big)$ into both upper- and lower-triangular form before finding the eigenvectors by the method of back substitution.

Moving from left to right along the principal diagonal, we search for the first element that is less than 10^{-8} in the upper-triangular matrix. A one is placed in the corresponding position of the eigenvector. If no element is $<10^{-8}$, then the element that is smallest in magnitude is chosen and a one is placed in that position. Zeros are placed in all eigenvector positions below the integer one. The remaining components of the eigenvector are computed by a method that is most easily explained by the following example.

Assume that we have four mesh points and we work with only the upper-triangular form of the decomposed matrix. This we denote by B. Let the eigenvector which is associated with a chosen nonzero, real eigenvalue be called X. Thus we have $BX = 0$:

$$
\begin{pmatrix} b_{11} & b_{12} & b_{13} & b_{14} \\ 0 & b_{22} & b_{23} & b_{24} \\ 0 & 0 & b_{33} & b_{34} \\ 0 & 0 & 0 & b_{44} \end{pmatrix}
\begin{pmatrix} x_1 \\ x_2 \\ x_3 \\ x_4 \end{pmatrix}
=
\begin{pmatrix} 0 \\ 0 \\ 0 \\ 0 \end{pmatrix}.
$$

Assume that the diagonal of B is searched, moving from left to right, and b_{33} is the first element $<10^{-8}$:

$$
b_{33} < 10^{-8} \rightarrow x_3 = 1 \text{ and } x_4 = 0.
$$

We now have

$$
X = \begin{pmatrix} x_1 \\ x_2 \\ 1 \\ 0 \end{pmatrix},
$$

in which x_1 and x_2 must be found.

We therefore calculate

$$b_{22}x_2 + b_{23} = 0 \quad \text{or} \quad x_2 = -\frac{b_{23}}{b_{22}},$$

$$b_{11}x_1 + b_{12}x_2 + b_{13} = 0 \quad \text{or} \quad x_1 = \frac{-b_{13} - b_{12}(-b_{23}/b_{22})}{b_{11}}.$$

Thus we compute eigenvectors for real nonzero values of $1/\lambda h$. If the imaginary part of $1/\lambda h$ is $>10^{-8}$, then the machine considers $1/\lambda h$ to be complex and no eigenvector is computed for this value. We should not be concerned about imaginary values of λ unless the ratio $\text{Im}(\lambda)/\text{Re}(\lambda)$ is large.

Example.

$$\lambda \int_0^{\pi/2} \sin(x+y)f(y)\,dy = f(x),$$

$$k(x, y) = \sin(x+y),$$

$$a = 0, \quad b = \pi/2.$$

Solution. Let $N = 7 = n + 1$. Then $h = [(\pi/2) - 0]/6 = $ length of each interval. Any mesh point x_i is given by

$$x_i = a + h(i - 1), \quad i = 1, 2, \ldots, 7.$$

Replacing

$$\int_0^{\pi/2} \sin(x+y)f(y)\,dy = (1/\lambda)f(x)$$

by Gregory's integration formula, we have, for a fixed mesh point x_i,

$$\tfrac{1}{2}\sin(x_i + x_1)f(x_1) + \sin(x_i + x_2)f(x_2) + \cdots + \sin(x_i + x_6)f(x_6)$$

$$+ \tfrac{1}{2}\sin(x_i + x_7)f(x_7) + c(x_i) = \frac{1}{\lambda\pi/12}f(x_i).$$

Letting i take on all possible values $i = 1, 2, \ldots, 7$, we have the following set of seven algebraic equations:

$$\tfrac{1}{2}\sin(x_1 + x_1)f(x_1) + \sin(x_1 + x_2)f(x_2) + \cdots + \sin(x_1 + x_6)f(x_6) + \tfrac{1}{2}\sin(x_1 + x_7)f(x_7) + c(x_1) = \frac{1}{\lambda\pi/12}f(x_1),$$

$$\tfrac{1}{2}\sin(x_2 + x_1)f(x_1) + \sin(x_2 + x_2)f(x_2) + \cdots + \sin(x_2 + x_6)f(x_6) + \tfrac{1}{2}\sin(x_2 + x_7)f(x_7) + c(x_2) = \frac{1}{\lambda\pi/12}f(x_2),$$

$$\vdots$$

$$\tfrac{1}{2}\sin(x_7 + x_1)f(x_1) + \sin(x_7 + x_2)f(x_2) + \cdots + \sin(x_7 + x_6)f(x_6) + \tfrac{1}{2}\sin(x_7 + x_7)f(x_7) + c(x_7) = \frac{1}{\lambda\pi/12}f(x_7).$$

Writing the set of algebraic equations in matrix form, we have

$$AF + c = \frac{1}{\lambda\pi/12}F,$$

where

$$F = \begin{pmatrix} f(x_1) \\ f(x_2) \\ \vdots \\ f(x_7) \end{pmatrix} \quad \text{(F is to be found)}, \quad c = \begin{pmatrix} c(x_1) \\ c(x_2) \\ \vdots \\ c(x_7) \end{pmatrix},$$

$$A = \begin{pmatrix} \frac{1}{2}\sin(x_1 + x_1) & \sin(x_1 + x_2) & \cdots & \sin(x_1 + x_6) & \frac{1}{2}\sin(x_1 + x_7) \\ \frac{1}{2}\sin(x_2 + x_1) & \sin(x_2 + x_2) & \cdots & \sin(x_2 + x_6) & \frac{1}{2}\sin(x_2 + x_7) \\ \vdots & & & & \vdots \\ \frac{1}{2}\sin(x_7 + x_1) & \sin(x_7 + x_2) & \cdots & \sin(x_7 + x_6) & \frac{1}{2}\sin(x_7 + x_7) \end{pmatrix}.$$

In order to reduce the problem to standard eigenvalue form, we must expand c; including any significant differences in the expansion.

Computation of differences of $k(x_i, x_j)$ for $i = 2, 3, 6$ reveal that

$$|\Delta^6 - \nabla^6| \geq |\Delta^5 - \nabla^5|$$

for each i. Hence, five differences add significantly to $c(x_2)$, $c(x_3)$, and $c(x_6)$. Each $c(x_i)$, $i = 1, 2, \ldots, 7$ is now expanded up through the fifth difference, thus expressing each correction term as a linear combination of the f's. We rewrite c as CF, where the nonzero elements of C are of the form $zk(x_i, x_j)$. The constant z is the product of the appropriate Gregory coefficient and the signed binomial coefficient. Hence

$$C = \begin{pmatrix} ak(x_1, x_1) & bk(x_1, x_2) & \cdots & gk(x_1, x_7) \\ ak(x_2, x_1) & bk(x_2, x_2) & \cdots & gk(x_2, x_7) \\ \vdots & & & \vdots \\ ak(x_7, x_1) & bk(x_7, x_2) & \cdots & gk(x_7, x_7) \end{pmatrix}.$$

We now solve $(A + C)F = [1/(\lambda\pi/12)]F$. The eigenvalues associated with $(A + C)$ are

$$\begin{aligned} +0.490\ 965\ 68 \times 10^{+1} &= 12/\lambda_1\pi, \\ -0.109\ 034\ 21 \times 10^{+1} &= 12/\lambda_2\pi, \\ -0.249\ 771\ 39 \times 10^{-8} &= 12/\lambda_3\pi, \\ 0, & \\ 0, & \\ -0.111\ 758\ 71 \times 10^{-7} &= 12/\lambda_6\pi, \\ -0.753\ 404\ 24 \times 10^{-8} &= 12/\lambda_7\pi. \end{aligned}$$

We note that the only usable values of $1/(\lambda h)$ are the first and the second. The eigenvalues associated with the integral equation are

$$\begin{aligned} 0.778\ 001\ 14 &= \lambda_1, \\ -0.350\ 322\ 93 \times 10^{+1} &= \lambda_2. \end{aligned}$$

Since the imaginary values of $1/\lambda h$ are zero, it follows that all imaginary values of λ are also zero.

In this example we know that two nonzero values of $1/\lambda$ are given by $1/\lambda = \frac{1}{2} \pm \pi(1/4)$, and the associated eigenfunctions are of the form $f(x) = \cos(x) \pm \sin(x)$. Comparing our machine answers with the results, we have

Machine Answer $1/\lambda$:

$0.128\ 534\ 51 \times 10^{+1} = 1/\lambda_1$
$-0.285\ 450\ 91 = 1/\lambda_2$

True Answer $1/\lambda$:

$0.128\ 539\ 81 \times 10^{+1}$
$-0.285\ 398\ 16$

Machine Eigenvectors:

$$\begin{pmatrix} 0.999\ 999\ 78 \\ 0.122\ 474\ 46 \times 10^{+1} \\ 0.136\ 602\ 51 \times 10^{+1} \\ 0.141\ 421\ 33 \times 10^{+1} \\ 0.136\ 602\ 52 \times 10^{+1} \\ 0.122\ 474\ 39 \times 10^{+1} \\ 0.099\ 999\ 99 \times 10^{+1} \end{pmatrix} \quad \text{for } \lambda_1$$

True Eigenvectors:

$$\begin{pmatrix} 0.099\ 999\ 99 \times 10^{+1} \\ 0.122\ 474\ 48 \times 10^{+1} \\ 0.136\ 602\ 54 \times 10^{+1} \\ 0.141\ 421\ 35 \times 10^{+1} \\ 0.136\ 602\ 54 \times 10^{+1} \\ 0.122\ 474\ 48 \times 10^{+1} \\ 0.099\ 999\ 99 \times 10^{+1} \end{pmatrix}$$

Machine Eigenvectors:

$$\begin{pmatrix} -0.999\ 999\ 86 \\ -0.707\ 106\ 66 \\ -0.366\ 025\ 30 \\ 0.653\ 106\ 62 \times 10^{-7} \\ 0.366\ 025\ 43 \\ 0.707\ 106\ 44 \\ 0.099\ 999\ 99 \times 10^{+1} \end{pmatrix} \quad \text{for } \lambda_2$$

True Eigenvectors:

$$\begin{pmatrix} 0.099\ 999\ 99 \times 10^{+1} \\ 0.707\ 106\ 78 \\ 0.366\ 025\ 40 \\ 0.745\ 058\ 06 \times 10^{-8} \\ -0.366\ 025\ 40 \\ -0.707\ 106\ 78 \\ -0.999\ 999\ 99 \end{pmatrix}$$

When $N = 13$, we have

Machine Answer $1/\lambda$:

$0.128\ 539\ 798 \times 10^{+1}$
$-0.285\ 398\ 357$

Machine Eigenvectors:

$$\begin{pmatrix} 0.999\ 999\ 74 \\ 0.112\ 198\ 08\ 10^{+1} \\ 0.122\ 474\ 45\ 10^{+1} \\ 0.130\ 656\ 27\ 10^{+1} \\ 0.136\ 602\ 51\ 10^{+1} \\ 0.140\ 211\ 45\ 10^{+1} \\ 0.141\ 421\ 33\ 10^{+1} \\ 0.140\ 211\ 46\ 10^{+1} \\ 0.136\ 602\ 52\ 10^{+1} \\ 0.130\ 656\ 16\ 10^{+1} \\ 0.122\ 474\ 48\ 10^{+1} \\ 0.112\ 197\ 09\ 10^{+1} \\ 0.999\ 999\ 99 \end{pmatrix} \quad \text{for } \lambda_1$$

True Eigenvectors:

$$\begin{pmatrix} 0.099\ 999\ 99\ 10^{+1} \\ 0.112\ 197\ 10\ 10^{+1} \\ 0.122\ 474\ 48\ 10^{+1} \\ 0.130\ 656\ 29\ 10^{+1} \\ 0.136\ 602\ 54\ 10^{+1} \\ 0.140\ 211\ 47\ 10^{+1} \\ 0.141\ 421\ 35\ 10^{+1} \\ 0.140\ 211\ 47\ 10^{+1} \\ 0.136\ 602\ 54\ 10^{+1} \\ 0.130\ 656\ 29\ 10^{+1} \\ 0.122\ 474\ 48\ 10^{+1} \\ 0.112\ 197\ 10\ 10^{+1} \\ 0.099\ 999\ 99\ 10^{+1} \end{pmatrix}$$

Machine Eigenvectors:

$$\begin{pmatrix} -0.999\ 999\ 81 \\ -0.860\ 918\ 54 \\ -0.707\ 106\ 64 \\ -0.541\ 195\ 97 \\ -0.366\ 025\ 30 \\ -0.184\ 491\ 84 \\ 0.560\ 939\ 10\ 10^{-7} \\ 0.184\ 591\ 93 \\ 0.366\ 025\ 43 \\ 0.541\ 196\ 09 \\ 0.707\ 106\ 79 \\ 0.860\ 918\ 13 \\ 0.999\ 999\ 99 \end{pmatrix} \quad \text{for } \lambda_2$$

True Eigenvectors:

$$\begin{pmatrix} 0.099\ 999\ 99\ 10^{+1} \\ 0.860\ 918\ 67 \\ 0.707\ 106\ 78 \\ 0.541\ 196\ 10 \\ 0.366\ 025\ 40 \\ 0.184\ 591\ 93 \\ 0.745\ 058\ 06\ 10^{-8} \\ -0.184\ 591\ 91 \\ -0.366\ 025\ 40 \\ -0.541\ 198\ 08 \\ -0.707\ 106\ 78 \\ -0.860\ 918\ 66 \\ -0.999\ 999\ 99 \end{pmatrix}$$

20.10 SUPPLEMENTARY REFERENCES

For a more extensive study of integral equations see Kantorovich [82], Lovitt [98], Tricomi [151] and

a) L. Fox and E. T. Goodwin, "The Numerical Solution of Non-Singular Linear Integral Equations," *Phil. Trans. Roy. Soc. London*, Series A, **245** (1953) 501–534.

b) J. Irving and N. Mullineux, *Mathematics in Physics and Engineering*, Chapter XII, Academic, New York, 1959.

c) M. A. Krasnosel'skii, *Topological Methods in the Theory of Non-Linear Integral Equations*, Macmillan, New York, 1964.

d) M. G. Krein, "Integral Equations on a Half-Line with Kernel Depending on the Difference of the Arguments," *Amer. Math. Soc. Trans.*, Series 2, **22** (1962).

e) N. I. Muskhelishvili, *Singular Integral Equations*, P. Noordhoff, Groningen, 1953.

f) P. Samuelson, "Rapidly Converging Solutions to Integral Equations," *J. Math. Phys.* **31** (1953) 276–286.

CHAPTER 21

NUMERICAL SOLUTION OF
VIBRATION PROBLEMS

21.1 INTRODUCTION

An important problem in dynamics is one in which a system executes small vibrations in the neighborhood of a stable equilibrium position. Frictional forces are always present in physical systems. In many cases they are so small that they may be neglected and the system treated as a so-called conservative system. Suppose, however, that viscous damping is present in a system and is so large it cannot be neglected. The system is then treated as a so-called nonconservative system.

We may divide the analytical determination of the vibration behavior of a physical system into four steps:

1) The choice of a mathematical model which is to be used to represent the physical system. (If the system were the wing of an aircraft, for instance, it would have to be decided whether to treat it as a continuous beam in flexure and/or torsion, as a plate or box-like structure, as some lumped-mass system, or as some other type of system.)

2) The derivation of the equations of motion of the mathematical model.

3) The determination of the physical constants occurring in the mathematical equations. (These constants—lengths, masses, stiffnesses, or spring constants, etc.—will have to be determined from the given data, which, itself, will often have been determined experimentally.)

4) The solution of the mathematical equations.

We will be concerned almost wholly with the last step of the problem. The first two steps will be discussed briefly in order to define some of the quantities encountered in the fourth step.

We conveniently divide vibrating systems into two types, discrete and continuous. The distinction is mathematical, and not physical. A discrete system is one whose exact equations of motion may be expressed as a set of ordinary differential equations in a finite number of unknowns $q_1, q_2, \ldots, q_n$, functions of time t alone. For the small oscillations with which we are concerned, the equations will be linear and have constant coefficients. Discrete systems will then be characterized by having a finite number of natural frequencies and corresponding modes of free vibration. Although exactly discrete systems never occur in practice, many physical systems are discrete for most practical purposes. An example of such a

271

system is a set of massive flywheels on a light shaft which is undergoing torsional vibration. It is possible to write down a set of linear, ordinary, differential equations governing the angular deflections $\theta_1, \theta_2, \ldots, \theta_n$ of the flywheels, and obtain from them results which conform with experiment over a very large frequency range. The system may be regarded as discrete within this range.

A continuous system is one whose exact equations of motion may be expressed as one or more partial differential equations, with boundary conditions, governing certain displacements which are functions of the space variables x, y, z and the time t. For small oscillations, the equations will be linear, but the coefficients will not necessarily be constant. Equations governing a continuous system may usually be expressed in an alternative form involving integral equations. Continuous systems are characterized by having an infinity of natural frequencies and corresponding modes of free vibration.

Although it is possible to make an absolute distinction between discrete and continuous systems in mathematics, no such clear-cut distinction is possible in the real world. In practice, the decision about whether to treat a system as discrete or continuous depends on arguments involving convenience and accuracy. The increased complication of the equations may not be justified by a comparable increase in accuracy for the ordinary working range of frequencies. The class of systems for which it is possible to write down the equations of motion as one or more partial differential equations which can be solved exactly in terms of known functions is comparatively small. When it is impossible, or difficult, to obtain an exact solution of the partial differential equations governing a continuous system, the system is almost always reduced to discrete form. In this chapter we are concerned with the properties of the equations governing a vibrating system which has been reduced to discrete form.

Often it is convenient to have a formulation of the equations of motion which makes use of quantities relating to the system as a whole, not to the elements from which it is made up. For a lumped-mass system such a formulation is provided by Lagrange's equations

$$\frac{d}{dt}\left(\frac{\partial T}{\partial \dot{q}_r}\right) - \frac{\partial T}{\partial q_r} + \frac{\partial U}{\partial q_r} = F_r, \qquad r = 1, 2, \ldots, n. \qquad (21.1.1)$$

Here T and U are the kinetic and potential energies of the system and the quantities $q_1, q_2, \ldots, q_n$ are a set of generalized coordinates—a set of quantities in terms of which all linear and angular displacements involved in the problem may be expressed.

The kinetic energy T and the potential energy U can be expressed as multiple integrals involving only the displacements and their space derivatives. These integrals may take various forms, depending on the geometric configuration of the system. Whatever the form of the integrals, substitution of the generalized coordinates leads to the following equations for the kinetic energy and potential energy in terms of the displacements and their derivatives.

1) For the kinetic energy:

$$T = \tfrac{1}{2}[m_{11}\dot{q}_1^2 + m_{22}\dot{q}_2^2 + \cdots + m_{nn}\dot{q}_n^2 + 2m_{12}\dot{q}_1\dot{q}_2 + \cdots + 2m_{n-1,n}\dot{q}_{n-1}\dot{q}_n],$$
(21.1.2)

where the m_{ij} are constants for small vibrations about some datum configuration, which will usually be one of stable or neutral equilibrium.

2) For the potential energy:

$$U = k_0 + k_1 q_1 + k_2 q_2 + \cdots + k_n q_n + \tfrac{1}{2}[k_{11}q_1^2 + k_{22}q_2^2$$
$$+ k_{33}q_3^2 + \cdots + k_{nn}q_n^2 + 2k_{12}q_1 q_2 + \cdots + 2k_{n-1,n}q_{n-1}q_n],$$
(21.1.3)

where the k's are constants. If the datum configuration is one of stable or neutral equilibrium, then

$$k_1 = k_2 = \cdots = k_n = 0,$$

and if the datum level of the potential energy is taken to be zero, so that $k_0 = 0$, then (21.1.3) reduces to

$$U = \tfrac{1}{2}[k_{11}q_1^2 + \cdots + k_{nn}q_n^2 + 2k_{12}q_1 q_2 + \cdots + 2k_{n-1,n}q_{n-1}q_n].$$
(21.1.4)

21.2 THE EQUATIONS OF MOTION

Consider a system having n degrees of freedom, a convenient set of generalized coordinates being the quantities $q_1, q_2, \ldots, q_n$. The datum configuration, in which all these coordinates vanish, is assumed to be one of stable or neutral equilibrium.

If the system executes a small motion about its datum configuration, its kinetic energy T will be a quadratic form given by (21.1.2) in the quantities $\dot{q}_1$, $\dot{q}_2, \ldots, \dot{q}_n$. The quantities $m_{11}, m_{22}, m_{12}, \ldots, m_{nn}$ are constants; they are known as the coefficients of inertia or mass coefficients of the system and are such that T is positive or zero for all values of $\dot{q}_1, \dot{q}_2, \ldots, \dot{q}_n$.

We can write the kinetic energy T in the alternative form

$$T = \tfrac{1}{2}\sum_{i=1}^{n}\sum_{j=1}^{n} m_{ij}\dot{q}_i\dot{q}_j.$$
(21.2.1)

From the above we also see that T may be expressed as

$$T = \tfrac{1}{2}[\dot{q}_1\dot{q}_2 \cdots \dot{q}_n]\begin{bmatrix} m_{11} & m_{12} & \cdots & m_{1n} \\ m_{21} & m_{22} & \cdots & \\ \vdots & & & \vdots \\ m_{n1} & \cdots & & m_{nn} \end{bmatrix}\begin{bmatrix} \dot{q}_1 \\ \dot{q}_2 \\ \vdots \\ \dot{q}_n \end{bmatrix}$$
(21.2.2)

$$= \tfrac{1}{2}\dot{Q}^t M \dot{Q}.$$
(21.2.3)

In this equation $\dot{Q}$ is a column matrix or vector, $\dot{Q}^t$ is its transpose, and M (which is symmetric) is the inertia or mass matrix.

The matrix M is positive definite if $\dot{Q}^t M \dot{Q} > 0$ for all possible nonnull column vectors $\dot{Q}$. A necessary and sufficient condition for the symmetric matrix M to be positive definite is given in Section 7.8.

For a small distortion of the system from its equilibrium configuration, the potential energy U will be a quadratic form given by (21.1.4) in the quantities $q_1, q_2, \ldots, q_n$. The quantities $k_{11}, k_{22}, k_{12}, \ldots, k_{nn}$ are called the stiffness coefficients or spring constants. We can write the potential energy U in the alternative form

$$U = \tfrac{1}{2} \sum_{i=1}^{n} \sum_{j=1}^{n} k_{ij} q_i q_j. \tag{21.2.4}$$

Or we may write it in matrix form as

$$U = \tfrac{1}{2}[q_1, q_2, \ldots, q_n] \begin{bmatrix} k_{11} & k_{12} & \cdots & k_{1n} \\ k_{21} & k_{22} & \cdots & \\ \vdots & & & \vdots \\ k_{n1} & & \cdots & k_{nn} \end{bmatrix} \begin{bmatrix} q_1 \\ q_2 \\ \vdots \\ q_n \end{bmatrix} \tag{21.2.5}$$

$$= \tfrac{1}{2} Q^t K Q. \tag{21.2.6}$$

In this matrix equation, Q is the displacement vector, Q^t is its transpose, and K is the stiffness or spring matrix.

The equations of motion of any system reduced to discrete form may be expressed by means of Lagrange's equations (21.1.1). The quantities $F_1, F_2, \ldots, F_n$ are the generalized forces or driving forces which produce an excitation of the system. If the expressions (21.1.2) and (21.1.4) are substituted for T and U in (21.1.1), we obtain the equations

$$\left. \begin{array}{l} m_{11}\ddot{q}_1 + \cdots + m_{1n}\ddot{q}_n + k_{11}q_1 + \cdots + k_{1n}q_n = f_1 \\ m_{21}\ddot{q}_1 + \cdots + m_{2n}\ddot{q}_n + k_{21}q_1 + \cdots + k_{2n}q_n = f_2 \\ \vdots \\ m_{n1}\ddot{q}_1 + \cdots + m_{nn}\ddot{q}_n + k_{n1}q_1 + \cdots + k_{nn}q_n = f_n \end{array} \right\} \tag{21.2.7}$$

These equations may be written in matrix form as

$$M\ddot{Q} + KQ = F. \tag{21.2.8}$$

This differential matrix equation is very similar to the ordinary differential equation

$$m\ddot{y} + ky = f(t)$$

in the function $y(t)$. We could prove that the general solution of (21.2.8) is the sum of two parts—the complementary function and a particular integral. The complementary function is the general solution of the equation

$$M\ddot{Q} + KQ = 0, \tag{21.2.9}$$

and represents the free vibration of the system. The particular integral is a particular solution of the equation (21.2.8) and represents the forced motion of the system.

Lord Raleigh showed that one may allow for viscous damping forces by introducing a third function, the dissipation function V, into the Lagrangian equations. The dissipation function is defined as half the instantaneous rate of energy dissipation, and is expressed in the form

$$V = \tfrac{1}{2}[d_{11}\dot{q}_1^2 + d_{22}\dot{q}_2^2 + \cdots + d_{nn}\dot{q}_n^2 + 2\,d_{12}\dot{q}_1\dot{q}_2 + \cdots + 2\,d_{n-1,n}\dot{q}_{n-1}\dot{q}_n]$$

$$= \tfrac{1}{2}\sum_{i=1}^{n}\sum_{j=1}^{n}d_{ij}\dot{q}_i\dot{q}_j$$

$$= \tfrac{1}{2}\dot{Q}^t D\dot{Q}. \tag{21.2.10}$$

In this equation the d_{ij} are constants known as the damping coefficients, $\dot{Q}$ is a velocity vector, $\dot{Q}^t$ is its transpose, and D is called the damping matrix.

The Lagrangian equations now take the form

$$\frac{d}{dt}\left(\frac{\partial T}{\partial \dot{q}_r}\right) - \frac{\partial T}{\partial q_r} + \frac{\partial U}{\partial q_r} + \frac{\partial V}{\partial \dot{q}_r} = F_r, \qquad r = 1, 2, \ldots, n. \tag{21.2.11}$$

If we substitute the expressions for T, U, and V into (21.2.11), then we write n equations of motion found in this way as the single matrix equation

$$M\ddot{Q} + D\dot{Q} + KQ = F. \tag{21.2.12}$$

21.3 ANALOGS OF LINEAR, TORSIONAL, AND ELECTRICAL SYSTEMS

The equations of motion in the previous section were developed in terms of a linear mechanical system involving mass, spring stiffness, and damping. Identical equations exist for torsional systems and electrical systems. The analogs of the three systems are given in Table 21.3.1.

For example, in electrical oscillations we substitute inductance for mass, resistance for damping, the reciprocal value of the capacitance for elastic restraint, and the impressed electromotive force for the impressed mechanical force. The

Table 21.3.1

Linear system		Torsional system		Series electrical system	
Mass	m	Moment of inertia	I	Inductance	L
Spring stiffness	k	Torsional stiffness	K	Elastance	$1/C$
Damping	d	Torsional damping	R	Resistance	R
Impressed Force	$F(t)$	Impressed torque	$T(t)$	Impressed voltage	$E(t)$
Displacement	$Q(t)$	Angular displacement	$\theta(t)$	Capacitor charge	$Q_c(t)$
Velocity	$\dot{Q}(t)$	Angular velocity	$\dot{\theta}(t)$	Current	$I(t) = \dot{Q}_c(t)$

analysis of a coupled circuit often leads to a system of second-order differential equations with constant coefficients. The dependent functions involved in the derivatives may be capacitor charges Q_i, currents I_i, or voltages E_i, depending on the particular interest and manner in which the equations are set up. In illustration, one system of differential equations for the circuit diagram (Fig. 21.3.1) is as follows:

$$L_1 \frac{d^2Q_1}{dt^2} + R\frac{d}{dt}(Q_1 - Q_2) + \frac{1}{C_1}Q_1 + \frac{1}{C_2}(Q_1 - Q_2) = E,$$

$$L_2 \frac{d^2Q_2}{dt^2} - R\frac{d}{dt}(Q_1 - Q_2) - \frac{1}{C_2}(Q_1 - Q_2) = 0.$$

This system of equations, in matrix form, is

$$
\begin{bmatrix} L_1 & 0 \\ 0 & L_2 \end{bmatrix}
\begin{bmatrix} \ddot{Q}_1 \\ \ddot{Q}_2 \end{bmatrix}
+
\begin{bmatrix} R & -R \\ -R & R \end{bmatrix}
\begin{bmatrix} \dot{Q}_1 \\ \dot{Q}_2 \end{bmatrix}
+
\begin{bmatrix} \frac{1}{C_1} + \frac{1}{C_2} & -\frac{1}{C_2} \\ -\frac{1}{C_2} & \frac{1}{C_2} \end{bmatrix}
\begin{bmatrix} Q_1 \\ Q_2 \end{bmatrix}
=
\begin{bmatrix} E \\ 0 \end{bmatrix}
$$

This may be written as the matrix equation

$$L\ddot{Q} + R\dot{Q} + CQ = F,$$

which is identical with the matrix equation given in (21.2.12).

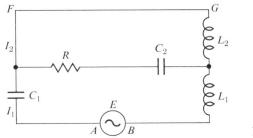

Figure 21.3.1

21.4 THE TRANSFORMED EQUATIONS OF MOTION

One of the best approaches for numerically solving the equations of motion of a system on a computer is through the transformed equations.

Taking the Laplace transform of (21.2.8), we obtain the transform matrix equation of a conservative system. That is,

$$M[s^2 Q(s) - sQ(0) - \dot{Q}(0)] + KQ(s) = F(s) \qquad (21.4.1)$$

or

$$[Ms^2 + K]Q(s) = G(s), \qquad (21.4.2)$$

where

$$G(s) = M[sQ(0) + \dot{Q}(0)] + F(s). \qquad (21.4.3)$$

If $Q(0) = \dot{Q}(0) = 0$, that is, if the initial conditions are zero, then $G(s) = F(s)$.

If we take the transformed matrix of coefficients, we may set up the eigenproblem that represents the free vibrations of the system,

$$|Ms^2 + K|X = 0. \qquad (21.4.4)$$

Substituting $s = j\omega$ or $s^2 = -\omega^2$, we obtain

$$|K - M\omega^2|X = 0. \qquad (21.4.5)$$

Multiplying by M^{-1} and setting $M^{-1}K = L$, we have

$$|L - I\omega^2|X = 0. \qquad (21.4.6)$$

The equation $|L - I\omega^2| = 0$ is called the frequency equation of degree n for ω^2. The n roots ω^2 may be designated by $\omega_1^2, \omega_2^2, \ldots, \omega_n^2$. The terms $\omega_1, \omega_2, \ldots, \omega_n$ are called the natural frequencies of the system, and the lowest frequency is called the fundamental frequency.

However, since $s^2 = -\omega^2$, we have $2n$ values of s:

$$s = j\omega_1, -j\omega_1, j\omega_2, -j\omega_2, \ldots, j\omega_n, -j\omega_n.$$

We now observe that these $2n$ values of s are the $2n$ eigenvalues of the general eigenproblem as given in Eq. (21.4.4):

$$|Ms^2 + K|X = 0.$$

This may also be considered a special case of the generalized eigenproblem $|As^2 + Bs + C|X = 0$, where $A = M$, $B = 0$, and $C = K$.

Corresponding to the n roots ω_i^2 for Eq. (21.4.6), are n eigenvectors, X_i, each with n components. These eigenvectors are called principal modes of oscillation and are proportional to the amplitudes of the principal oscillations. The eigenvector corresponding to the fundamental frequency ω_1 is called the fundamental mode of oscillation. When the eigenvectors are normalized, they are called the normal modes of oscillation.

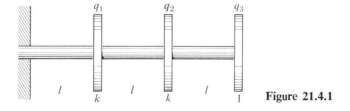

Figure 21.4.1

The following example with static coupling only illustrates the principles enunciated above. A shaft (Fig. 21.4.1) with uniform torsional stiffness C carries three disks of equal shape and size at three equidistant points. The shaft is fixed at $x = 0$. At $x = 3l$ the shaft has a free end. The moment of inertia of each disk is I. Angular deflection of the three disks is noted by q_1, q_2, and q_3. If $c = C/l$, the equations of motion are

$$I\ddot{q}_1 + 2cq_1 - cq_2 = 0,$$
$$I\ddot{q}_2 - cq_1 + 2cq_2 - cq_3 = 0,$$
$$I\ddot{q}_3 - cq_2 + cq_3 = 0.$$

Dividing through by c, taking the Laplace transform, and substituting $s = j\omega$, we obtain the frequency equation

$$\begin{vmatrix} 2 - \dfrac{I\omega^2}{c} & -1 & 0 \\ -1 & 2 - \dfrac{I\omega^2}{c} & -1 \\ 0 & -1 & 2 - \dfrac{I\omega^2}{c} \end{vmatrix} = 0.$$

Or, with $\lambda = I\omega^2/c$, we have the eigenproblem

$$\begin{vmatrix} 2 - \lambda & -1 & 0 \\ -1 & 2 - \lambda & -1 \\ 0 & -1 & 1 - \lambda \end{vmatrix} = 0.$$

The eigenvalues are approximately $\lambda_1 = 0.1981$, $\lambda_2 = 1.555$, and $\lambda_3 = 3.247$. From these we compute

$$\omega_1 = 0.445 \cdot \sqrt{c/I}, \qquad \omega_2 = 1.247 \cdot \sqrt{c/I}, \qquad \text{and} \qquad \omega_3 = 1.801 \cdot \sqrt{c/I}.$$

Associated with λ_1, λ_2, and λ_3 are the corresponding normalized eigenvectors

$$x_1 = (0.328, 0.591, 0.736),$$
$$x_2 = (-0.736, -0.328, 0.591), \qquad \text{and} \qquad x_3 = (0.591, -0.736, 0.328).$$

If we denote these vectors by $x_1 = (\phi_1^1, \phi_2^1, \phi_3^1)$, $x_2 = (\phi_1^2, \phi_2^2, \phi_3^2)$, and $x_3 = (\phi_1^3, \phi_2^3, \phi_3^3)$, the general solution of the problem is

$$q_i = \sum_{r=1}^{3} c_r \phi_i^r \sin(\omega_r t + \psi_r),$$

and the angular deflections are

$$q_1 = c_1 \phi_1^1 \sin(\omega_1 t + \psi_1) + c_2 \phi_1^2 \sin(\omega_2 t + \psi_2) + c_3 \phi_1^3 \sin(\omega_3 t + \psi_3),$$
$$q_2 = c_1 \phi_2^1 \sin(\omega_1 t + \psi_1) + c_2 \phi_2^2 \sin(\omega_2 t + \psi_2) + c_3 \phi_2^3 \sin(\omega_3 t + \psi_3),$$
$$q_3 = c_1 \phi_3^1 \sin(\omega_1 t + \psi_1) + c_2 \phi_3^2 \sin(\omega_2 t + \psi_2) + c_3 \phi_3^3 \sin(\omega_3 t + \psi_3),$$

where c_1, c_2, and c_3 are arbitrary constants.

Consider the first mode of oscillation. Here

$$q_1 = c_1 \phi_1^1 \sin(\omega_1 t + \psi_1),$$
$$q_2 = c_1 \phi_2^1 \sin(\omega_1 t + \psi_1),$$
$$q_3 = c_1 \phi_3^1 \sin(\omega_1 t + \psi_1),$$

are the equations of a segment of a straight line (in the q_i space) along which the mass oscillates, and ϕ_1^1, ϕ_2^1, ϕ_3^1 are the direction cosines of this line ($x_i \cdot x_j = 1$ for $i = j$).

The displacement of the mass at time t is

$$\sqrt{q_1^2 + q_2^2 + q_3^2} = c_1 \sin(\omega_1 t + \psi_1).$$

Treating the second and third principal modes of oscillation in a similar manner, we find that $(\phi_1^2, \phi_2^2, \phi_3^2)$ and $(\phi_1^3, \phi_2^3, \phi_3^3)$ are the direction cosines of the two lines along which the mass oscillates in these two modes.

We note that these three lines satisfy the orthogonality principle:

$$x_i \cdot x_j = 0, \quad \text{for } i \neq j.$$

The principal oscillations take place therefore along straight lines that are perpendicular to each other. Hence, any oscillation of a mass in space is made up by superposition of three linear oscillations in three perpendicular directions.

Taking the Laplace transform of (21.2.12), we obtain the transform matrix equation of a nonconservative system. That is,

$$[Ms^2 + Ds + K]Q(s) = G(s), \tag{21.4.7}$$

where

$$G(s) = [Ms + D]Q(0) + M\dot{Q}(0) + F(s). \tag{21.4.8}$$

If $Q(0) = \dot{Q}(0) = 0$, that is, the initial conditions are zero, then $G(s) = F(s)$.

If we take the transformed matrix of coefficients, we may set up the eigenproblem that represents the free vibrations of the nonconservative system. That is,

$$|Ms^2 + Ds + K|X = 0. \tag{21.4.9}$$

Solving this problem we find the eigenvalues to determine the natural frequencies and the eigenvectors to determine the modes of free oscillations. This may be done by reducing the problem to the simple eigenproblem,

$$|L + Is|X = 0, \tag{21.4.10}$$

by the method of Section 14.19. The eigenvalues and eigenvectors are found by one of the methods of Chapter 9.

The time response or frequency response of (21.4.2) or (21.4.7) are found by obtaining and using the transfer functions discussed in Chapter 15.

21.5 OTHER VIBRATION TYPE PROBLEMS

Certain problems in aircraft flutter analysis are special cases of the general problem (21.4.7). In general, flutter velocity v appears in the aerodynamic coefficients d_{ij} and k_{ij}, and is replaced by a quantity in terms of the flutter frequency ω. In solving the system of differential equations, one is led to a system of linear algebraic equations (with complex coefficients if m_{ij}, d_{ij}, and k_{ij} are complex). After finding the eigenvalues of the matrix of linear equations, one ultimately finds the flutter velocity v as a function of the flutter frequency ω and the structural damping coefficients.

Many problems of structural analysis lead to homogeneous problems of free vibrations and buckling. These problems may be expressed as various forms of the matrix equations discussed above, with the associated eigenproblem. Solving the eigenproblem gives eigenvalues which represent natural frequencies or critical loads, and eigenvectors which determine mode shapes of vibration, bending, or buckling.

21.6 SUPPLEMENTARY REFERENCES

For a more intensive study of vibration problems a number of references are recommended. They are Duncan [38–39], Karman [83], Oldenburger [115], Pipes [125], Scott [137], Timoshenko [148], and

a) R. E. BISHOP and D. C. JOHNSON, *The Mechanics of Vibration*, Cambridge University Press, Cambridge, 1960.

b) R. E. BISHOP, G. M. GLADWELL, and S. MICHAELSON, *The Matrix Analysis of Vibration*, Cambridge University Press, Cambridge, 1965.

c) E. T. WHITTAKER, *Treatise on the Analytical Dynamics of Particles and Rigid Bodies*, Cambridge University Press, Cambridge, 1959.

CHAPTER 22

PADÉ APPROXIMATION TO A FUNCTION

22.1 INTRODUCTION

It is sometimes convenient to approximate a nonpolynomial function by a function which involves only polynomials. For example, a transfer function, due to the input or forcing functions of a system, may involve exponentials or trigonometric functions. One method of approximating these functions is by means of a Padé approximation. Let

$$F_{m,n}(x) = \frac{P_m(x)}{Q_n(x)} \tag{22.1.1}$$

be a rational approximation to a function $f(x)$, where $P_m(x)$ and $Q_n(x)$ are polynomials of degree m and n respectively. We call $N = m + n$ the index of $F_{m,n}(x)$. The number of coefficients in $F_{m,n}(x)$ is $N + 1$ since one of the $N + 2$ coefficients in the numerator and denominator is redundant. In general, it is true that the greater the index, the higher the accuracy of the approximation.

22.2 GENERATING THE APPROXIMATION

Our approach toward generating approximations of the form (22.1.1) will be, for a given m and n, to choose $P_m(x)$ and $Q_n(x)$ so that $f(x)$ and $F_{m,n}(x)$ are equal at $x = 0$ and have as many derivatives as possible equal at $x = 0$. In the case $n = 0$, the approximation is then just the Maclaurin expansion for $f(x)$. We will assume that the Maclaurin series for $f(x)$ exists in some neighborhood of $x = 0$. There are two reasons for the arbitrary choice of $x = 0$:

1) It makes the manipulations much simpler than for any other x.

2) The interval over which we wish to approximate most functions will contain zero, and when it does not, a simple change of variable can be made to make it contain zero.

We also assume that $P_m(x)$ and $Q_n(x)$ have no common factors. Let

$$P_m(x) = \sum_{j=0}^{m} a_j x^j,$$

$$Q_n(x) = \sum_{j=0}^{n} b_j x^j, \quad b_0 = 1. \tag{22.2.1}$$

281

It is permissible to let the constant term in $Q_n(x)$ equal 1, because the constant term cannot be zero if the approximation is to exist at $x = 0$, and the value of $F_{m,n}(x)$ is unchanged if the numerator and denominator are divided by the same constant.

Let $f(x)$ have a Maclaurin series

$$f(x) = \sum_{j=0}^{\infty} c_j x^j. \tag{22.2.2}$$

Now we consider the difference

$$f(x) - F_{m,n}(x) = \frac{(\sum_{j=0}^{\infty} c_j x^j)(\sum_{j=0}^{n} b_j x^j) - \sum_{j=0}^{m} a_j x^j}{\sum_{j=0}^{n} b_j x^j}. \tag{22.2.3}$$

Since we have $N + 1$ constants, $m + 1$ a_j's, and n b_j's, to compute, we hope to make $f(x) - F_{m,n}(x)$ and its first N derivatives equal to zero at $x = 0$. We shall achieve this if the numerator of the right member of (22.2.3) is such that its leading power is of degree $N + 1$. Thus we may write

$$\left(\sum_{j=0}^{\infty} c_j x^j\right)\left(\sum_{j=0}^{n} b_j x^j\right) - \sum_{j=0}^{m} a_j x^j = \sum_{j=N+1}^{\infty} d_j x^j. \tag{22.2.4}$$

The vanishing of the coefficients of the first $N + 1$ powers of x on the left-hand side of (22.2.4) is equivalent to the equations

$$\sum_{j=0}^{n} c_{N-s-j} b_j = 0, \qquad s = 0, 1, \ldots, N - m - 1, \tag{22.2.5}$$

$$(c_j = 0 \text{ if } j < 0, b_0 = 1),$$

$$a_r = \sum_{j=0}^{r} c_{r-j} b_j, \qquad r = 0, 1, \ldots, m, \tag{22.2.6}$$

$$(b_j = 0 \text{ if } j > n).$$

When this set of $N + 1$ linear equations in the $N + 1$ unknowns has a solution, it provides us with the desired approximation in the form (22.1.1). Solving the first set of equations (22.2.5) for the b_j's, we can then solve the second set of equations (22.2.6) for the a_r's.

Example. Compute the Padé approximation, $F_{2,3}(x)$, for $f(x) = e^{-kx}$.

Solution. For $F_{2,3}(x)$ we have $m = 2$, $n = 3$, and $N = 2 + 3 = 5$. The Maclaurin expansion for e^{-kx} given to six terms is

$$e^{-kx} = 1 - kx + \frac{k^2 x^2}{2!} - \frac{k^3 x^3}{3!} + \frac{k^4 x^4}{4!} - \frac{k^5 x^5}{5!}.$$

Therefore, we have

$$c_0 = 1, \quad c_1 = -k, \quad c_2 = \tfrac{1}{2}k^2, \quad c_3 = -\tfrac{1}{6}k^3, \quad c_4 = \tfrac{1}{24}k^4, \quad c_5 = -\tfrac{1}{120}k^5.$$

From (22.2.5) we have

$$\left.\begin{array}{l} c_5 b_0 + c_4 b_1 + c_3 b_2 + c_2 b_3 = 0 \\ c_4 b_0 + c_3 b_1 + c_2 b_2 + c_1 b_3 = 0 \\ c_3 b_0 + c_2 b_1 + c_1 b_2 + c_0 b_3 = 0 \end{array}\right\}$$

or

$$\left.\begin{array}{l} -\tfrac{1}{120}k^5 + \tfrac{1}{24}k^4 b_1 - \tfrac{1}{6}k^3 b_2 + \tfrac{1}{2}k^2 b_3 = 0 \\ \tfrac{1}{24}k^4 - \tfrac{1}{6}k^3 b_1 + \tfrac{1}{2}k^2 b_2 - k b_3 = 0 \\ -\tfrac{1}{6}k^3 + \tfrac{1}{2}k^2 b_1 - k b_2 + b_3 = 0 \end{array}\right\}.$$

Solving the above system we obtain

$$b_1 = \tfrac{3}{5}k, \quad b_2 = \tfrac{3}{20}k^2, \quad b_3 = \tfrac{1}{60}k^3.$$

Now, from (22.2.6) we have

$$\left.\begin{array}{l} a_0 = c_0 b_0 \\ a_1 = c_1 b_0 + c_0 b_1 \\ a_2 = c_2 b_0 + c_1 b_1 + c_0 b_2 \end{array}\right\}.$$

Substituting the b_j's from above we have

$$a_0 = 1, \quad a_1 = -\tfrac{2}{5}k, \quad a_2 = \tfrac{1}{20}k^2.$$

We can now write the Padé approximation for $f(x)$:

$$F_{2,3}(x) = \frac{1 - \tfrac{2}{5}kx + \tfrac{1}{20}k^2 x^2}{1 + \tfrac{3}{5}kx + \tfrac{3}{20}k^2 x^2 + \tfrac{1}{60}k^3 x^3}$$

or

$$e^{kx} \sim \frac{60 - 24kx + 3k^2 x^2}{60 + 36kx + 9k^2 x^2 + k^3 x^3},$$

22.3 ACCURACY OF THE APPROXIMATION

One disadvantage of the derivation given in the last section is that it does not provide us with an error term in closed form. However, our emphasis here is on finding the maximum error on an interval, and error terms which contain a derivative of the function but cannot be evaluated are not of basic interest to us. Rather we must be able to find the error at any point in the interval, and this we do by actual evaluation of the approximation and comparing this evaluation with the true function.

We shall show this by considering an example. Let us consider the problem of approximating e^x on the interval $(-1.25, 1.25)$, with $x = 0$ at the center of the interval and $N = 4$. Using the method of the previous section we can obtain

Table 22.3.1

(m, n) \ x	(4, 0)	(3, 1)	(2, 2)	(1, 3)	(0, 4)
−1.25	−0.02095	−0.12074	−0.00133	0.00118	−0.00264
−1.00	−0.00712	0.00121	−0.00054	0.00053	−0.00135
−0.75	−0.00175	0.00033	−0.00016	0.00018	−0.00050
−0.50	−0.000240	0.000049	−0.000027	0.000032	−0.000104
−0.25	−0.0000078	0.0000018	−0.0000011	0.0000014	−0.0000052
0.25	0.0000086	−0.0000023	0.0000018	−0.0000029	0.0000129
0.50	0.000284	−0.000088	0.000073	−0.000134	0.000653
0.75	0.00225	−0.00079	0.00072	−0.00147	0.00783
1.00	0.00995	−0.00394	0.00400	−0.00899	0.05162
1.25	0.03180	−0.01440	0.01610	−0.04030	0.23780

five approximations with $N = 4$. These are

$$F_{4,0}(x) = 1 + x + \tfrac{1}{2}x^2 + \tfrac{1}{6}x^3 + \tfrac{1}{24}x^4,$$

$$F_{3,1}(x) = \frac{24 + 18x + 6x^2 + x^3}{24 - 6x},$$

$$F_{2,2}(x) = \frac{12 + 6x + x^2}{12 - 6x + x^2},$$

$$F_{1,3}(x) = \frac{24 + 6x}{24 - 18x + 6x^2 - x^3},$$

$$F_{0,4}(x) = \frac{1}{1 - x + \tfrac{1}{2}x^2 - \tfrac{1}{6}x^3 + \tfrac{1}{24}x^4}.$$

The approximation $F_{m,0}(x)$ is always the truncated Maclaurin series. Our interest is in the errors in these various approximations over the interval $(-1.25, 1.25)$. Some sample values of the error $e^x - F_{m,n}(x)$ have been computed and listed in Table 22.3.1.

We note an important empirical fact that applies to most functions for which we want computer approximations. That is, the Padé approximations for $m = n$ or $m = n + 1$, in general, give the smallest minimum-maximum error for a given N.

Usually, we have two alternatives when an approximation for a given N is not sufficiently good over the whole interval:

1) Break up the interval into subintervals and use an appropriate approximation over each subinterval.

2) Use a larger value of N to get more accuracy.

On a digital computer the latter is more desirable. In case subintervals are used, $x = 0$ can be made the center of each subinterval by a simple transformation of variables.

22.4 APPLICATIONS OF APPROXIMATIONS

There are many reasons for wanting an accurate approximation to certain functions, particularly on a digital computer. For example, in Chapter 15 the time response and the frequency response are computed numerically from transfer functions expressed as one polynomial divided by another polynomial. However, the transfer function of a given system may involve input or forcing functions which are not polynomials. For example, in Section 12.8 the transform of the unit-step function $U(t - a)$ is e^{-as}/s, and the transform of the unit-impulse function $U'(t - a)$ is e^{-as}. Other examples of functions involving the form e^{-as} in their transforms are given in the exercises at the end of Chapter 15. When these functions are involved in a transfer function, the form of the transfer function can be changed to one of a polynomial divided by a polynomial by using a Padé approximation for the e^{-as}. We derived one such approximation in Section 22.2.

CHAPTER 23

GRAM-SCHMIDT ORTHOGONALIZATION PROCEDURE

23.1 INTRODUCTION

Suppose that we are given two nonzero vectors $\mathbf{A}_1$ and $\mathbf{A}_2$; if $\mathbf{A}_2$ is not an exact multiple of $\mathbf{A}_1$ the two vectors are linearly independent. We wish to construct a vector $\mathbf{Z}$ that lies in the space spanned by $\mathbf{A}_1$ and $\mathbf{A}_2$ and whose inner product with $\mathbf{A}_1$ is zero. The method of doing this is as follows: Let

$$\mathbf{Z} = \mathbf{A}_2 - \alpha\mathbf{A}_1. \tag{23.1.1}$$

Find the constant α such that $\mathbf{A}_1 \cdot \mathbf{Z} = 0$:

$$\mathbf{A}_1 \cdot \mathbf{Z} = \mathbf{A}_1 \cdot (\mathbf{A}_2 - \alpha\mathbf{A}_1) = \mathbf{A}_1 \cdot \mathbf{A}_2 - \alpha(\mathbf{A}_1 \cdot \mathbf{A}_1) = 0. \tag{23.1.2}$$

Obviously, $\mathbf{A}_1 \cdot \mathbf{A}_1 > 0$, hence,

$$\alpha = \frac{\mathbf{A}_1 \cdot \mathbf{A}_2}{\mathbf{A}_1 \cdot \mathbf{A}_1}. \tag{23.1.3}$$

As long as $\mathbf{A}_1$ and $\mathbf{A}_2$ are independent, then $\mathbf{Z} \neq 0$. If $\mathbf{A}_1 = \mu\mathbf{A}_2$, then $\alpha = 1/\mu$ and $\mathbf{Z} = \mathbf{A}_2 - \mathbf{A}_2 = 0$.

By a similar process one generates a set of m orthogonal vectors from m independent vectors. That is,

$$\mathbf{Z}_q = \mathbf{A}_q - \sum_{i=1}^{q-1} \frac{\mathbf{Z}_i \cdot \mathbf{A}_q}{\mathbf{Z}_i \cdot \mathbf{Z}_i} \mathbf{Z}_i. \tag{23.1.4}$$

Note in passing that α adjusts the vector $\mathbf{A}_1$ to a new length, such that the absolute value of the difference vector $\mathbf{A}_2 - \alpha\mathbf{A}_1$ is a minimum with respect to α; α is analogous to the correlation coefficient of two pulse signals. (See Fig. 23.1.1.)

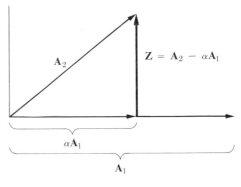

Figure 23.1.1

23.2 NUMERICAL COMPUTATION

In computer computation the situation is not as clear-cut as our simple example. No matter whether floating-point or fixed-point computation is used, the resulting $\mathbf{Z}$ will usually not be such that $\mathbf{A}_1 \cdot \mathbf{Z} = 0$.

In general there are two ways that $\mathbf{A}_1 \cdot \mathbf{Z}$ can be near zero:

1) The angle ϕ between $\mathbf{A}_1$ and $\mathbf{Z}$ can be very close to $\pi/2$, or

2) The magnitude of at least one of the two vectors can be very small.

We can eliminate the second possibility by converting each given vector to a unit vector before the orthogonalization procedure begins.

Consider the case in which each component of $\mathbf{A}_1$ and $\mathbf{A}_2$, given in decimal, has a minimum of t digits, and each vector is made into a unit vector before the orthogonalization procedure begins. In this case $\mathbf{A}_1 \cdot \mathbf{Z} = \cos \phi$. For machine purposes $\mathbf{A}_1$ and $\mathbf{Z}$ could be considered orthogonal if $\phi = \pi/2 + \epsilon$, $\epsilon = \theta(10^{-t})$, in which case $\mathbf{A}_1 \cdot \mathbf{Z} = \theta(10^{-t})$.

The true vector $\mathbf{Z}$ can be determined as accurately as needed if we are given $\mathbf{A}_1$ and $\mathbf{A}_2$ as exact vectors and if we are willing to work to a sufficiently high precision. In practice, of course, $\mathbf{A}_1$ and $\mathbf{A}_2$ have rounded components. We can compensate as much as possible for further rounding errors by computing all scalar products in double precision. We may assume two distinct nonzero vectors to be orthogonal as long as their inner product is equal to or less than 10^{-8}.

Example. Given $H = \{\mathbf{A}_1, \mathbf{A}_2\}$, $\mathbf{A}_1 \neq \mu \mathbf{A}_2$, $\mathbf{A}_1 \neq 0$, $\mathbf{A}_2 \neq 0$. Generate a set of mutually orthogonal unit vectors.

Solution. Let $H' = \{\mathbf{B}_1, \mathbf{B}_2\}$, where

$$\mathbf{B}_1 = \frac{\mathbf{A}_1}{|\mathbf{A}_1|} \quad \text{and} \quad \mathbf{B}_2 = \frac{\mathbf{A}_2}{|\mathbf{A}_2|}.$$

Let $\mathbf{Z}_1 = \mathbf{B}_1$, then

$$\mathbf{Z}_2 = \mathbf{B}_2 - \alpha_1 \mathbf{B}_1, \qquad \alpha_1 = \frac{\mathbf{B}_1 \cdot \mathbf{B}_2}{\mathbf{B}_1 \cdot \mathbf{B}_1} = \mathbf{B}_1 \cdot \mathbf{B}_2.$$

If $\mathbf{B}_1 \cdot (\mathbf{Z}_2/|\mathbf{Z}_2|) \leq 10^{-8}$, then we assume that $\mathbf{B}_1$ and $\mathbf{Z}_2/|\mathbf{Z}_2|$ are orthogonal and $\mathbf{Z}_2/|\mathbf{Z}_2|$ is one of the desired vectors. If $\mathbf{B}_1 \cdot (\mathbf{Z}_2/|\mathbf{Z}_2|) > 10^{-8}$, then we assume that the angle between $\mathbf{B}_1$ and $\mathbf{Z}_2/|\mathbf{Z}_2|$ is not near enough to $\pi/2$, in which case reorthogonalization takes place. That is,

$$\mathbf{Z}_2' = \frac{\mathbf{Z}_2}{|\mathbf{Z}_2|} - \alpha_1' \mathbf{B}_1, \qquad \alpha_1' = \frac{\mathbf{Z}_2}{|\mathbf{Z}_2|} \cdot \mathbf{B}_1.$$

If $\mathbf{Z}_2'/|\mathbf{Z}_2'| \cdot \mathbf{B}_1 \leq 10^{-8}$, then $\mathbf{Z}_2'/|\mathbf{Z}_2'|$ is considered as the desired vector. If, after two reorthogonalizations, the inner product of $\mathbf{B}_1$ with the calculated $\mathbf{Z}$ is not equal to or less than 10^{-8}, we stop and accept $\mathbf{Z}_2''/|\mathbf{Z}_2''|$ as the required vector.

23.3 COMMENTS ON NUMERICAL COMPUTATION

Before the orthogonalization procedure begins the computer converts the given vectors to a set of unit vectors. If the given set is linearly dependent, then the computed set of unit vectors will usually not be linearly dependent, due to rounding error.   Thus, when the orthogonalization procedure begins, the computer is operating on a linearly independent set of unit vectors and, hence the procedure will result in a set of mutually orthogonal unit vectors.

If by chance the computed set of unit vectors contains at least one vector that is dependent to eight decimal places upon any of the remaining vectors, then the resulting orthonormal set will contain at least one zero vector. It is therefore desirable, if possible, to determine if the set of vectors contains any linearly dependent vectors before machine computation begins.

Numerical Example.   Given the two vectors

$$\mathbf{A}_1 = \begin{bmatrix} 0.213625 \\ 0.314317 \\ 0.412135 \end{bmatrix} \quad \text{and} \quad \mathbf{A}_2 = \begin{bmatrix} 0.174681 \\ 0.257023 \\ 0.336951 \end{bmatrix},$$

find a vector $\mathbf{Z}$ which is orthogonal to $\mathbf{A}_1$ to working accuracy, i.e., absolute value of $(\mathbf{Z} \cdot \mathbf{A}_1) \leq 10^{-8}$.

Solution.   Let

$$\mathbf{B}_1 = \frac{\mathbf{A}_1}{|\mathbf{A}_1|} = \begin{bmatrix} 0.38105661 \\ 0.56066739 \\ 0.73515163 \end{bmatrix} \quad \text{and} \quad \mathbf{B}_2 = \frac{\mathbf{A}_2}{|\mathbf{A}_2|} = \begin{bmatrix} 0.38108516 \\ 0.56072299 \\ 0.73509442 \end{bmatrix}.$$

Then let $\mathbf{Z}_1 = \mathbf{B}_1$.   Thus

$$\mathbf{Z}_2 = \mathbf{B}_2 - \alpha\mathbf{B}_1, \quad \alpha = \mathbf{B}_2 \cdot \mathbf{B}_1 = 0.99999998,$$

$$\mathbf{Z}_2 = \begin{bmatrix} 0.28559142 \\ 0.55616215 \\ -0.57189126 \end{bmatrix} 10^{-4}, \quad \frac{\mathbf{Z}_2}{|\mathbf{Z}_2|} = \begin{bmatrix} 0.33705561 \\ 0.65638377 \\ -0.67494730 \end{bmatrix},$$

$$\mathbf{B}_1 \cdot \frac{\mathbf{Z}_2}{|\mathbf{Z}_2|} = 0.26163863 \times 10^{-3}.$$

We see that $\mathbf{Z}_2/|\mathbf{Z}_2|$ is not orthogonal to $\mathbf{B}_1$ within working accuracy.   Therefore, reorthogonalization is necessary:

$$\mathbf{Z}_2' = \frac{\mathbf{Z}_2}{|\mathbf{Z}_2|} - \alpha'\mathbf{B}_1, \quad \alpha' = \frac{\mathbf{Z}_2}{|\mathbf{Z}_2|} \cdot \mathbf{B}_1,$$

$$\mathbf{Z}_2' = \begin{bmatrix} 0.33695591 \\ 0.65623707 \\ -0.67513964 \end{bmatrix}, \quad \frac{\mathbf{Z}_2'}{|\mathbf{Z}_2'|} = \begin{bmatrix} 0.33695593 \\ 0.65623710 \\ -0.67513967 \end{bmatrix}.$$

The absolute value of $(\mathbf{Z}_2'/|\mathbf{Z}_2'|) \cdot \mathbf{B}_1 = 0.53461607 \times 10^{-8}$. Therefore, $\mathbf{Z}_2'/|\mathbf{Z}_2'|$ is orthogonal to $\mathbf{B}_1$.

We now have two orthogonal unit vectors formed from $\mathbf{A}_1$ and $\mathbf{A}_2$. That is,

$$\begin{bmatrix} 0.38105661 \\ 0.56066739 \\ 0.73515163 \end{bmatrix} \quad \text{and} \quad \begin{bmatrix} 0.33695593 \\ 0.65623710 \\ -0.67513967 \end{bmatrix}.$$

23.4 SUPPLEMENTARY REFERENCES

Suggested references for study in conjunction with the above material are Kunz [87], and

a) J. H. WILKINSON, *Rounding Errors in Algebraic Processes*, Prentice Hall, Englewood Cliffs, N. J., 1963.

b) S. J. MASON, and H. J. ZIMMERMANN, *Electronic Circuits, Signals, and Systems*, Wiley, New York, 1960.

CHAPTER 24

COMPUTER METHODS OF FUNCTIONAL MINIMIZATION

24.1 INTRODUCTION

The problem of functional minimization or maximization often arises in handling scientific problems involving curve-fitting, systems of linear equations, or calculus and differential equations. Essentially, the problem consists of finding a point $X' = (x'_1, x'_2, \ldots, x'_N)$, such that a given function, $f = f(x_1, x_2, \ldots, x_N)$, attains a local minimum or maximum at X'. Since the maximization of a function may be considered as the minimization of the negative of the function, we will consider only the problem of minimization and, in particular, how it may be effected on a digital computer. For the present, no restrictions will be placed on the function or the procedure, since it is anticipated that certain restrictions will arise soon enough from the inherent nature of the problem.

24.2 CRITERIA FOR COMPARING MINIMIZATION PROCEDURES

The first consideration is that of time; that is, computing time. We wish to find a minimization procedure which will require as few computer operations, and hence, as little computing time, as possible. The second consideration is accuracy. Since nearly all, if not all, functions can be dealt with by digital computers only in the sense of numerical approximation, we can only wish that any minimization procedure be capable of approximating the true minimum of a function with a high degree of accuracy. Even at this early stage, our intuition tells us that these demands will exert opposing pressures on our procedure, so that accuracy will be directly proportional to time. Our goal, then, is to devise a minimization procedure, such that the constant of proportionality between time and accuracy is as small as possible. This, in itself is a minimization problem.

24.3 DEFINITIONS AND FUNCTION EVALUATIONS

Unless explicitly stated otherwise, the following definitions will be used throughout the remainder of this chapter:

  a) Variable—an independent variable,
  b) Point—an ordered set of N variables,
  c) Function—a function of N variables,
  d) Function value—the numerical value of a function at a given point,
  e) Function evaluation—the sequence of steps executed by a computer in order to find the function value at a given point.

Past experience with computer minimization procedures has shown that the time and effort expended in making a function evaluation is much greater than that expended in deciding where (that is, at what point) to make the evaluation. Hence we try to minimize computing time by seeking a minimization procedure which will require as few function evaluations as possible.

24.4 DIRECT MATHEMATICAL APPROACH

It is relatively common mathematical knowledge that the necessary and sufficient conditions for a function $f = f(x_1, x_2, \ldots, x_N)$ to attain a relative minimum at $X' = (x'_1, x'_2, \ldots, x'_N)$ are that

$$\frac{\partial f(X')}{\partial x_i} = 0, \qquad i = 1, 2, \ldots, N, \tag{24.4.1}$$

and that the matrix

$$\left| \frac{\partial^2 f}{\partial x_i \, \partial x_j} \right|, \qquad i, j = 1, 2, \ldots, N \tag{24.4.2}$$

be positive definite. See references (a), (b), and (h) at the end of the chapter. Hence, it seems logical to apply these conditions to form some sort of an iterative procedure that can be executed by a digital computer. In general, the so-called gradient methods of minimization seek to do exactly this.

24.5 GRADIENT METHODS OF MINIMIZATION

Perhaps the most basic of the gradient methods of minimization is the method of steepest descent. A point

$$X = (x_1, x_2, \ldots, x_N)$$

is picked at random and each of the N first partial derivatives are evaluated at X. This evaluation is effected through the use of partial difference formulas. That is, $\partial f(X)/\partial x_i$ is approximated by

$$\frac{f(x_1 x_2, \ldots, x_i + h, \cdots x_N) - f(x_1, x_2, \ldots, x_i, \ldots x_N)}{h} \tag{24.5.1}$$

for some small $h > 0$. A second point $X_1 = (x_{11}, x_{12}, \ldots, x_{1N})$ is then found according to the formula

$$x_{1i} = x_i - K \frac{\partial f(X)}{\partial x_i}, \qquad i = 1, 2, \ldots, N, \tag{24.5.2}$$

where K is a small positive constant. We can also express this procedure by the equation

$$X_1 = X - K \nabla f(X). \tag{24.5.3}$$

Hence the name, gradient method. Similarly, a third point

$$X_2 = (x_{21}, x_{22}, \ldots, x_{2N})$$

is found according to the formula

$$x_{2i} = x_{1i} - K\frac{\partial f(X_1)}{\partial x_i}, \qquad i = 1, 2, \ldots, N, \tag{24.5.4}$$

and then a fourth point X_3 is found from X_2, and so on. It can be shown that the sequence of points

$$\{X, X_1, X_2, X_3, \ldots\}, \tag{24.5.5}$$

thus obtained, converges to the point where f is a minimum. See references (c), (d), (g), (h), and (l).

In practice, the procedure can be made most efficient by starting with rather large values of h and K and gradually reducing both in size. The procedure is usually terminated when all of the first partial derivatives become less than a small positive constant.

If it is assumed that f is a quadratic polynomial in N variables, the theorem of parallel chords can be applied to speed up the minimization procedure. This yields the method of mixed descents which uses the method described above to minimize the function f along certain hyperplanes. See reference (k). Other gradient methods, all using the method of steepest descent at least in part, have been devised for certain special classes of functions. See references (i) and (l).

Since all gradient methods of minimization use the method of steepest descent in some way, perhaps their common weakness can best be explained in terms of that procedure. First, it should be observed that the sequence of points $\{X, X_1, X_2, X_3, \ldots\}$ which converges to the point where f is a minimum is an infinite sequence of points. Then, Cauchy's condition must necessarily apply; that is, for any $\epsilon > 0$, there exists an M such that for all m and $n > M$, the distance between X_n and X_m is less than ϵ. This means simply that, once X_m is found, it is senseless to go further, since the procedure is obviously grossly inefficient. However, this manifestation of the law of diminishing return is not unique to gradient methods, but is present in all computer minimization procedures. It means simply that high accuracy in approximating the minimum will always demand considerable computing time, and that considerable discretion must be exercised in each individual situation to determine how much time should be spent to achieve a certain accuracy.

A major weakness of the gradient methods is that, owing to the digital nature of the computer, the first partial derivatives must be approximated by partial difference formulas (24.5.1). As h is reduced in size to improve the accuracy and efficiency of the procedure, truncation and/or overflow cause considerable error in the approximation of the first partial derivatives. This, in turn, seriously affects the convergence of the sequence of points $\{X, X_1, X_2, X_3, \ldots\}$, which results in considerable error in finding the point where the function is a minimum. Some of the more complicated gradient methods have sought to avoid this through various devices, but since the point of difficulty lies precisely in evaluating the gradient itself, all gradient methods are predestined to only partial success at best.

24.6 OTHER METHODS OF MINIMIZATION

Several other methods which do not depend on the gradient of the function have been explored with more or less limited success. These methods belong to a group generally known as search procedures. The best known of these procedures are the sequential min-max procedures, the random sampling procedures, and the "direct search" procedures.

The sequential min-max procedures have shown some success on functions of a peculiar shape. Unfortunately, except for functions of one independent variable, the methods have not been developed sufficiently to reach their full potential.

Minimization methods based on taking a random sampling of function values at a number of points—the so-called shotgun methods—have been tried with only limited success. First, it seems that the number of function evaluations is excessive—directly proportional to 2^N, where N is the number of independent variables—and, second, the criteria for convergence, if they exist, are quite complex and difficult to determine.

One of the most promising methods is a search technique developed by Hooke and Jeeves (Section 24.8j), which they call *Direct Search*. We now summarize this method for the problem of minimizing the function $f(x_1, x_2, \ldots, x_n)$. One assumes a set of points P which represent possible solutions, and also some means of saying that one point P_i is closer to the solution than another point P_j. Point P_i is said to be a better solution than P_j if and only if

$$f(x_{1i}, x_{2i}, \ldots, x_{ni}) < f(x_{1j}, x_{2j}, \ldots, x_{nj}).$$

Dictated by various aspects of the problem and our knowledge of the structure of the solution space, we choose a point P_0 to be the first *base point*, B_0. New trial points are selected by a set of *states*. There is an initial state and a final state which stops the search. The other states represent conditions which arise as a function of the results of the trials made. For example, each of the independent variables is increased and/or decreased in turn and the function is evaluated each time. When increasing or decreasing any variable results in an increase or no change in the value of the function, the original value of the variable is restored. If a decrease in the value of the function results, however, the variable is changed, and a new base point with associated state is obtained.

By systematically increasing and/or decreasing each of the variables in cyclic fashion, one obtains a sequence of base points with associated states. This sequence converges, we hope, to the minimum of the function. It is evident that difficulties can arise if the function is "flat" or if there are several minimums in close proximity.

Hooke and Jeeves gives a more formal description of the method, several modifications of the method and a number of examples.

24.7 CONCLUSIONS

It would be useful to be able to compare the various methods so that one could select a particular method for a given function. This is generally a very difficult, if not impossible, problem. In practice, however, one of the gradient methods is best if the gradient of the function is analytically available, if the function around the minimum depends primarily on its second derivatives, and if the function does not have several minimums in close proximity.

If the gradient of the function cannot be determined analytically, a finite difference approximation to the gradient must be made. In that case it would appear that the *direct search* procedure would be preferable. *Direct search* techniques offer an approach, not only to a variety of numerical problems for which classical methods have proved unfeasible, but also to many hitherto "unsolvable" problems.

24.8 SUPPLEMENTARY REFERENCES

Listed below are the references given in the text.

a) E. BURGER, "On Extrema with Side Conditions," *Econometrica*, **23** (1955) 451–452.

b) C. CARATHEODORY, *Variationsrechnung*, B. G. Teubner, Berlin-Leipzig, 1935.

c) J. B. CROCKETT and H. CHERNOFF, "Gradient Methods of Maximization," *Pacific Journal of Math.* **5** (1955) 35–50.

d) H. B. CURRY, "The Method of Steepest Descent for Non-Linear Minimization Problems," *Quart. Applied Math.* **2** (1944) 258–261.

e) W. C. DAVIDSON, "Variable Metric Method for Minimization," *AEC Research and Development Report* ANL-5990 Rev. (November, 1959).

f) M. DAVIS, *Computability and Unsolvability*, McGraw-Hill, New York, 1958.

g) G. E. FORSYTHE, "Solving Linear Algebraic Equations Can be Interesting," *Bull. Amer. Math. Soc.* **59** (1953) 299–329.

h) G. E. FORSYTHE, "Selected References on Use of High-Speed Computers for Scientific Computation," *Math. Tab. Aids Comp.* **10** (1956).

i) G. E. FORSYTHE, "Computing Constrained Minima with Lagrange Multipliers," *J. Soc. Indust. Appl. Math.* **3** (1955) 173–178.

j) R. HOOKE and T. A. JEEVES, "Direct Search Solution of Numerical and Statistical Problems," *J. Assoc. Comp. Mach.* **8** (1961) 212–229.

k) R. C. KLINE, JR., "Project 435 Least Squares Fitting Technique," *APL Memo SRA-35-61* (February 1958).

l) C. B. TOMPKINS, *Methods of Steep Descent, in Modern Mathematics for the Engineer*, E. F. Beckenbach, ed., McGraw-Hill, New York, 1956.

CHAPTER 25

ELEMENTARY STATISTICS

25.1 INTRODUCTION

The purpose of this chapter is to discuss a few of the elementary statistical concepts and formulas used in the solution of some statistical problems which admit
of computer aid. The speed of computation and data storage capacity can be used
effectively in the tabulation and reduction of statistical data.

Statistics is the branch of applied mathematics concerned with experimental
design, summary analysis of data, and valid inference based upon such analysis.

The design of experiments is a field of study in itself. Prior to conducting an
experiment, a theoretical model is hypothesized. Analytic and computational
procedures are derived on the basis of this theoretical model. The experiment is
then designed to ensure compatibility of the theoretical model and the real world
situation. The criterion of design is the adequacy of the model to explain experimental results with maximum economy.

The tabulation and arithmetic computations necessary for summarizing data
afford ample opportunity for profitable use of the computer. Anyone who has
attempted any statistical analysis using hand computational methods welcomes
the aid of high-speed computers.

The problem of presenting the results of an experiment concisely may be
solved in a number of different ways. One of the more common methods of
handling large amounts of observational data is graphically by means of the
frequency distribution. Data are simply grouped into carefully chosen intervals
and plotted for visual inspection. Three types of curves are used:

1) the frequency histogram,

2) the frequency polygon to illustrate direct frequency counts,

3) the cumulative frequency curve to show the number of observations less
than or equal to a particular value.

25.2 MEASURES OF CENTRAL TENDENCY AND DISPERSION

Statistics designed to summarize data may be grouped into two categories, those
which measure central tendency and those which measure dispersion or variation.
The most common measures of central tendency are the mean, median, and mode.

The mean is the arithmetic average of a set of N numbers. That is,

$$\bar{x} = \sum_{i=1}^{N} \frac{x_i}{N}. \tag{25.2.1}$$

The mode is that value which occurs most frequently and the median is that value below which half of the observations fall.

Dispersion is most often measured in terms of the variance

$$s^2 = \sum_{i=1}^{N} \frac{(x_i - \bar{x})^2}{N - 1}, \tag{25.2.2}$$

or the standard deviation s, which is the square root of the variance.

A theoretical population is sometimes infinite and impossible to sample completely. Often the physical set up of an experiment does not warrant a complete sampling even in the case of a finite population. A representative sample is then chosen to aid in determining the characteristics of the theoretical population. For a theoretical population the mean is denoted by μ, the standard deviation by σ, and the variance by σ^2.

25.3 PROBABILITY DISTRIBUTIONS

A probability distribution is most conveniently defined in terms of a random variable (or variate), where, roughly speaking, a (one-dimensional) random variable is a numerical-valued function on a sample space. For example the simple coin toss experiment yields the two point sample spaces, heads and tails. A random variable is obtained by associating the numbers 0 and 1, respectively, with these two points. The simple (perfect) coin toss probability distribution is obtained in turn by associating the probability 0.5 with each of these numbers. Thus, a discrete probability distribution, such as the simple coin toss distribution, is a numerical-valued function on a random variable.

The binomial distribution,

$$P(k) = \binom{n}{k} p^k (1 - p)^{n-k}, \qquad k = 1(1)n, \tag{25.3.1}$$

is a generalization of the simple coin toss experiment. Let p be the probability of obtaining heads in a single toss of a perhaps imperfect coin. The random variable k is the number of heads obtained in n tosses.

Another example of a discrete distribution often encountered in practice is the Poisson distribution:

$$P(k) = \frac{\lambda^k e^{-\lambda}}{k!}, \qquad k = 1, 2, 3, \ldots, \tag{25.3.2}$$

which is, in a certain sense, a limit of the binomial distribution. That is, for large

n, small p, and $np < 1$,

$$\binom{n}{k} p^k (1 - p)^{n-k} \doteq \frac{(np)^k}{k!} e^{-np}. \tag{25.3.3}$$

Indeed, for $n > 100$ and $p < 0.01$, the two sides of (25.3.3) agree to about three decimal places for every k (see J. R. McCord and R. M. Moroney, *Probability Theory*, MacMillan, 1964). Consequently, the random variable k can be interpreted as the number of heads obtained in many tosses of a very imperfect coin. The parameter λ then represents the expected number of heads.

A continuous probability distribution must be defined somewhat differently since $P(X) = 0$ for each value X of a continuous random variable. This difficulty is readily overcome by use of the cumulative distribution function,

$$F(x) = P(X \leq x). \tag{25.3.4}$$

Thus, F is a continuous, nondecreasing function defined for all real x, and

$$F(-\infty) = 0 \qquad \text{while } F(\infty) = 1. \tag{25.3.5}$$

The frequency distribution function

$$f(x) = dF/dx \tag{25.3.6}$$

is sometimes more convenient to use than F. Note that if $x_1 \leq x_2$, then

$$P(x_1 \leq X \leq x_2) = \int_{x_1}^{x_2} f(t) \, dt = F(x_2) - F(x_1). \tag{25.3.7}$$

As an important example of a continuous distribution, consider the Gaussian distribution:

$$f(x) = \frac{1}{\sigma \sqrt{2\pi}} e^{-(x-\mu)^2/2\sigma^2}, \tag{25.3.8}$$

where μ is the population mean and σ^2 is the population variance. In particular, for mean zero and variance one, the equation

$$P(-2 \leq X \leq 2) = \frac{1}{\sqrt{2\pi}} \int_{-2}^{2} e^{-t^2/2} \, dt = 0.9545 \tag{25.3.9}$$

can be confirmed by referring to tables for the definite integral. Stated another way, 95 percent of the time, X is expected to assume values between -2 and 2.

Some probability distributions are of major importance in hypothesis testing and estimation. In general, the chi-square distribution is used in those tests in which the test statistic can be expressed as a sum of squares of normal and independently distributed variables. The F distribution is often used in those instances when the test statistic is expressed as the ratio of two such sums of squares. A third distribution used under certain conditions is the t distribution. These distributions will be discussed later in relation to the testing of parameters.

25.4 FISHER'S MAXIMUM-LIKELIHOOD ESTIMATION

Let $f(x, \theta)\, d\theta$ be a probability density, where θ is an unknown parameter. Assume that n independent observations $(x_1, x_2, \ldots, x_n)$ are taken from a population with the above probability density. Since the joint density of independent variables is the product of their densities, one has

$$f(x_1, \theta)f(x_2, \theta) \cdots f(x_n, \theta)\, dx_1\, dx_2 \cdots dx_n \qquad (25.4.1)$$

for the joint density. The product $L = f(x_1, \theta)f(x_2, \theta) \cdots f(x_n, \theta)$ is called the likelihood function when regarded as a function of θ. The maximum-likelihood estimator is a value $\theta = T$ which maximizes L. Since the log of the likelihood has its maximum at the same point as the likelihood, it is convenient to take the log and set the partial derivatives with respect to $\theta = 0$. Thus

$$\log L = \sum_{i=1}^{n} \log f(x_i, \theta). \qquad (25.4.2)$$

Differentiating and setting equal to zero, we have

$$\sum_{i=1}^{n} \frac{f_\theta(x_i, \theta)}{f(x_i, \theta)} = 0. \qquad (25.4.3)$$

If $f(x_1, x_2, \ldots, x_n, \theta_1, \theta_2)$ is the density for a random sample of size n from a population with two parameters θ_1, θ_2, the maximum likelihood estimators are obtained from

$$\sum_{i=1}^{n} \frac{f_{\theta_1}(x_i, \theta_1, \theta_2)}{f(x_i, \theta_1, \theta_2)} = 0 \quad \text{and} \quad \sum_{i=1}^{n} \frac{f_{\theta_2}(x_i, \theta_1, \theta_2)}{f(x_i, \theta_1, \theta_2)} = 0. \qquad (25.4.4)$$

Example. The joint density function of a sample of n observations, taken from a normal population with normal density function

$$\frac{1}{\sqrt{2\pi}\,\sigma} \exp\left[-\frac{1}{2\sigma^2}(x - \mu)^2\right]$$

of unknown parameters μ and σ, is given by

$$\prod_{i=1}^{n} \frac{1}{\sqrt{2\pi}\,\sigma} \exp\left[-\frac{1}{2\sigma^2}(x_i - \mu)^2\right] = \left(\frac{1}{2\pi\sigma^2}\right)^{n/2} \exp\left[-\frac{1}{2\sigma^2}\sum_{i=1}^{n}(x_i - \mu)^2\right].$$

Taking the logarithm and setting the partials with respect to μ and σ^2 equal to zero, we have

$$\frac{1}{\sigma^2}\sum_{i=1}^{n}(x_i - \mu) = 0, \qquad -\frac{n}{2\sigma^2} + \frac{1}{2\sigma^4}\sum_{i=1}^{n}(x_i - \mu)^2 = 0.$$

Simultaneous solution of the above for μ and σ^2 gives

$$T_1 = \frac{1}{n} \sum_{i=1}^{n} x_i = \bar{x}, \qquad T_2 = \frac{1}{n} \sum_{i=1}^{n} (x_i - \bar{x})^2.$$

25.5 METHOD OF CONFIDENCE INTERVALS

When a parameter θ is estimated by T, we want to obtain information about the accuracy of the estimate. One method is to indicate an interval and a statement of confidence that the interval will include the value θ, such as

$$\text{Prob } \{\theta_0 - h \le T \le \theta_0 + h\} \ge 1 - \alpha. \tag{25.5.1}$$

From $\theta - h \le T \le \theta + h$, we have

$$T - h \le \theta \le T + h. \tag{25.5.2}$$

The interval $(T - h, T + h)$ covers θ_0 in a proportion of $1 - \alpha$ of the cases. It is called the confidence interval and $1 - \alpha$ is called the confidence coefficient.

Example 1. Suppose we wish to estimate the mean μ of a normal population from $\bar{x}$, the mean of a sample with standard deviation s.

Solution. We assume a significance level α and obtain a value of the statistic

$$t_\alpha = \frac{\bar{x} - \mu}{s} \sqrt{n - 1}$$

from a table with $n - 1$ degrees of freedom, where n is the size of the sample. Since the mean of a random sample may be greater or less than the population mean, one has

$$P\left(-t_\alpha \le \frac{\bar{x} - \mu}{s} \sqrt{n - 1} \le t_\alpha\right) = 1 - \alpha$$

which, when simplified, gives

$$P\left(\bar{x} - t_\alpha \frac{s}{\sqrt{n - 1}} \le \mu \le \bar{x} + t_\alpha \frac{s}{\sqrt{n - 1}}\right) = 1 - \alpha.$$

The two quantities on either side of μ provide confidence limits for μ. Together they define a confidence interval. Note that t_α is not unique, and we may choose as limits any two values t_1 and t_2 such that

$$\int_{t_1}^{t_2} h(t)\, dt = 1 - \alpha,$$

where $h(t)$ is the t frequency distribution. By selecting the two values symmetrically (t_α and $-t_\alpha$), we obtain the smallest confidence interval when the distribution is symmetric, as is the case with $h(t)$.

If $(X - \mu)/\sigma$ is known to be normally distributed, we may calculate $-n_\alpha$ and n_α from the normal distribution table in a similar way. The probability statement given above may be interpreted so that, in successive calculations of confidence intervals at the indicated significance level for samples of equal size taken from the population, the intervals will be found to cover the population mean $100(1 - \alpha)$ percent of the time. Before the sample was drawn, $1 - \alpha$, a measure of confidence, was the probability that the interval to be constructed would contain the population mean.

For a normal distribution, 95 percent of the population has a value of the variate $X - \mu$ lying between 1.96σ and -1.96σ, and 99 percent of the population has a value of the variate $X - \mu$ lying between 2.58σ and -2.58σ.

Example 2. To obtain a confidence interval for the variance of a normal distribution, note that for samples of n observations the expression

$$\chi^2 = \frac{ns^2}{\sigma^2}$$

follows the chi-square law with $n - 1$ degrees of freedom. As before, one uses

$$P\left[\frac{\sum(x_i - \bar{x})^2}{\chi_\alpha'^2} \leq \sigma^2 \leq \frac{\sum(x_i - \bar{x})^2}{\chi_\alpha''^2}\right] = 1 - \alpha,$$

where χ'^2 and χ''^2 are two values of chi-square which yield the value $1 - \alpha$ for $n - 1$ degrees of freedom as obtained from a table. This gives the desired confidence interval for σ^2.

25.6 TESTING OF PARAMETERS

We now describe very briefly three tests of importance.

a) *Student t-test.* The ratio of the deviation of the mean $\bar{x}$ of a particular sample from the population mean to its standard deviation $s/\sqrt{n - 1}$ is known as Student t, where

$$t = \frac{\bar{x} - \mu}{s/\sqrt{n - 1}}.\tag{25.6.1}$$

By computing t and then entering the t-table at a prescribed level with $n - 1$ degrees of freedom, one compares the value of t from the table with the calculated value. The hypothesis that the sample and population means are the same at the prescribed significance level is rejected if the computed result exceeds the value of the table, otherwise it is accepted.

In a similar manner the t-test serves to determine whether two sample means $\bar{x}$ and $\bar{\bar{x}}$ came from the same population by calculating

$$t = \frac{|\bar{x} - \bar{\bar{x}}|}{s}\sqrt{\frac{n_1 n_2}{n_1 + n_2}},\tag{25.6.2}$$

where n_1 and n_2 are the sample sizes and s is the standard deviation of the two samples combined.

For large samples, e.g., exceeding 30 items, the normal distribution may be used as an approximation to the t-distribution.

b) *The chi-square test*. Chi-square is defined as the sum of the squares of a number of independent variates from a normal population with zero mean and unit standard deviation. The number of independent variables determines the number of degrees of freedom $n - 1$, associated with chi-square.

It is used to decide whether the estimate of variance from a sample of normally distributed observations is consistent with their having been drawn from a population of specified variance. It is also used to test whether the numbers of observations found in different classes agree (within limits of random error) with the numbers expected in those classes.

As a goodness-of-fit test, it is usually used as follows:

$$\chi^2 = \sum \frac{(\text{number observed} - \text{number expected})^2}{\text{number expected}} \qquad (25.6.3)$$

is computed. Entering the chi-square table with $n - 1$ degrees of freedom, we determine if this number is less than or greater than that indicated at the highest significance levels. If the computer value exceeds the value from the table, the fitness of the curve is rejected at that significance level.

c) *The F-test* (Variance-ratio test). The ratio of two estimates of variance obtained from two independent samples drawn from a normal population has the F-distribution. This distribution may be used to decide whether two independent estimates of variance can be accepted as being the variance of a single normally distributed population.

Thus, for the two samples of sizes n_1 and n_2 and variances s_1^2 and s_2^2, we calculate the expression

$$F = \frac{n_1 s_1^2/(n_1 - 1)}{n_2 s_2^2/(n_2 - 1)}. \qquad (25.6.4)$$

This value is compared with that obtained from the F-table with corresponding degrees of freedom ($n_1 - 1$ and $n_2 - 1$) for the two samples. It is also compared at a prescribed significance level to determine whether the variances are significantly different or whether they may be taken as estimates of the variance of a normally distributed population.

25.7 REGRESSION AND ANALYSIS OF VARIANCE

Regression analysis consists primarily in obtaining a functional relationship between characteristics (variables) of a population when that relationship exists. The functions can assume various forms—linear, polynomial, logarithmic, exponential, etc. Regression analysis differs from a simple curve fit in that statistical inference is made about a theoretical population on the basis of the sampling data

used to obtain that fit. It is not therefore unreasonable that certain hypotheses
on the sampling data be satisfied in order to preserve the validity of that inference.
In general the hypotheses satisfied and the behavior of the sampling data under
those hypotheses determine the form of the functional relationship and allowable
inference.

   Multiple linear regression presents perhaps the simplest example for development of necessary theory and computational procedure. For a population of k
variables the functional relationship then becomes

$$Y = \beta_0 + \beta_1 X_1 + \beta_2 X_2 + \cdots + \beta_i X_i + \cdots + \beta_k X_k, \qquad (25.7.1)$$

where the β_i are the population regression coefficients to be estimated. The likelihood function used to determine the maximum-likelihood estimates of the β_i is
then an implicit function, i.e., the normal distribution with usual parameters
μ and σ^2, where μ is expressed as a function of the β_i:

$$L(\theta_1, \theta_2, \ldots, \theta_k) = \left\{ \frac{1}{\sqrt{2\pi\sigma^2}} e^{\frac{-[Y - \mu(\theta_1, \theta_2, \ldots, \theta_k)]^2}{2\sigma^2}} \right\}^n, \qquad (25.7.2)$$

$$\ln L(\theta_1, \theta_2, \ldots, \theta_k) = -\frac{n}{2} \ln 2\pi\sigma^2 - \frac{1}{2\sigma^2} \sum^k [Y_i - \mu(\theta_1, \theta_2, \ldots, \theta_k)]^2, \qquad (25.7.3)$$

$$\frac{\partial \ln L(\theta_1, \ldots, \theta_k)}{\partial \theta_i} = -\frac{1}{2\sigma^2} \frac{\partial}{\partial \theta_i} \sum^k (Y_i - \hat{Y})^2. \qquad (25.7.4)$$

It now becomes apparent that the estimators which maximize the likelihood are
identical with those obtained by a least squares fit, that is, those estimators
which minimize

$$\sum_{i=1}^{n} (Y_i - \hat{Y}_i)^2 = \sum_{i=1}^{n} (Y_i - b_0 - b_1 X_{1i} - \cdots - b_j X_{ji} - \cdots - b_k X_{ki})^2. \qquad (25.7.5)$$

   Taking first partial derivatives with respect to each of the b_j's and equating
to zero yields the set of equations. (For simplicity of notation the subscript i
denoting summation over the observations will be dropped.) We have

$$\left.\begin{aligned}
\sum Y &= nb_0 &&+ \sum X_1 b_1 &&+ \cdots + \sum X_j b_j &&+ \cdots + \sum X_k b_k \\
\sum X_1 Y &= \sum X_1 b_0 + \sum X_1^2 b_1 &&+ \cdots + \sum X_1 X_j b_j &&+ \cdots + \sum X_1 X_k b_k \\
\sum X_2 Y &= \sum X_2 b_0 + \sum X_2 X_1 b_1 &&+ \cdots + \sum X_2 X_j b_j &&+ \cdots + \sum X_2 X_k b_k \\
&\ \ \vdots \\
\sum X_k Y &= \sum X_k b_0 + \sum X_k X_1 b_1 &&+ \cdots + \sum X_k X_j b_j &&+ \cdots + \sum X_k^2 b_k
\end{aligned}\right\} .$$

$$(25.7.6)$$

   The solution of this system of equations is the basic computational problem
for the multiple linear regression. Any of the many mathematical procedures

which are designed to solve this system is valid. Cramer's method, though certainly not a good method for computers, is applicable for small values of k. For the simple linear model with $k = 1$ an analytical determination of formulas and straightforward substitution in these formulas appear more efficient.

It would be well at this point to clarify notation. The letter Y denotes the theoretical value of the regression equation, Y_i is the observed value for X_i, and $\hat{Y}$ denotes the estimate of Y obtained by the fitted regression equation. For simplicity of notation and algebraic manipulation, lower-case letters are used to denote the deviations of x and y about their respective means, $x = (X - \bar{X})$ and $y = (Y - \bar{Y})$. As is the convention, Greek letters are used to designate theoretical population values and Roman letters to denote observed or computed sample values.

The simple linear case yields the regression equation:

$$Y = \alpha + \beta X. \tag{25.7.7}$$

It is desirable then to minimize the expression

$$Q = \sum_{i=1}^{n} (\hat{Y}_i - a - bX_i)^2. \tag{25.7.8}$$

Taking partials with respect to a and b and solving the normal equations, we have

$$b = \frac{\sum_{i=1}^{n} x_i y_i}{\sum_{i=1}^{n} x_i^2}, \tag{25.7.9}$$

$$a = \bar{Y} - b\bar{X}. \tag{25.7.10}$$

This is the "best" linear fit to the data in the least-squares sense and is valid regardless of the distribution of the data. If, however, we want to attach confidence bands and perform tests of significance, certain hypotheses are made:

1) X is fixed prior to sampling.

2) For any X, the possible Y values are normal and independently distributed.

3) The means of the Y-values fall on a straight line, $\mu_{Y/X} = \alpha + \beta X$.

4) Homogeneity of variance among the Y-distributions, that is, $\sigma_{Y/X}^2$ is constant for all X.

The regression equation gives a functional description of data by which dependent variable values may be predicted. Confidence bands and tests of hypotheses give some measure of the ability of the regression equation to perform these functions.

Under the hypotheses, the standard error of estimate (σ_E^2, $\sigma_{Y/X}^2$, or $\sigma_{Y \cdot X}^2$)^2 is equal for all X. It is justifiable then to form a pooled estimate of variance as

$$S_E^2 = \frac{\sum_{i=1}^{n} (Y_i - \hat{Y}_i)^2}{n - 2} = \frac{1}{(n-2)} \left[\sum_{i=1}^{n} y_i^2 - \frac{(\sum_{i=1}^{n} x_i y_i)^2}{\sum_{i=1}^{n} x_i^2} \right], \tag{25.7.11}$$

since $\hat{Y}_i$ is the estimate of a line through the mean of the Y_i sample populations. Knowing S_E^2, we can derive the variance of those quantities for which inference is desirable. Obviously, the confidence in estimating any variable is a function of the variability of that variable.

Confidence bands are simply a form of hypothesis testing. Usually the formulas for the confidence bands can be derived algebraically from the analogous test statistic. Define $\hat{Y}_0$ as the value of the estimated regression line at the point X_0, where X_0 takes on all X_i values in the fit interval and takes on μ_0 as the mean of the theoretical population. Also define

$$S_{\hat{Y}_0} = S_E\sqrt{1/n + (X_0 - \overline{X})^2/\sum_{i=1}^{n}(X_i - \overline{X})^2}. \qquad (25.7.12)$$

The two-tailed t-test on the mean yields the test statistic

$$t_{\alpha,n-2} = \frac{\hat{Y}_0 - \mu_0}{S_{\hat{Y}_0}}. \qquad (25.7.13)$$

That is, $|t_{\alpha,n-2}| > (\hat{Y}_0 - \mu_0)/S_{\hat{Y}_0}$ is the acceptance region for $H_0: \mu_{Y/X_0} = \mu_0$. Therefore with $(1 - \alpha)$-percent confidence

$$\hat{Y}_0 - t_{\alpha,n-2}S_{\hat{Y}_0} < \mu_0 < \hat{Y}_0 + t_{\alpha,n-2}S_{\hat{Y}_0}. \qquad (25.7.14)$$

Substituting X_i and $\hat{Y}_i$, $i = 1(1)n$, for X_0 and $\hat{Y}_0$ yields the set of points determining the confidence bands for the computed regression line over the fit interval. With $(1 - \alpha)$-percent confidence the theoretical population regression equation

$$Y = \alpha + \beta X \qquad (25.7.15)$$

falls within these bands.

If $\hat{Y}_p$ is the predicted value for a specific value X_p, then the confidence interval becomes

$$\hat{Y}_p - t_{\alpha,n-2}S_{\hat{Y}_p} < \mu_p < \hat{Y}_p + t_{\alpha,n-2}S_{\hat{Y}_p}, \qquad (25.7.16)$$

where

$$S_{\hat{Y}_p} = \sqrt{1 + 1/n + (X_p - \overline{X})^2/\sum_{i=1}^{n}(X_i - \overline{X})^2}. \qquad (25.7.17)$$

For a single predicted value $\hat{Y}_p$, the confidence interval is wider than if prediction is made over an interval.

The same procedure is applied to the intercept and regression coefficient. Defining

$$S_a = S_E\sqrt{1/n + \overline{X}^2/\sum_{i=1}^{n}(X_i - \overline{X})^2}$$

and   (25.7.18)

$$S_b = S_E(1/\sqrt{\sum_{i=1}^{n}x_i^2}),$$

we find the appropriate t-tests which are

$$t_{\alpha,n-2} = \frac{a - \alpha_0}{s_a} \quad \text{and} \quad t_{\alpha,n-2} - \frac{b - \beta_0}{s_b}, \qquad (25.7.19)$$

and the corresponding confidence intervals

$$a - t_{\alpha,n-2} s_a < \alpha_0 < a + t_{\alpha,n-2} s_a$$

and   (25.7.20)

$$b - t_{\alpha,n-2} s_b < \beta_0 < b + t_{\alpha,n-2} s_b.$$

The most common value of α_0 and β_0 is zero. When $a = 0$, the regression line passes through the origin. When $H_0 : \beta_0 = 0$ is accepted, the data should be re-examined in terms of the hypothesized linear model.

One more quantity is of interest in regression analysis. The sample correlation coefficient,

$$r = \frac{\sum x_1 x_2}{\sqrt{\sum x_1^2 \sum x_2^2}}, \qquad |r| \le 1,   (25.7.21)$$

is a numerical measure of the linear relationship between X_1 and X_2. A value of r equal to 1 would indicate a perfect positive correlation between X_1 and X_2. Large values of X_1 are associated with large values of X_2 in a direct linear relation. An r of -1 would indicate a corresponding relationship between small values of both variables. An r of 0 would denote a lack of linear relationship between the variables. Intermediate values of r would show varying degrees of linear relationship, the significance of which would vary with the type of experimental data.

The presentation of the results of a regression analysis is often done in the form of an analysis of variance table. The purpose of an *anova* table is to present the results of an experiment in terms of partitioned sums of squares. For the regression problem, the total variation in the experiment is expressed as the total corrected, i.e., corrected by the mean, sum of squares of the dependent variable, $\sum_{i=1}^{n} y_i^2$. The total variation can be partitioned into the variation which was explained by regression and the variation which is left unexplained.

The square of the correlation coefficient r^2 is the proportion of variation explained by a linear relation. In the regression analysis, $r^2 \cdot \sum_{i=1}^{n} y_i^2$ is that portion of the sum of squares explained by linear regression, and $(1 - r^2) \cdot \sum_{i=1}^{n} y_i^2$ is that portion of variation due to deviations from the regression line. With each sum of squares is associated corresponding degrees of freedom.

The analysis of variance for simple linear regression is shown in Table 25.7.1.

Table 25.7.1

Source of variation	d.f.	Sum of squares	Mean sum of squares
Explained by regression	1	$r^2 \sum y_i^2$	$(\sum xy)^2 / \sum x^2$
Deviations from regression	$n - 2$	$(1 - r^2) \sum y_i^2$	$[\sum y^2 - (\sum xy)^2 / \sum x^2] / (n - 2)$
Total	$n - 1$	$\sum y_i^2$	

The formula for the mean sum of squares for the deviation from regression can be recognized as the expression for S_E^2. Recalling that the sample variance is an unbiased estimate of the population variance, we find that the expected value of the mean square deviations about regression is σ_E^2. We can show that the expected value of the mean sum of squares explained by regression is

$$\sigma_E^2 + \beta^2 \sum_{i=1}^{n} (X_i - \overline{X})^2. \tag{25.7.22}$$

Under the H_0: $\beta = 0$ the ratio of these two estimators of σ_E^2 follows an $F_{1,n-2}$ distribution. The equation

$$F = \frac{r^2(n - 2)}{1 - r^2} \tag{25.7.23}$$

is then an alternative to the t-test for the H_0: $\beta = 0$.

Multiple linear regression analysis follows the same type of procedure except that it becomes necessary to solve a system of linear equations in order to obtain the b_i's. The maximum-likelihood estimates of the b_i's yield a set of equations (25.7.6). The solution of that system of equations is perfectly valid. However, since computer time for solving such a system of equations is approximately proportional to k^3, and the sums of squares are needed in the final analysis, another procedure is suggested.

Divide the first equation by n and solve for

$$b_0 = \overline{Y} - b_1\overline{X}_1 - b_2\overline{X}_2 - \cdots - b_k\overline{X}_k. \tag{25.7.24}$$

Substitute the value thus obtained in the quantity to be minimized:

$$\begin{aligned}
\sum(Y - \hat{Y})^2 &= \sum(Y - (b_0 + b_1X_1 + \cdots + b_kX_k))^2 \\
&= \sum(Y - \overline{Y} + b_1\overline{X}_1 + b_2\overline{X}_2 + \cdots + b_k\overline{X}_k \\
&\quad - b_1X_1 - b_2X_2 - \cdots - b_kX_k)^2 \\
&= \sum(Y - \overline{Y} - b_1(X - \overline{X}_1) - \cdots - b_k(X_k - \overline{X}_k))^2 \\
&= \sum(y - bx_1 - bx_2 - \cdots - b_kx_k)^2. \tag{25.7.25}
\end{aligned}$$

Taking first partials and equating to zero yields the following set of equations:

$$\left.\begin{aligned}
\sum x_1 y &= b_1\sum x_1^2 + b_2\sum x_1x_2 + \cdots + b_k\sum x_1x_k \\
\sum x_2 y &= b_1\sum x_1x_2 + b_2\sum x_2^2 + \cdots + b_k\sum x_2x_k \\
&\;\;\vdots \\
\sum x_k y &= b_1\sum x_1x_k + b_2\sum x_2x_k + \cdots + b_k\sum x_k^2
\end{aligned}\right\}. \tag{25.7.26}$$

Gaussian elimination provides a simple method of solving for the b_i and obtaining the inverse elements at the same time. The matrix of coefficients of the b_i's is augmented by the vector on the left-hand side of the equations and the identity matrix.

Example. Assume we have data which gives the following sums of squares:
$\sum x_i x_j$:

i \ j	1	2	3	$\sum x_i y$	$\overline{X}_i$	$\sum y^2$
1	16.6840	1.9279	0.8204	1.5057	13.10	0.6831
2		0.9924	0.3351	0.5989	9.61	
3			0.2248	0.1848	3.28	

One procedure is to use a method of tabulation shown in Table 25.7.2. We find that

$$b_0 = 6.5900 - (0.0291)(13.10) = (0.6148)(9.61) - (-0.2011)(3.28)$$
$$= 0.9602,$$
$$\hat{Y} = 0.9602 - 0.0291 X_1 + 0.6148 X_2 - 0.2011 X_3.$$

The presentation of the results in the *anova* table (Table 25.7.3) is straightforward:

$$r^2 \sum_{i=1}^{n} y_i^2 = b_1 \sum x_1 y + b_2 \sum x_2 y + \cdots + b_k \sum x_k y,$$

$$r^2 \sum_{i=1}^{44} y_i^2 = (0.0291)(1.5057) + (0.6148)(0.5989) + (-0.2011)(0.1848) = 0.3749,$$

$$\sum_{i=1}^{n} (Y_i - \hat{Y}_i)^2 = (1 - r^2) \sum_{i=1}^{n} y_i^2 = \sum_{i=1}^{n} y_i^2 - r^2 \sum_{i=1}^{n} y_i^2$$
$$= 0.6831 - 0.3749 = 0.3082,$$

$$F_c = \frac{0.1249}{0.0077} = 16.2, \qquad F_{3,40} = 2.8387, \qquad \alpha = 0.05.$$

The computed regression equation then explains a significant proportion of the variation in the dependent variable.

Confidence bands, test statistics, and the needed variances are computed in a manner analogous to simple linear regression. The standard error of Y estimated by the X_i becomes

$$S_{\hat{Y} \cdot 12 \cdots k}^2 = \frac{\sum_{i=1}^{n} (Y_i - \hat{Y}_i)^2}{n - k - 1} = \frac{1}{(n - k - 1)} \left[\sum_{i=1}^{n} y_i^2 - r^2 \sum_{i=1}^{n} y_i^2 \right]. \quad (25.7.27)$$

Although confidence bands are used less frequently for the multiple regression, they may be obtained by using ($k = 3$) as the standard error of estimate. Hence

$$S_{Y_0}^2 = S_{Y \cdot 123}^2 [(1/n) + c_{11}(X_{01} - \overline{X}_1)^2 + c_{22}(X_{02} - \overline{X}_2)^2$$
$$+ c_{33}(X_{03} - \overline{X}_3)^2 + 2c_{12}(X_{01} - \overline{X}_1)(X_{02} - \overline{X}_2)$$
$$+ 2c_{13}(X_{01} - \overline{X}_1)(X_{03} - \overline{X}_3) + 2c_{23}(X_{02} - \overline{X}_2)(X_{03} - \overline{X}_3)]. \quad (25.7.28)$$

Table 25.7.2

$\sum x_i x_j$			$\sum x_i y$		I		
16.6840	1.9279	0.8240	1.5057	1	0		0
1.9279	0.9924	0.3351	0.5989	0	1		0
0.8240	0.3351	0.2248	0.1848	0	0		1
13.6636	0.6997	0	0.8284	1	0		−3.6655
0.6996	0.4929	0	0.3234	0	1		−1.4906
3.6655	1.4906	1	0.8220	0	0		4.4484
12.6705	0	0	0.3693	1	−1.4195		−1.5495
1.4194	1	0	0.6561	0	2.0288		−3.0241
1.5497	0	1	−0.1560	0	−3.0241		8.9551

I			b_i		c_{ij}		
1	0	0	0.0291	0.0789	−0.1120		−0.1223
0	1	0	0.6148	−0.1120	2.1878		−2.8505
0	0	1	−0.2011	0.1223	−2.8505		9.1446

Table 25.7.3

Source of variation	d.f.	Sum of squares
Due to regression	k	$r^2 \sum_{i=1}^{n} y_i^2$
Deviations from regression	$n - k - 1$	$(1 - r^2) \sum_{i=1}^{n} y_i^2$
Total	$n - 1$	$\sum_{i=1}^{n} y_i^2$

Source of variation	d.f.	SS	MSS
Due to regression	3	0.3749	0.1249
Deviations from regression	40	0.3082	0.0077
Total	43	0.6831	

The sample value X_0 is extended to (X_{01}, X_{02}, X_{03}), where X_{0i} takes on all values of X_i in the fit interval. For a single predicted $\hat{Y}$, one is added to the quantity in brackets as in the simple linear case.

The test of H_0: $\beta_i = 0$ is of greater practical interest. The variance of the partial regression coefficients is computed as

$$S_{b_i}^2 = S_{Y \cdot 12 \cdots k}^2 c_{ii}, \qquad i = 1(1)k, \qquad (25.7.29)$$

and the test statistic is

$$t = \frac{b_i}{S_{b_i}}. \tag{25.7.30}$$

If H_0 is rejected, the variable X_i is contributing significantly to the estimation of Y. If H_0 is accepted, it may be desired to delete X_i from the experiment.

The test of H_0: $\beta_i = 0$ only tests the individual β_i for significance. A comparison of the relative importance of the β_i's is better performed on the standard partial regression coefficients

$$b_i' = b_i \frac{\sqrt{\sum x^2}}{\sqrt{\sum y^2}}. \tag{25.7.31}$$

25.8 THE MONTE CARLO METHOD

The Monte Carlo method consists in formulating a game of chance or a stochastic process which produces a random variable whose expected value is the solution of the given problem. An approximation to the expected value is then obtained by means of sampling from the resulting distribution. As in all numerical procedures, only an approximation to the correct solution is obtained. Instead of the main source of error being due to roundoff, it is due to the fact that only a finite sample can be taken. The degree of accuracy depends on the sample size.

The name *Monte Carlo* is generally credited to Metropolis and Ulam. One of the earliest applications was in solving integral equations of the Fredholm type. Another was in solving difference equations associated with elliptic partial differential equations. With the advent of high-speed computers it became feasible to obtain large samples. When the method was first used on high-speed computers, some considered the method a panacea. However, it is now considered as another numerical tool especially suited for certain types of problems.

The method has been used with varying degrees of success in evaluating integrals and boundary value problems in both ordinary and partial differential equations. It has also been used in solving linear systems and matrix inversion.

All Monte Carlo techniques require a random number source. Therefore, knowledge about generating random numbers is of utmost importance. The literature on this subject is quite extensive.

The application of the Monte Carlo method to formulated mathematical problems has been the only one mentioned thus far. However, the method may be much more fruitful in the case where one formulates the Monte Carlo process from the physical process without first translating the process into a type of mathematical expression. In fact, it is sometimes not feasible to formulate the problem mathematically. This is particularly true in such problems as particle physics, nuclear reactions, and missile impact point studies.

No attempt has been made here to discuss the method. This could not be adequately done without an extensive presentation of the method as applied to a large number of special types of problems with a thorough analysis of each. This has been adequately done in the literature. Some references, suggested for the detailed study of this subject, are given in the supplementary references.

25.9 SUPPLEMENTARY REFERENCES

Suggested references for further study of the material given in this chapter are Bennett and Franklin [8], Brownlee [14], Dixon and Massey [34], Ostle [118], Snedecor [141], and

a) R. L. ANDERSON and T. A. BANCROFT, *Statistical Theory in Research*, McGraw-Hill, New York, 1952.

b) W. G. COCHRAN and G. M. COX, *Experimental Designs*, Wiley, New York, 1950.

c) T. C. FRY, *Probability and its Engineering Uses*, 2nd Ed., Van Nostrand, Princeton, N. J., 1965.

d) A. HALD, *Statistical Theory with Engineering Applications*, Wiley, New York, 1952.

e) P. G. HOEL, *Introduction to Mathematical Statistics*, 2nd Ed., Wiley, New York, 1966.

f) A. M. MOOD, *Introduction to the Theory of Statistics*, McGraw-Hill, New York, 1950.

g) L. SIMON, *Engineer's Manual of Statistical Methods*, Wiley, New York, 1941.

h) W. F. BAUER, "The Monte Carlo Method," *J. Soc. Indust. Appl. Math.*, Vol. 6, No. 4, (December, 1958) 438–451.

i) N. METROPOLIS and S. ULAM, "The Monte Carlo Method," *J. Am. Statist. Assoc.* **44** (1949) 335–341.

j) H. KAHN, "Stochastic (Monte Carlo) Attenuation Analysis," Rand Corp., Santa Monica, Calif., Report No. R-163, (June 1949).

k) R. COURANT, K. FRIEDRICHS, and H. LEVY, "Uber die Partiellen Differenzengleichungen der Mathemischen Physik," *Math. Ann.* **100** (1928) 32–74.

l) W. WASOW, "Random Walks and the Eigenvalues of Elliptic Difference Equations," *J. Res. Nat. Bur. Standards* **46** No. 1, (January 1951).

m) R. E. CUTKOSKY, "A Monte Carlo Method for Solving a Class of Integral Equations," *J. Res. Nat. Bur. Standards* **47,** No. 2, (August 1951).

n) J. H. CURTISS, "Monte Carlo Methods for the Iteration of Linear Operators," *J. Math. Phys.* **37** (1954) 209–232.

o) J. VON NEUMANN, "Various Techniques Used in Connection with Random Digits, Monte Carlo Method," *Nat. Bur. Standards Applied Math. Series* **12** (June 1951).

p) B. JANSSON, *Random Number Generators*, Almquist and Wiksell, Stockholm, 1966.

q) A. PAPOULIS, *Probability Random Variables and Stochastic Processes*, McGraw-Hill, New York, 1965.

BIBLIOGRAPHY

1. N. ACHIESER, *Theory of Approximations*, Ungar, New York, 1956.
2. Advanced Numerical Analysis, University of Michigan Summer Session, 1958.
3. *Advances in Computation*, **1, 2, 3,** Academic, New York, 1960, 1961, 1962.
4. T. APOSTOL, *Mathematical Analysis*, Addison-Wesley, Reading, Mass., 1960.
5. B. ARDEN, *An Introduction to Digital Computing*, Addison-Wesley, Reading, Mass., 1963.
6. F. BAUER, "Optimal Scaling of Matrices and the Importance of the Minimal Condition," *Proc. IFIP Congress*, **62,** Munich, North Holland Co., Amsterdam, 1962, 198–206.
7. R. BELLMAN, *Introduction to Matrix Analysis*, McGraw-Hill, New York, 1960.
8. C. BENNETT and N. FRANKLIN, *Statistical Analysis in Chemistry and the Chemical Industry*, Wiley, New York, 1954.
9. E. BODEWIG, *Matrix Calculus*, Interscience, New York, 1959.
10. A. BOOTH, *Numerical Methods*, Academic, New York, 1955.
11. F. BOTHWELL, "Nyquist Diagrams and the Routh-Hurwitz Stability Criterion," *Proc. IRE*, **38,** 1950, 1345.
12. R. BOXER, "A Note on Numerical Transform Calculus," *Proc. IRE*, 1957, 1401.
13. J. BRENNER, "A Set of Matrices for Testing Computer Programs," MRC Technical Summary Report No. 325, May 1962.
14. K. BROWNLEE, *Statistical Theory and Methodology in Science and Engineering*, Wiley, New York, 1960.
15. G. CALDWELL, "A Note on the Downhill Method," *J. Assoc. Comput. Mach.*, **6,** 1959, 223.
16. H. CARSLAW, *Introduction to the Theory of Fourier's Series and Integrals*, Dover, New York, 1930.
17. R. CHURCHILL, *Introduction to Complex Variables*, McGraw-Hill, New York, 1948,
18. E. CODDINGTON and N. LEVINSON, *Theory of Ordinary Differential Equations.* McGraw-Hill, New York, 1955.
19. G. COHN and B. SALZBERG, "Solution of Nonlinear Differential Equations by the Reversion Method," *J. Appl. Phys.*, **24,** 1953, 180.
20. L. COLLATZ, *Numerical Treatment of Differential Equations*, 3rd Ed., Springer, Berlin, 1960.

21. R. COURANT and D. HILBERT, *Methods of Mathematical Physics*, **1**, 1953, **2**, 1962, Interscience, New York.

22. R. COURANT, K. FRIEDRICHS, and H. LEWY, "Partielle Differenzengleichungen der Physik," *Mathematische Annalen*, 1928.

23. R. COURANT and P. LAX, "On Nonlinear Partial Differential Equations with Two Independent Variables," *Commun. Pure Appl. Math.*, 1949.

24. J. CRANK and P. NICHOLSON, "A Practical Method for Numerical Evaluation of Solutions of Partial Differential Equations of the Heat Conduction Type," *Proc. Cambridge Philos. Soc.*, **42**, 1946, **43**, 1947.

25. J. CROCKETT and H. CHERNOFF, "Gradient Methods of Maximization," *Pacific J. Math.*, **5**, 1955, 33.

26. H. CROSS, *Numerical Methods of Analysis in Engineering*, Macmillan, New York, 1949.

27. W. CUNNINGHAM, *Introduction to Nonlinear Analysis*, McGraw-Hill, New York, 1958.

28. H. CURRY, "The Method of Steepest Descent for Nonlinear Minimization Problems," *Quart. Appl. Math.*, **2**, 1944, 258.

29. J. CURTISS, *Numerical Analysis*, McGraw-Hill, New York, 1956.

30. W. DAVIDSON, "Variable Metric Method for Minimization," Argonne National Laboratory Report 5990, 1959.

31. H. DAVIS, "Introduction to Nonlinear Differential and Integral Equations," U.S.A.E.C., 1961.

32. M. DAVIS, *Computability and Unsolvability*, McGraw-Hill, New York, 1958.

33. L. DEDERICK, "Construction and Selection of Smoothing Formulas," BRL Report No. 863, Aberdeen Proving Ground, May 1953.

34. W. DIXON and F. MASSEY, *Introduction to Statistical Analysis*, McGraw-Hill, New York, 1957.

35. A. DOODSON, "A Method for the Smoothing of Numerical Tables," *Quart. J. Mech. Appl. Math.*, **3**, 1950, 217

36. J. DOUGLAS, "A Survey of Numerical Methods for Parabolic Differential Equations," *Advances in Computers*, **2**, 1961, 1.

37. J. DOUGLAS and B. JONES, "On Predictor-Corrector Methods for Nonlinear Parabolic Differential Equations," *J. Soc. Indust. Appl. Math.*, **11**, 1963, 195.

38. W. DUNCAN and A. COLLAR, "Solution of Oscillation Problems by Matrices," *Phil. Mag.*, **17**, 1934, 865.

39. W. DUNCAN and A. COLLAR, "Matrices Applied to the Motions of Damped Systems," *Phil. Mag.*, **19**, 1935, 197.

40. R. EDDY, "Stability in the Numerical Solution of Initial Value Problems in Partial Differential Equations," Naval Ord. Lab. Memo 10232, 1949.

41. L. EHRLICH, "Roots of Polynomials with Complex Coefficients," Johns Hopkins Appl. Phys. Lab., BCC-281, Nov. 1962.

42. L. EHRLICH and M. HORTON, "The Quotient-Difference (QD) and Biorthogonalization (BO) Algorithms," Johns Hopkins Appl. Phys. Lab., BCC-318, Nov. 1963.

43. a) V. FADDEEVA, *Computational Methods of Linear Algebra*, Dover, New York, 1959.

43. b) D. FADDEEV and V. FADDEEVA, *Computational Methods of Linear Algebra*, Freeman, San Francisco, 1963.

44. G. FORSYTHE and P. ROSENBLOOM, *Numerical Analysis and Partial Differential Equations*, Wiley, New York, 1958.

45. G. FORSYTHE and W. WASOW, *Finite Difference Methods for Partial Differential Equations*, Wiley, New York, 1960.

46. G. FORSYTHE, "A Numerical Analyst's Fifteen-Foot Shelf," *MTAC*, 1953, 221–228.

47. G. FORSYTHE, "Generation and Use of Orthogonal Polynomials for Data Fitting with a Digital Computer," *J. Soc. Indust. Appl. Math.*, **5,** 1957.

48. G. FORSYTHE and M. ASCHER, "SWAC Experiments on the Use of Orthogonal Polynomials for Data Fitting," *J. Assoc. Comput. Mach.*, **5,** Jan. 1958.

49. G. FORSYTHE, "Crout, Algorithm No. 16," *Comm. ACM*, Sept. 1960, 507.

50. G. FORSYTHE, "Computing Constrained Minima with Lagrange Multipliers," *J. Soc. Indust. Appl. Math.*, **3,** 1955, 173.

51. L. FOX, *Numerical Solution of Two Point Boundary Problems in Ordinary Differential Equations*, Oxford University Press, Oxford, 1957.

52. a) L. FOX, *Numerical Solution of Ordinary and Partial Differential Equations*, Pergamon, London, 1962.

52. b) L. FOX, *Introduction to Numerical Linear Algebra*, Clarendon, Oxford, 1964.

53. I. FRANCIS, The QR-Transformation: A Unitary Analogue to the LR-Transformation — Part 1, *Comput. J.*, **4,** No. 3, p. 265; Part 2, *Comput. J.*, **4,** No. 4, 1961–1962, 332.

54. B. FRIEDMAN, *Principles and Techniques of Applied Mathematics*, Wiley, New York, 1961.

55. D. FULKERSON and P. WOLFE, "An Algorithm for Scaling Matrices," *SIAM Rev.*, **4,** No. 2, April 1962.

56. A. FULLER, "Stability Criteria for Linear Systems and Realizability Criteria for *RC* Networks," *Proc. Cambridge Phil. Soc.*, **53,** 1957, 878–885, 895.

57. F. GANTMACHER, *Application of the Theory of Matrices*, Interscience, New York, 1959.

58. W. GIVENS, "Numerical Computation of the Characteristic Values of a Real Symmetric Matrix," Oak Ridge National Laboratory Report ORNL-1574, 1954.

59. H. GOLDSTEIN and J. VON NEUMANN, "Numerical Inverting of Matrices of High Order," *Bull. Am. Math. Soc.*, **53,** 1947, 1021–1099.

60. H. GOLDSTEIN and J. VON NEUMANN, "Numerical Inverting of Matrices of High Order," *Proc. Am Math. Soc.*, **2,** 1951, 188.

61. S. GORN, "Divergence Points for Newton's Method," *Ann. Math.*, **59,** 1954.

62. C. GRAM, *Selected Numerical Methods*, Regnecentralen, Copenhagen, 1962.

63. T. GREVILLE, "On Smoothing a Finite Table: A Matrix Approach," *J. Soc. Indust. Appl. Math.*, **5,** No. 3, 1957, 137.

64. J. HADAMARD, *Lectures on Cauchy's Problem in Linear Partial Differential Equations*, Dover, New York, 1952.

65. R. HAMMING, *Numerical Methods for Scientists and Engineers*, McGraw-Hill, New York, 1962.

66. H. HARMAN, *Factor Analysis*, Wiley, New York, 1959.

67. W. HART and T. MOTZKIN, "A Composite Newton-Raphson Gradient Method for the Solution of Systems of Equations," *Pacific J. Math.*, **6**, 1959, 691.

68. D. HARTREE, *Numerical Analysis*, Oxford University Press, Oxford, 1952.

69. C. HASTINGS, *Approximations for Digital Computers*, Princeton University Press, Princeton, N. J., 1955.

70. P. HENRICI, *Discrete Variable Methods in Ordinary Differential Equations*, Wiley, New York, 1962.

71. P. HENRICI, "The Quotient-Difference Algorithm," Natl. Bur. Std. Appl. Math. Series No. 49, 1958, 23.

72. M. HESTENES, "Inversion of Matrices by Biorthogonalization and Related Results," *J. Soc. Indust. Appl. Math.*, **6**, No. 1, 1958, 51.

73. F. HILDEBRAND, *Introduction to Numerical Analysis*, McGraw-Hill, New York, 1956.

74. F. HILDEBRAND, *Methods of Applied Mathematics*, Prentice-Hall, Englewood Cliffs, N. J., 1952.

75. R. HOOKE and T. JEEVES, "Direct Search Solution of Numerical and Statistical Problems," *J. Assoc. Comput. Mach.*, **8**, 1961, 212.

76. A. HOUSEHOLDER, *Principles of Numerical Analysis*, McGraw-Hill, New York, 1953.

77. A. HOUSEHOLDER, *Theory of Matrices in Numerical Analysis*, Ginn, Boston, 1964.

78. A. HOUSEHOLDER, "The Approximate Solution of Matrix Problems, "*J. Assoc. Comput. Mach.*, **5**, 1958, 205.

79. J. INDRITZ, *Methods in Analysis*, Macmillan, New York, 1963.

80. H. JEFFREYS and B. JEFFREYS, *Methods of Mathematical Physics*, Cambridge University Press, Cambridge, 1956.

81. F. JOHN, *Advanced Numerical Analysis*, Gordon and Breach, New York, 1964.

82. L. KANTORIVICH and V. KRYLOV, *Approximation Methods of Higher Analysis*, Interscience, New York, 1958.

83. T. KARMAN and M. BIOT, *Mathematical Methods in Engineering*, McGraw-Hill, New York, 1940.

84. M. KENDALL, *A Course in Multivariate Analysis*, Hafner, New York, 1957.

85. K. KNOPP, *Theory of Functions*, Dover, New York, 1945, 1947.

86. Z. KOPAL, *Numerical Analysis*, Wiley, New York, 1955.

87. K. KUNZ, *Numerical Analysis*, McGraw-Hill, New York, 1957.

88. G. LANCE, "Solution of Algebraic and Transcendental Equations on an Automatic Digital Computer," *J. Assoc. Comput. Mach.*, **6**, 1959, 97.

89. C. LANCZOS, *Applied Analysis*, Prentice-Hall, Englewood Cliffs, N. J., 1956.

90. R. Langer, *On Numerical Approximations*, U. of Wis. Press, Madison, Wis., 1959.

91. R. Langer, *Boundary Value Problems in Differential Equations*, U. of Wis. Press, Madison, Wis., 1960.

92. J. Laning and R. Battin, *Random Processes in Automatic Control*, McGraw-Hill, New York, 1956.

93. H. Lass, *Elements of Pure and Applied Mathematics*, McGraw-Hill, New York, 1957.

94. S. Lefschetz, "Contributions to the Theory of Nonlinear Oscillations," *Ann. Math. Studies*, **1**, No. 20, 1950; **2**, No. 29, 1952; **3**, No. 36, 1956; **4**, No. 41, 1958; Princeton University Press, Princeton, N. J.

95. M. Lighthill, *Fourier Analysis and Generalized Functions*, Cambridge University Press, London, 1958.

96. G. Lindamood, "Computer Methods of Functional Minimization," Johns Hopkins Appl. Phys. Lab., BCC-243, 1961.

97. M. Lotkin, "Experiments in the Smoothing of Data," *Quart. of Appl. Math.*, **16**, No. 2, 1958.

98. W. Lovitt, *Linear Integral Equations*, Dover, New York, 1951.

99. W. McKeeman, "Crout with Equilibration and Iteration," *Commun. ACM*, Nov. 1962, 553.

100. N. McLachlan, *Complex Variable and Operational Calculus*, Cambridge University Press, London, 1942.

101. N. McLachlan, *Ordinary Nonlinear Differential Equations in Engineering and Physical Sciences*, Oxford University Press, Oxford, 1950.

102. T. McRobert, *Functions of a Complex Variable*, Macmillan, New York, 1933.

103. H. Meyer, *Symposium on Monte Carlo Methods*, Wiley, New York, 1956.

104. F. Miller, *Partial Differential Equations*, Wiley, New York, 1941.

105. W. Milne, *Numerical Calculus*, Princeton University Press, Princeton, N. J., 1949.

106. W. Milne, *Numerical Solution of Differential Equations*, Wiley, New York, 1953.

107. L. Milne-Thompson, *Calculus of Finite Differences*, Macmillan, New York, 1951.

108. N. Minorsky, *Introduction to Non-Linear Mechanics*, J. W. Edwards, Ann Arbor, 1947.

109. Modern Computing Methods, 2nd Ed., completely revised, "Notes on Applied Science," No. 16, National Physical Laboratory, London, 1962.

110. C. Moler, "Numerical Matrix Inversion with Iterative Improvement," Jet Propulsion Laboratory Report No. 32–394, March 1963.

111. D. Muller, "A Method for Solving Algebraic Equations Using an Automatic Computer," *MTAC*, **10**, 1956, 208.

112. K. Nielson, *Methods in Numerical Analysis*, Macmillan, New York, 1956.

113. A. Nordsieck, "On Numerical Integration of Ordinary Differential Equations," *Math. Computat.*, Jan. 1962.

114. G. Obrien, M. Hyman and S. Kaplan, "A Study of the Numerical Solution of Partial Differential Equations," *J. Math. and Phys.*, **29–30**, 1950, 223.

115. R. Oldenberger, *Frequency Response*, Macmillan, New York, 1956.

116. E. Osborn, "On Acceleration and Matrix Deflation Processes Used with the Power Method," *J. Indust. Appl. Math.*, **6**, 1958, 279.

117. W. Osgood, *Functions of a Complex Variable*, Stechert, New York, 1938.

118. B. Ostle, *Statistics in Research*, 2nd Ed., Iowa State, Ames, Iowa, 1963.

119. A. Ostrowski, *Solutions of Equations and Systems of Equations*, Academic, New York, 1960.

120. B. Parlett, "Applications of Laguerre's Method to the Matrix Eigenvalue Problem," Tech. Report No. 21, Appl. Math. and Stat. Lab., Stanford Univ., 1962.

121. S. Perlis, *Theory of Matrices*, Addison-Wesley, Reading, Mass., 1952.

122. I. Petrovsky, *Lectures on Partial Differential Equations*, Interscience, New York, 1954.

123. J. Pierpont, *Functions of a Complex Variable*, Ginn, Boston, 1914.

124. L. Pipes, "Solution of Nonlinear Differential Equations by the Reversion Method," *J. Appl. Phys.*, **23**, 1952, 202.

125. L. Pipes, "The Matrix Theory of Torsional Oscillations," *J. Appl. Phys.*, **13**, 1942, 434.

126. A. Ralston and H. Wilf, *Mathematical Methods for Digital Computers*, Wiley, New York, 1960.

127. K. Redish, *An Introduction to Computational Methods*, Wiley, New York, 1961.

128. R. Rich and H. Shaw, "A Method for Finding All the Zeros of $f(z)$," *J. Assoc. Comput. Mach.*, Oct. 1963.

129. L. Richardson, "The Approximate Arithmetic Solution by Finite Differences of Physical Problems Involving Differential Equations," *Phil. Trans. Roy. Soc. London*, Series A, **210**, 1910, 307.

130. R. Richtmyer, *Difference Methods for Initial Value Problems*, Interscience, New York, 1957.

131. S. Rushton, "On Least Squares Fitting by Orthonormal Polynomials Using the Choleski Method," *J. Roy. Stat. Soc.*, **13**, 1951, 92–99.

132. T. Salty, *Mathematical Methods of Operations Research*, McGraw-Hill, New York, 1959.

133. M. Salvadori and M. Baron, *Numerical Methods in Engineering*, Prentice-Hall, Englewood Cliffs, N. J., 1961.

134. J. Scarborough, *Numerical Mathematical Analysis*, Johns Hopkins, Baltimore, 1958.

135. I. Schoenberg, "Some Analytical Aspects of the Problem of Smoothing," *Courant Anniversary Volume, Studies and Essays*, Interscience, 1948, 351.

136. I. Schoenberg, "On Smoothing Operations and their Generating Functions," *Bull. Am. Math. Soc.*, **59**, No. 3, 1953, 199.

137. E. Scott, *Transform Calculus*, Harper, New York, 1955.

138. S. Seshu and N. Balabanian, *Linear Network Analysis*, Wiley, New York, 1959.

139. S. SIMPSON, "Least Squares Polynomial Fitting to Gravitational Data and Density Plotting by Digital Computers," *Geophysics*, **19**, 1954, 255.

140. M. SMITH, "A Review of Methods of Filtering Seismic Data," *Geophysics*, **19**, 1954, 402.

141. G. SNEDECOR, *Statistical Methods Applied to Experiments in Agriculture and Biology*, Iowa State, Ames, Iowa, 1961.

142. E. STIEFEL, *An Introduction to Numerical Mathematics*, Academic, New York, 1963.

143. E. STIEFEL, "Kernel Polynomials and Their Numerical Applications," Multilithed Lecture Notes, American University, 1955.

144. J. STOKER, *Nonlinear Vibrations in Mechanical and Electrical Systems*, Interscience, New York, 1950.

145. R. STRUBLE, *Nonlinear Differential Equations*, McGraw-Hill, New York, 1962.

146. C. SWARTZ and V. SOKOLEFF, "Filtering Associated with Selective Sampling of Geophysical Data," *Geophysics*, **19**, 1954, 402.

147. W. THOMSON, *Laplace Transformation*, Prentice-Hall, Englewood Cliffs, N. J., 1950.

148. S. TIMOSHENKO, *Vibration Problems in Engineering*, Van Nostrand, Princeton, 1955.

149. J. TODD, *Survey of Numerical Analysis*, McGraw-Hill, New York, 1962.

150. J. TODD, "The Condition of a Matrix," *Proc. Cambridge Phil. Soc.*, **46**, 1949, 116–118.

151. F. TRICOMI, *Integral Equations*, Interscience, New York, 1957.

152. L. TURNER, "Solution of Nonlinear Systems," *Ann. N. Y. Acad. Sci.*, **86**, 1960, 817.

153. M. VAN VALKENBURG, *Network Analysis*, Prentice-Hall, Englewood Cliffs, N. J., 1956.

154. R. VARGA, *Matrix Iterative Analysis*, Prentice-Hall, Englewood Cliffs, N. J., 1962.

155. H. WALL, *Analytic Theory of Continued Fractions*, Van Nostrand, Princeton, N. J., 1948.

156. J. WARD, "The Downhill Method of Solving $f(z) = 0$," *J. Assoc. Comput. Mach.*, **4**, 1957, 148.

157. E. WHITTAKER and G. ROBINSON, *The Calculus of Observations*, Blackie and Son, Glasgow, 1949.

158. E. WHITTAKER and G. WATSON, *Modern Analysis*, 4th Ed., Cambridge University Press, London, 1935.

159. D. WIDDER, *The Laplace Transform*, Princeton University Press, Princeton, N. J., 1941.

160. J. WILKINSON, *Rounding Errors in Algebraic Processes*, Prentice-Hall, Englewood Cliffs, N. J., 1964.

161. J. WILKINSON, "Error Analysis of Floating Point Computation," *Numer. Math.*, **2**, 1960, 319.

162. J. WILKINSON, "Error Analysis of Direct Methods of Matrix Inversion," *J. Assoc. Comput. Mach.*, **8**, 1961, 281.

163. J. WILKINSON, "Householder's Method for the Solution of the Algebraic Eigenproblem," *Comput. J.*, **3**, 1960, 23.

164. J. WILKINSON, *The Algebraic Eigenvalue Problem*, Oxford University Press, Oxford, 1965.

165. J. WILKINSON, "The Evaluation of Zeros of Ill-Conditioned Polynomials," *Numer. Math.*, **1**, 1959, 155.

166. F. WILLERS, *Practical Analysis*, Dover, New York, 1947.

167. R. WOOLDRIDGE, *An Introduction to Computing*, Oxford University Press, Oxford, 1962.

APPENDIXES

MATHEMATICAL THEOREMS

1) *Weierstrass approximation theorem.* Every function which is continuous in an interval (a, b) can be represented in that interval, to any desired degree of accuracy, by a polynomial; that is, it is possible to find a polynomial $P(x)$ such that $|f(x) - P(x)| < \epsilon$ for every value of x in the interval (a, b), where ϵ is any preassigned positive quantity.

2) If $f(x)$ is continuous for $a \leq x \leq b$, and if $f(a)$ and $f(b)$ are of opposite signs, then $f(\xi) = 0$ for at least one number ξ, such that $a < \xi < b$.

3) If $f(x)$ is continuous for $a \leq x \leq b$, and if λ_1 and λ_2 are positive constants, then $\lambda_1 f(a) + \lambda_2 f(b) = (\lambda_1 + \lambda_2) f(\xi)$ for at least one ξ, such that $a \leq \xi \leq b$.

4) *Rolle's theorem.* If $f(x)$ is continuous for $a \leq x \leq b$ and $f'(x)$ is continuous for $a < x < b$, and if $f(a) = f(b) = 0$, then $f'(\xi) = 0$ for at least one ξ, such that $a < \xi < b$.

5) *Mean-value theorem.* If $f(x)$ is continuous for $a \leq x \leq b$ and $f'(x)$ is continuous for $a < x < b$, then $f(b) - f(a) = (b - a)f'(\xi)$ for at least one ξ such that $a < \xi < b$.

6) Assuming the integral exists and $b > a$, if $|f(x)| \leq M$ in (a, b), where M is a constant, then

$$\left| \int_a^b f(x)\, dx \right| \leq \int_a^b |f(x)|\, dx \leq M(b - a).$$

7) *First law of the mean.* If $f(x)$ is continuous for $a \leq x \leq b$, then

$$\int_a^b f(x)\, dx = (b - a)f(\xi)$$

for at least one ξ such that $a < \xi < b$.

8) If $m \leq f(x) \leq M$ and $g(x)$ is nonnegative for $a \leq x \leq b$, then

$$m \int_a^b g(x)\, dx \leq \int_a^b f(x)g(x)\, dx \leq \int_a^b g(x)\, dx.$$

9) *Second law of the mean.* If $f(x)$ is continuous for $a \leq x \leq b$ and $g(x)$ does not change sign inside (a, b), then

$$\int_a^b f(x)g(x)\, dx = f(\xi) \int_a^b g(x)\, dx$$

for at least one ξ such that $a < \xi < b$.

Theorems Involving Parameters

10) If a and b are finite constants and $F(x, s)$ is continuous in x and s, then

$$\lim_{x \to c} \int_a^b F(x, s)\, ds = \int_a^b F(c, s)\, ds.$$

11) If a and b are finite constants and if $\partial F/\partial x$ is continuous, then

$$\frac{d}{dx} \int_a^b F(x, s)\, ds = \int_a^b \frac{\partial F(x, s)}{\partial x}\, ds.$$

12) If a is a finite constant, u is a differentiable function of x, and $\partial F/\partial x$ is continuous, then

$$\frac{d}{dx} \int_a^u F(x, s)\, ds = \int_a^u \frac{\partial F(x, s)}{\partial x}\, ds + F(x, u)\frac{du}{dx}.$$

13) If $F_n(x)$ denotes the result of integrating $F(x)$ successively n times over (a, x), then

$$F_n(x) = \frac{1}{(n-1)!} \int_a^x (x - s)^{n-1} F(s)\, ds.$$

FORMULA DERIVATION BY MATRIX METHODS

If $\mathbf{0}$ is some linear operator, operating on $f(x)$, we may assume a form

$$\mathbf{0}\{f(x)\} = W_1 f(x_1) + W_2 f(x_2) + \cdots + W_n f(x_n). \tag{1}$$

For the special case $f(x) = 1, x, x^2, \ldots, x^k$, let $\mathbf{0}\{f(x)\} = \mathbf{0}\{x^k\} = c_k$, then (1) can be written

$$
\begin{aligned}
W_1 \quad + W_2 \quad + W_3 \quad + \cdots + W_n \quad &= c_0, \\
W_1 x_1 + W_2 x_2 + W_3 x_3 + \cdots + W_n x_n &= c_1, \\
W_1 x_1^2 + W_2 x_2^2 + W_3 x_3^2 + \cdots + W_n x_n^2 &= c_2, \\
&\vdots \\
W_1 x_1^{n-1} + W_2 x_2^{n-1} + W_3 x_3^{n-1} + \cdots + W_n x_n^{n-1} &= c_{n-1}.
\end{aligned} \tag{2}
$$

The system of equations (2) is written in matrix form as

$$XW = C.$$

The coefficient determinant X, called a Vandermonde determinant, is not zero if $x_i \neq x_j$. The vector of weighting coefficients W is found from the matrix equation

$$W = X^{-1} C.$$

We now determine a standard way of finding the inverse of X. The fundamental polynomials are defined as follows:

$$\pi_i(x) = (x - x_1)(x - x_2) \cdots (x - x_{i-1})(x - x_{i+1}) \cdots (x - x_n),$$

$$\pi_i(x) = \sum_{k=0}^{n-1} c_{i,k} x^k, \qquad i = 1, 2, \ldots, n,$$

where the ith factor $(x - x_i)$ is omitted from the ith polynomial. It follows that $\pi_i(x_j) = 0$, $(j \neq i)$ and $\pi_i(x_i) \neq 0$.

The mth row of X^{-1} is written

$$\frac{C_{m,k}}{\pi_m(x_m)}$$

because the product of this row times the jth column of X gives

$$\frac{\sum C_{m,k} x_j^k}{\pi_m(x_m)} = \frac{\pi_m(x_j)}{\pi_m(x_m)} = \begin{cases} 1, & j = m, \\ 0, & j \neq m. \end{cases}$$

As a simple example, return to Formula (1.5.2) and determine the weighting coefficients by this method.

If $x_1 = -1$, $x_2 = 0$, $x_3 = 1$, then

$$\pi_1(x) = 0 - x + x^2, \qquad \pi_1(x_1) = 2;$$
$$\pi_2(x) = -1 + 0x + x^2, \qquad \pi_2(x_2) = -1;$$
$$\pi_3(x) = 0 + x + x^2, \qquad \pi_3(x_3) = 2;$$

$$X^{-1} = \begin{bmatrix} 0 & -\frac{1}{2} & \frac{1}{2} \\ 1 & 0 & -1 \\ 0 & \frac{1}{2} & \frac{1}{2} \end{bmatrix}, \qquad C = \begin{bmatrix} 2 \\ 0 \\ \frac{2}{3} \end{bmatrix},$$

$$W = X^{-1}C,$$

$$\begin{bmatrix} W_{-1} \\ W_0 \\ W_1 \end{bmatrix} = \begin{bmatrix} 0 & -\frac{1}{2} & \frac{1}{2} \\ 1 & 0 & -1 \\ 0 & \frac{1}{2} & \frac{1}{2} \end{bmatrix} \begin{bmatrix} 2 \\ 0 \\ \frac{2}{3} \end{bmatrix},$$

$$\begin{bmatrix} W_{-1} \\ W_0 \\ W_1 \end{bmatrix} = \begin{bmatrix} \frac{1}{3} \\ \frac{4}{3} \\ \frac{1}{3} \end{bmatrix}.$$

These are the same weighting coefficients obtained in Eq. (1.5.3).

THEOREMS OF INTERPOLATION
FUNCTION THEORY

The material presented here is a summary of theorems from J. M. Whittaker, "Interpolatory Function Theory," *Cambridge Tracts in Mathematics and Mathematical Physics* **33**, Cambridge University Press, Cambridge, 1935.

C.1 Definitions

A function which is analytic (Section 8.3) everywhere, except at ∞, is called an integral function. A single-valued function shall, without regard to its behavior at infinity, be called meromorphic, if it has no singularities other than poles in the entire plane.

C.2 The Gregory-Newton Series

The earliest basic series was discovered by James Gregory in 1670. This is the series

$$f(0) + z\,\Delta f(0) + \frac{z(z-1)}{2!}\,\Delta^2 f(0) + \frac{z(z-1)(z-2)}{3!}\,\Delta^3 f(0) + \cdots, \quad (1)$$

where $\Delta f(0) = f(1) - f(0)$, $\Delta^2 f(0) = f(2) - 2f(1) + f(0)$, which solves the fundamental problem of interpolation, that is, the problem of finding a polynomial of degree n (or less) which has the given values $f(0), f(1), \ldots, f(n)$ at $z = 0, 1, \ldots, n$.

Theorem 1. Let $f(z)$ be an integral function which satisfies the condition

$$\lim_{r \to \infty} \frac{\log M(r)}{r} < \log 2, \quad (2)$$

where M is the maximum bound on $f(z)$ in a region of radius r. Then the series (1) converges to $f(z)$ uniformly in any finite region.

Let $d_0, d_1, d_2, \ldots$ be a sequence such that

$$\lim_{n \to \infty} |d_n|^{1/n} = k < 1. \quad (3)$$

Then the series

$$d_0 + z\,d_1 + \frac{z(z-1)}{2!}\,d_2 + \cdots \quad (4)$$

325

converges uniformly in any finite region of the plane to an integral function $g(z)$ which satisfies the condition

$$\lim_{r\to\infty} \frac{\log M(r)}{r} \leq \log \frac{1}{1-k}. \tag{5}$$

Theorem 2. If $f(z)$ is an integral function which satisfies (2), and if $f(0)$, $f(1)$, ... are integers, then $f(z)$ is a polynomial.

Theorem 3. Let $f(z) = \sum a_n z^n$ be regular in $|z| < 1$, and let $z = 1$ be the only singularity on $|z| = 1$, and let it be an isolated noncritical singularity. Then

$$a_n = g(n) + b_n, \tag{6}$$

where $g(z)$ is an integral function satisfying the conditions

$$\log \frac{M(r)}{r} \to 0 \tag{7}$$

and

$$\lim_{n\to\infty} |b_n|^{1/n} < 1. \tag{8}$$

Theorem 4. Let $f(z)$ be regular in $|z| < 1$; $|f(z)| \leq M(|z| < 1)$; $|f(a_k)| \leq L(k = 0, 1, \ldots, N)$; $a_0, a_1, a_2, \ldots, a_N$ being any distinct points in $|z| \leq \tau < 1$. Then

$$|f(z)| \leq M \left(\frac{2\tau}{1+\tau^2} \right)^{N+1} + \frac{6}{1-\tau^4} L\, \Delta (2\tau)^N, \qquad |z| \leq \tau, \tag{9}$$

where $\Delta = \sum_{k=0}^{N} \prod_i' \dfrac{1}{|a_i - a_k|}$, and the prime means $i = k$ is omitted.

Theorem 5. Let $f(z)$ be an integral function such that

$$\frac{\log M(r)}{r} \to 0,$$

and let α, λ be given positive numbers. Then

$$|f(z)| \geq e^{-\alpha n} (\lambda n \leq |z| \leq \lambda(n+1)) \tag{10}$$

for almost every integer n.

Theorem 6. If an integral function of finite order p has a Borel exceptional value, its power series has a density equal to one of the fractions

$$\frac{1}{p}, \frac{2}{p}, \frac{3}{p}, \ldots, \frac{p}{p}. \tag{11}$$

The density is defined as the limit of $q_{n/n}$ as $n \to \infty$, q_n being the number of coefficients which do not vanish. The limit may not exist. Only functions of integral order p can possess a Borel exceptional value, and a will be such a value for $G(z)$ if and only if

$$G(z) = a + e^{bz^p} F(z), \tag{12}$$

where b is a constant other than zero, and $F(z)$ is an integral function of order less than p.

Theorem 7. Let p be a positive integer, and let

$$G(z) = e^{z^p} F(z) = C_0 + C_1 z + C_2 z^2 + \cdots, \tag{13}$$

where $F(z)$ is an integral function either of order less than p, or of minimum type of order p. Then, the sequence

$$C_k, C_{k+p}, C_{k+2p}, \ldots \tag{14}$$

has the density 1, unless all its terms are zero.

C.3 The Newton-Gauss Series and the Cardinal Series

There are two formulas for interpolation at the points $0, \pm n$. They are the Newton-Gauss series

$$f(0) + \left\{ z\, \Delta f(0) + \frac{z(z-1)}{2!} \Delta^2 f(-1) \right\}$$

$$+ \left\{ \frac{z(z^2 - 1^2)}{3!} \Delta^3 f(-1) + \frac{z(z^2 - 1^2)(z-2)}{4!} \Delta^4 f(-2) \right\} + \cdots, \tag{15}$$

and the cardinal series

$$\frac{\sin \pi z}{\pi} \left[\frac{f(0)}{z} + \sum_{n=1}^{\infty} (-1)^n \left\{ \frac{f(n)}{z-n} + \frac{f(-n)}{z+n} \right\} \right]. \tag{16}$$

Steffensen (Section 3.12n) and Whittaker (Section 3.12a) showed that under certain conditions these series converge to the same sum, and the precise relationship was discovered by Ferrar (Section 3.12b and e).

If (16) is convergent, (15) converges to the same sum. If (15) is convergent, (16) is summable by the method of de la Vallée Poussin to the same sum.

The class of functions represented by (15) has been discussed by Norlund, "Sur les formules d'interpolation de Stirling et Newton," *Annales Sci. de l'Ecole Normale* **39** (1922) 343–403, **40** (1923) 35–54.

It includes all integral functions satisfying (7). The cardinal series represents a much more restricted class of integral functions, all of order one.

Ferrar's result, in a much more general form, can be deduced from the identity,

$$f(e_0) + (z - e_0)f(e_0, e_1) + \cdots + (z - e_0) \cdots (z - e_{n-1})f(e_0, e_1, \ldots, e_n)$$

$$= \phi(z) \sum_{i=0}^{n} \frac{f(e_i)}{\phi'(e_i)(z - e_i)}, \qquad (17)$$

where

$$\phi(z) = \prod_{i=0}^{n} \left(1 - \frac{z}{e_i}\right),$$

$$f(e_0, e_1) = \frac{f(e_1) - f(e_0)}{e_1 - e_0}, \text{ etc.}$$

The left-hand side of (17) is Newton's divided difference formula, and the right-hand side is Lagrange's formula.

Let $c_1, c_2, \ldots, c_n$ be a strictly increasing sequence of positive numbers such that $\sum c_n^{-2}$ converges, and let

$$H(z) = z \prod_{i=1}^{\infty} \left(1 - \frac{z^2}{c_i^2}\right), \qquad H_n(z) = z \prod_{i=1}^{n} \left(1 - \frac{z^2}{c_i^2}\right). \qquad (18)$$

Then Eq. (17) gives

$$f(0) + zf(0, c_1) + \cdots$$

$$+ z(z^2 - c_1)^2 \cdots (z^2 - c_{n-1}^2)(z - c_n)f(0, c_1 - c_1, \ldots, c_n, -c_n)$$

$$= H_n(z)\left[\frac{f(0)}{z} + \sum_{m=0}^{n} \left\{\frac{f(c_m)}{H_n'(c_m)(z - c_m)} + \frac{f(-c_m)}{H_n'(c_m)(z + c_m)}\right\}\right]$$

$$= H_n(z)\left[\frac{f(0)}{z} + \sum_{m=0}^{n} \phi(n, m)\left\{\frac{f(c_m)}{H_n'(c_m)(z - c_m)} + \frac{f(-c_m)}{H_n'(c_m)(z + c_m)}\right\}\right], \qquad (19)$$

where

$$\phi(n, m) = \frac{H'(c_m)}{H_n'(c_m)} = \prod_{i=n+1}^{\infty} \left(1 - \frac{c_m^2}{c_i^2}\right). \qquad (20)$$

Let $\lambda(n)$ be a decreasing positive function such that $\sum \lambda(n)$ converges, and let

$$\psi(n, m) = \prod_{i=n+1}^{\infty} \left\{1 - \frac{\lambda(i)}{\lambda(m)}\right\}, \qquad m = 0, 1, \ldots, n.$$

If $U_n = \sum_{m=0}^{n} \psi(n, m)u_n \to u$ as $n \to \infty$, the series $\sum u_n$ may be said to be summable $\{V.P. \lambda(n)\}$ to sum U. This method of summation sums every convergent series to the correct value. (Necessary and sufficient conditions to produce this case are found in P. Dienes, *The Taylor Series*, Oxford University Press, Oxford, 1931.)

If
$$\lambda(n) = \frac{1}{n^2},$$

then
$$\psi(n, m) = \prod_{i=n+1}^{\infty} \left(1 - \frac{m^2}{i^2}\right) = \frac{n!\,n!}{(n-m)!(n+m)!},$$

so that summability (V.P. $1/n^2$) is identical with the method used by de la Vallée Poussin to sum Fourier series.

Theorem 1. If the series
$$H(z)\left[\frac{f(0)}{z} + \sum_{n=0}^{\infty} \left\{\frac{f(c_n)}{H'(c_n)(z - c_n)} + \frac{f(-c_n)}{H'(c_n)(z + c_n)}\right\}\right] \tag{21}$$

is convergent, the series
$$\begin{aligned}
f(0) &+ \{zf(0, c_1) + z(z - c_1)f(0, c_1, -c_1) \\
&+ \{z(z^2 - c_1^2)f(0, c_1, -c_1, c_2) \\
&+ z(z^2 - c_1^2)(z - c_2)f(0, c_1, -c_1, c_2, -c_2)\} + \cdots \tag{22}
\end{aligned}$$

converges to the same sum. If Eq. (22) is convergent, (21) is summable (V.P. $1/c_n^2$) to the same sum.

Ferrar's result is the case $c_n = n$. It follows that, if the sequence $\{f(n)\}$ is bounded for all positive and negative values of n, the formulas (15) and (16) are equivalent, being either both divergent or both convergent to the same sum.

Theorem 2. Given any function of the form
$$\int_0^1 \{\cos \pi x t \, d\phi(t) + \sin \pi x t \, d\psi(t)\}, \tag{23}$$

where $\phi(t)$, $\psi(t)$ are continuous functions, the series
$$\frac{\sin \pi x}{\pi}\left[\frac{f(0)}{x} + \sum_{n=1}^{\infty} (-1)^n \left\{\frac{f(n)}{x - n} + \frac{f(-n)}{x + n}\right\}\right]$$

is summable $(c, 1)$ and its sum is $f(x)$.

If $a_{-2}, a_{-1}, a_0, a_1, a_2$ is a sequence such that
$$\sum_{n=1}^{\infty} \frac{1}{n}(|a_n| + |a_{-n}|) < \infty, \tag{24}$$

then
$$\sum_{n=1}^{\infty} \frac{1}{n}(a_n + a_{-n}) \sin \pi n t,$$

$$\sum_{n=1}^{\infty} \frac{1}{n}(a_n - a_{-n}) \cos \pi n t$$

converge to continuous functions, and there are continuous functions $\phi(t)$, $\psi(t)$, such that

$$a_0 = \int_0^1 d\phi(t), \tfrac{1}{2}(a_n + a_{-n}) = \int_0^1 \cos \pi nt \, d\phi(t), \tfrac{1}{2}(a_n - a_{-n})$$
$$= \int_0^1 \sin \pi nt \, d\psi(t).$$

If (24) is satisfied, the cardinal series

$$\frac{\sin \pi x}{\pi} \left\{ \frac{a_0}{x} + \sum_{n=1}^{\infty} (-1)^n \left(\frac{a_n}{x - n} + \frac{a_{-n}}{x + n} \right) \right\} \tag{25}$$

is absolutely convergent and its sum is of the form (23). This relates to the remarkable property of *consistency*, discovered by Ferrar.

TEST MATRICES WITH KNOWN INVERSES AND EIGENVALUES

D.1 Matrices with Known Inverses

a) $A_1 = [a_{ij}]$, where

Elements: $a_{ij} = (i + j)/p$, $p = n + 1$, n is order of A;

$$\left(\frac{i+j}{p}\right) = \begin{cases} 0, & \text{if } p \text{ divides } i + j \\ 1, & \text{if } i + j = x^2 \pmod{p}, x^2 \text{ an integer} \\ -1, & \text{otherwise.} \end{cases}$$

Inverse: $a_{ij}^{-1} = \dfrac{1}{p}\left[\left(\dfrac{i+j}{p}\right) - \dfrac{i}{p} - \dfrac{j}{p}\right]$.

Condition number: $(n + 1)^{1/2}$, where the condition number is defined as $|\lambda/\mu|$, and λ is the absolute value of largest root of A and μ is the absolute value of smallest root of A.

b) $A_2 = (A_1)^2$, where A_1 is defined in (a).

Inverse: $A_2^{-1} = (A_1^{-1})^2$.

Condition number: $n + 1$.

c) $A_3 = [a_{ij}]$, where

$$\text{Elements: } a_{ij} = \begin{cases} -2, & \text{if } i = j, \\ 1, & \text{if } |i - j| = 1, \\ 0, & \text{if } |i - j| \geq 2. \end{cases}$$

$$\text{Inverse: } a_{ij}^{-1} = \begin{cases} \dfrac{-i(n - j + 1)}{n + 1}, & \text{for } i \leq j, \\ a_{ji}, & \text{for } i > j. \end{cases}$$

Condition number: $\sim (4/\pi^2)n^2$.

d) $A_4 = [a_{ij}]$, where

Elements: $a_{ij} = 2 \min (i, j) - 1$.

Inverse: Tridiagonal

$$\frac{1}{2}\begin{bmatrix} -3 & -1 & & & \\ -1 & 2 & -1 & & \\ & & \ddots & & \\ & & -1 & 2 & -1 \\ & & & -1 & 1 \end{bmatrix}.$$

Condition number: $\sim (16/\pi^2)n^2$.

e) Elements: $A_5 = A_3^2$.
  Inverse: $A_5^{-1} = (A_3^{-1})^2$.
  Condition number: $\sim (16/\pi^4)n^4$.

f) Elements: $A_6 = A_3^3$.
  Inverse: $A_6^{-1} = (A_3^{-1})^3$.
  Condition number: $\sim (64/\pi^6)n^6$.

g) Elements: $A_7 = H^{-1}$, where H is a Hilbert matrix.
  Inverse: $A_7^{-1} = H$.
  Condition number: $\sim e^{3.5n}$.
  Restriction: $n \leq 7$, otherwise H^{-1} cannot be represented in single precision.

D.2 Generation of Exact Integer Matrices with Known Eigenvalues

a) $n = 8$

$$A = \begin{bmatrix} 4B & 3B \\ -2B & -B \end{bmatrix}, \qquad B = \begin{bmatrix} 0 & 1 & 2 & 2 \\ 4 & 11 & 0 & 11 \\ 3 & 7 & -7 & 2 \\ -4 & -9 & 7 & -4 \end{bmatrix}$$

Eigenvalues: $\pm 1, \pm 2, \pm 3, \pm 6$.

b) $n = 12$

$$A = \begin{bmatrix} 12 & 11 & & & & \\ 11 & 11 & 10 & & & \\ 10 & 10 & 10 & 9 & & \\ 9 & 9 & 9 & 9 & 8 & \\ & \vdots & & & & \\ 1 & 1 & 1 & \cdots & & 1 \end{bmatrix}.$$

Eigenvalues:

0.0310280606,	0.1436465198,	1.5539887091,	12.3110774009,
0.0495074292,	0.2847497206,	3.5118559486,	20.1989886459,
0.0812276592,	0.6435053190,	6.9615330856,	32.2288915016.

c) $n = 16$

$$A = \begin{bmatrix} B & 2B \\ 4B & 3B \end{bmatrix}, \qquad B = \begin{bmatrix} 5C & -C \\ 5C & C \end{bmatrix}, \qquad C = \begin{bmatrix} -2 & 2 & 2 & 2 \\ -3 & 3 & 2 & 2 \\ -2 & 0 & 4 & 2 \\ -1 & 0 & 0 & 5 \end{bmatrix}.$$

Eigenvalues:

$-3 \pm i$,	$-6 \pm 2i$,	$-9 \pm 3i$,	$-12 \pm 4i$,
$15 \pm 5i$,	$30 \pm 10i$,	$45 \pm 15i$,	$60 \pm 20i$.

D.3 References

a) M. NEWMAN and J. TODD, "The Evaluation of Matrix Inversion Programs," *SIAM J.* **6,** 4 (December 1958).

b) HSUAN-HENZ WANG, "On the Tridiagonalization of a Non-Hermitian Matrix Using Similarity Transformations," University of Texas Computation Center (May 1964).

TABLE OF LAPLACE TRANSFORMS

	$f(s)$	$f(t)$
(1)	$\dfrac{1}{s}(1 - e^{-bs})$	rectangular pulse
(2)	$\dfrac{1}{b}\left(\dfrac{1 - e^{-bs}}{s}\right)^2$	triangular pulse
(3)	$\dfrac{a}{s^2 + a^2}(1 + e^{-\pi s/a})$	sinusoidal pulse
(4)	$\dfrac{e^{-as}}{s}$	$U(t - a)$ unit-step function
(5)	$1/s$	1 or $U(t)$ unit-step function at $t = 0$
(6)	e^{-as}	$U'(t - a)$ unit impulse
(7)	1	$U'(t)$ unit impulse at $t = 0$
(8)	se^{-as}	$U''(t - a)$
(9)	$1/s^2$	t
(10)	$\dfrac{1}{s^n}\ (n = 1, 2, \ldots)$	$\dfrac{t^{n-1}}{(n - 1)!}$

(cont.)

333

	$f(s)$	$f(t)$
(11)	$\dfrac{1}{s^{1/2}}$	$\dfrac{1}{\sqrt{\pi t}}$
(12)	$\dfrac{1}{s^{3/2}}$	$2\sqrt{t/\pi}$
(13)	$\dfrac{1}{s^n} \quad n > 0$	$\dfrac{t^{n-1}}{\Gamma(n)}$
(14)	$\dfrac{1}{s+a}$	e^{-at}
(15)	$\dfrac{1}{(s+a)^2}$	te^{-at}
(16)	$\dfrac{1}{(s-a)^n} \quad n = 1, 2, \ldots$	$\dfrac{t^{n-1}e^{at}}{(n-1)!}$
(17)	$\dfrac{1}{(s-a)^\nu}, \quad \mathrm{Re}\,(\nu) > 0$	$\dfrac{t^{\nu-1}e^{at}}{\Gamma(\nu)}$
(18)	$\dfrac{1}{s(s-a)}$	$\dfrac{e^{at}-1}{a}$
(19)	$\dfrac{1}{(s-a)(s-b)}$	$\dfrac{e^{bt}-e^{at}}{b-a}$
(20)	$\dfrac{s}{(s-a)(s-b)}$	$\dfrac{be^{bt}-ae^{at}}{b-a}$
(21)	$\dfrac{s}{(s+a)^2}$	$e^{-at}(1-at)$
(22)	$\dfrac{1}{s(s+a)^2}$	$\dfrac{1}{a^2}[1-(1+at)e^{-at}]$
(23)	$\dfrac{s+b}{(s+a)^2}$	$[(b-a)t-1]e^{-at}$
(24)	$\dfrac{a}{s^2+a^2}$	$\sin at$

	$f(s)$	$f(t)$
(25)	$\dfrac{s}{s^2 + a^2}$	$\cos at$
(26)	$\dfrac{b}{(s + a)^2 + b^2}$	$e^{-at} \sin bt$
(27)	$\dfrac{s + a}{(s + a)^2 + b^2}$	$e^{-at} \cos bt$
(28)	$\dfrac{s}{(s^2 + a^2)^2}$	$\dfrac{t}{2a} \sin at$
(29)	$\dfrac{s^2 - a^2}{(s^2 + a^2)^2}$	$t \cos at$
(30)	$\dfrac{a}{s^2 - a^2}$	$\sinh at$
(31)	$\dfrac{s}{s^2 - a^2}$	$\cosh at$
(32)	$\dfrac{b}{(s + a)^2 - b^2}$	$e^{-at} \sinh bt$
(33)	$\dfrac{s + a}{(s + a)^2 - b^2}$	$e^{-at} \cosh bt$
(34)	$\dfrac{1}{s^2(s^2 + a^2)}$	$\dfrac{1}{a^3}(at - \sin at)$
(35)	$\dfrac{1}{s(s^2 + a^2)}$	$\dfrac{1}{a^2}(1 - \cos at)$
(36)	$\dfrac{1}{(s^2 + a^2)^2}$	$\dfrac{1}{2a^3}(\sin at - at \cos at)$
(37)	$\dfrac{1}{s\sqrt{s + 1}}$	$\operatorname{erf}(\sqrt{t})$
(38)	$\dfrac{1}{\sqrt{s}\,(s - 1)}$	$e^t \operatorname{erf}(\sqrt{t})$

(cont.)

$f(s)$	$f(t)$
(39) $\dfrac{e^{-a\sqrt{s}}}{s}$	$1 - \mathrm{erf}\left(\dfrac{a}{2\sqrt{t}}\right) = \mathrm{erfc}\left(\dfrac{a}{2\sqrt{t}}\right)$
(40) $\dfrac{1}{\sqrt{s^2 + a^2}}$	$J_0(at)$
(41) $\dfrac{1}{\sqrt{s^2 + a^2} + s}$	$\dfrac{1}{at} J_1(at)$
(42) $\dfrac{1}{\sqrt{s^2 + a^2}(\sqrt{s^2 + a^2} + s)^n}$	$\dfrac{1}{a^n} J_n(at)$

KEEPING UP WITH THE LITERATURE

Introduction

It is indeed difficult to keep up with all the literature being published in the field of numerical computation. It is almost impossible for a book in the process of being published to contain references to all the recent publications. Some of the more recent publications are given in the main Bibliography, Supplementary References at the end of the chapters, and in the text of this book. It is the purpose of this appendix to help bridge the gap of omissions by giving a Supplementary Bibliography and suggesting a guide, some periodicals, and three abstracting journals for keeping up with the literature.

Supplementary Bibliography

Some additional references not given elsewhere in the text are listed below.

1. B. ADLER, S. FERNBACH and M. ROTENBERG, *Methods in Computational Physics*, **1,** 1963, **2,** 1964, **3,** 1964, **4,** 1965, Academic, New York.
2. W. F. AMES, *Nonlinear Partial Differential Equations in Engineering*, Academic, New York, 1965.
3. A. V. BALAKRISHNAN and L. W. NEUSTADT, *Computing Methods in Optimization Problems*, Academic, New York, 1964.
4. R. BELLMAN and R. KALABA, *Modern Analytic and Computational Methods in Science and Mathematics*, **1,** 1963; **2,** 1964; **3,** 1965; **4,** in preparation, Elsevier, Amsterdam.
5. I. S. BEREZIN and N. P. ZHIDKOV, *Computing Methods*, **1** and **2,** Addison-Wesley, Reading, Mass., 1963.
6. W. G. BICKLEY, and R. S. H. G. THOMPSON, *Matrices, their Meaning and Manipulation*, English Universities Press, London, 1964.
7. J. H. BRAMBLE, *Numerical Solution of Partial Differential Equations*, Academic, New York, 1966.
8. R. BUTLER and E. KERR, *An Introduction to Numerical Methods*, Pitman, London, 1962.
9. E. D. CASHWELL and C. J. EVERETT, *A Practical Manual on the Monte Carlo Methods for Random Walk Problems*, Pergamon, London, 1959.
10. S. D. CONTE, *Elementary Numerical Analysis: An Algorithmic Approach*, McGraw-Hill, New York, 1965.

11. S. H. Crandall, *Engineering Analysis, a Survey of Numerical Procedures*, McGraw-Hill, New York, 1956.

12. G. B. Dantzig, *Linear Programming and Extensions*, Princeton University Press, Princeton, N. J., 1963.

13. P. J. Davis, *Interpolation and Approximation*, Blaisdell, New York, 1963.

14. R. Dorfman, P. A. Samuelson and R. M. Solow, *Linear Programming and Economic Analysis*, McGraw-Hill, New York, 1958.

15. A. Fletcher, J. Miller and L. Rosenhead, *An Index of Mathematical Tables*, 2nd ed., **1** and **2,** Addison-Wesley, Reading, Mass., 1962.

16. L. Fox, *An Introduction to Numerical Linear Algebra*, Oxford University Press, Oxford, 1965.

17. W. Freiberger and W. Prager, *Applications of Digital Computers*, Ginn, New York, 1963.

18. Carl-Erik Fröberg, *Introduction to Numerical Analysis*, Addison-Wesley, Reading, Mass., 1965.

19. H. L. Garabedian, *Approximation of Functions*, Elsevier, Amsterdam, 1965.

20. S. K. Godunov and V. S. Ryabenki, *Theory of Difference Schemes*, North Holland, Amsterdam, 1964.

21. R. L. Graves and P. Wolfe, *Recent Advances in Mathematical Programming*, McGraw-Hill, New York, 1963.

22. D. Greenspan, *Introductory Numerical Analysis of Elliptic Boundary Value Problems*, Harper and Row, New York, 1965.

23. F. Gruenberger and G. Jaffray, *Problems for Computer Solution*, Wiley, New York, 1965.

24. P. G. Guest, *Numerical Methods of Curve Fitting*, Cambridge University Press, London, 1961.

25. G. F. Hadley, *Linear Programming*, Addison-Wesley, Reading, Mass., 1962.

26. G. F. Hadley, *Nonlinear and Dynamic Programming*, Addison-Wesley, Reading, Mass., 1964.

27. J. M. Hammersley and D. C. Handscomb, *Monte Carlo Methods*, Wiley, New York, 1964.

28. P. Henrici, *Elements of Numerical Analysis*, Wiley, New York, 1964.

29. J. G. Herriot, *Methods of Mathematical Analysis and Computation*, Wiley, New York, 1963.

30. F. E. Hohn, *Applied Boolean Algebra, An Elementary Introduction*, Macmillan, New York, 1960.

31. I. M. Khabaza, *Numerical Analysis*, Pergamon, London, 1965.

32. A. N. Khovanskii, *The Application of Continued Fractions and Their Generalizations to Problems in Approximation Theory*, Noordhoff, Groningen, Netherlands, 1963.

33. V. I. Krylov, *Approximate Calculation of Integrals*, Macmillan, New York, 1962.

34. L. Lapidus, *Digital Computation for Chemical Engineers*, McGraw-Hill, New York, 1962.

35. L. A. Lyusternik, O. A. Chervonenkis and A. R. Yanpol'skii, *Handbook for Computing Elementary Functions*, Pergamon, London, 1965.

36. J. M. McCormick and M. G. Salvadori, *Numerical Methods in Fortran*, Prentice-Hall, Englewood Cliffs, N. J., 1964.

37. D. D. McCracken and W. S. Dorn, *Numerical Methods and Fortran Programming*, Wiley, New York, 1964.

38. S. J. McMinn, *Matrices for Structural Analysis*, E. and F. N. Spon, Ltd., London, 1964.

39. N. Macon, *Numerical Analysis*, Wiley, New York, 1963.

40. National Bureau of Standards, *Handbook of Mathematical Functions with Formulas, Graphs, and Mathematical Tables*, Applied Mathematics Series 55, Washington, D. C., 1964.

41. I. P. Natanson, *Constructive Function Theory* (3 Vols.), **1,** Uniform Approximation, 1964; **2,** Approximation in the Mean, 1965; **3,** Interpolation and Approximation Quadratures, Ungar, New York, 1965.

42. B. Noble, *Numerical Methods*, **1** and **2,** Oliver and Boyd, Edinburgh, 1964.

43. W. Prager, *Introduction to Basic Fortran Programming and Numerical Methods*, Blaisdell, New York, 1965.

44. L. B. Rall, *Error in Digital Computation*, **1** and **2,** Wiley, New York, 1965.

45. K. A. Redish, *An Introduction to Computational Methods*, Wiley, New York, 1965.

46. J. R. Rice, *The Approximation of Functions*, **1,** Linear Theory, Addison-Wesley, Reading, Mass., 1964.

47. A. Sard, "Linear Approximation, Mathematical Surveys," No. 9, *Am. Math. Soc.,* 1963.

48. V. K. Saul'yev, *Integration of Equations of Parabolic Type by the Method of Nets*, Macmillan, New York, 1964.

49. J. Singer, *Elements of Numerical Analysis*, Academic, New York, 1964.

50. G. D. Smith, *Numerical Solution of Partial Differential Equations*, Oxford University Press, Oxford, 1965.

51. R. W. Southworth and S. L. DeLeeuw, *Digital Computation and Numerical Methods*, McGraw-Hill, New York, 1965.

52. K. D. Tocher, *The Art of Simulation*, Van Nostrand, Princeton, N. J., 1963.

53. J. Todd, *Introduction to the Constructive Theory of Functions*, Academic, New York, 1963.

54. J. F. Traub, *Iterative Methods for the Solution of Equations*, Prentice-Hall, Englewood Cliffs, N. J., 1964.

55. N. Ya Vilenkin, *Successive Approximation*, Macmillan, New York, 1964.

Suggested Guide

There are several guides to the literature, but one of the most up-to-date for numerical computation is the following:

Price, J. F., "Numerical Analysis and Related Literature for Scientific Computer Users," 2nd ed., Mathematical Note No. 456, Document No. D1-82-0517, Mathematical Research Laboratory, Boeing Scientific Research Laboratories, March 1966.

Periodicals

The following is a list of suggested periodicals for keeping up with the literature related to numerical computation:

1) *Mathematics of Computation*

2) *Numerische Mathematik*

3) *SIAM Journal on Applied Mathematics*

4) *SIAM Journal on Numerical Analysis*

5) *SIAM Review*

6) *Journal of ACM*

7) *Communications of ACM*

8) *Computer Journal*

9) *Journal of Mathematics and Physics*

10) *Journal of Research, National Bureau of Standards*

11) *IBM Journal of Research*

Abstracting Journals.

If one has a limited amount of time, or is limited in the number of periodicals at his disposal, the following are highly recommended:

1. *Mathematical Reviews*, American Mathematical Society.

2. *Computer Abstracts*, Technical Information Co., Chancery House, London.

3. *Computing Reviews*, Association for Computing Machinery.

ANSWERS TO SELECTED EXERCISES

Chapter 1

1. $w_0 = \frac{7}{15}$, $w_1 = \frac{16}{15}$, $w_2 = \frac{7}{15}$, $w_3 = \frac{1}{15}$, $w_4 = -\frac{1}{15}$, $E_5 = 0$, $E_6 = \frac{16}{105}$

2. See (4.4.12) and (4.4.14)   **3.** $w_{-1} = -4/\pi^2$, $w_0 = 0$, $w_1 = 4/\pi^2$

5. $h^2 < 1/1.24$ **15.** $w_{-1} = w_0 = w_1 = \frac{2}{3}$, $x_1 = -\sqrt{2}/2$, $x_2 = 0$, $x_3 = \sqrt{2}/2$

17. $x_1 = 0.120$, $x_2 = 0.583$ **18.** $w_0 = 1$, $w_1 = -2$, $w_2 = 1$

Chapter 2

1. *Hint:* Using $y = x^2$, compute constant second difference, first two functional values, and construct a table similar to Table 2.12.1.

2. *Hint:* Using $y = x^3$, compute constant third difference, first three functional values, and construct a table similar to Table 2.12.1.

3. See (2.9.6).   **5.** See Table 2.12.1.

6. Construct a table similar to Table 2.13.2, make corrections in appropriate fourth differences, and correct the error in the eighth entry.

Chapter 3

1. It should be noted that choosing $x_0 = 0, 1, 2$ successively gives different results. It should also be noted that the error estimate cannot be computed by (3.3.7), since the divided difference involves the true functional value of $f(x)$, the quantity being approximated. The value of the first term omitted in (3.3.6) can be used as a crude estimate of the error.

2. See answer to Exercise 1.

3. See answer to Exercise 1.

4. If all entries are computed as defined in Figure 3.8.1, then all entries in the third computed column have the value 6.625.

5. $l_0(x) = -\frac{1}{6}(x^3 - 6x^2 - 11x + 6)$, $l_1(x) = \frac{1}{6}(3x^3 - 15x^2 + 18x)$,
$l_2(x) = -\frac{1}{6}(-3x^3 + 12x^2 - 9x)$, $l_3(x) = \frac{1}{6}(x^3 - 3x^2 + 2x)$;
$f(2.5) = 6.625$, $E(2.5) = 0$, since $l_4(2.5) = 0$.
[The $l_i(x)$ above are computed by using $x_0 = 0$.]

6. Using $x_0 = 0$, $f(s) = s^3 - 2s^2 + 3s - 4$, $f(2.5) = 6.625$ for $s = 2.5$; $E(s) = 0$, since $\Delta^4 f_0 = 0$.

7. Using $n = 4$, for $x = 2.5$ then $s = -1.5$; $E(s) = 0$, since $\nabla^4 f_4 = 0$.

Chapter 4

1. $f_0' = -\dfrac{1}{6h}(11f_0 - 18f_1 + 9f_2 - 2f_3) - \dfrac{h^3}{4}f^{(4)}(\xi)$

$f_1' = -\dfrac{1}{6h}(2f_0 + 3f_1 - 6f_2 + f_3) + \dfrac{h^3}{12}f^{(4)}(\xi)$

$f_2' = \dfrac{1}{6h}(f_0 - 6f_1 + 3f_2 + 2f_3) - \dfrac{h^3}{12}f^{(4)}(\xi)$

$f_3' = -\dfrac{1}{6h}(2f_0 - 9f_1 + 18f_2 - 11f_3) + \dfrac{h^3}{4}f^{(4)}(\xi)$

2. $hy_n' = -\frac{1}{2}(y_{n+2} - 4y_{n+1} + 3y_n)$

3. *Hint:* Use $\sinh^{-1} u = u - \dfrac{1}{2}\cdot\dfrac{u^3}{3} + \dfrac{1.3}{2.4}\cdot\dfrac{u^5}{5} - \dfrac{1.3.5}{2.4.6}\cdot\dfrac{u^7}{7} + \cdots$.

4. *Hint:* Assume $f(x) = f_k = K$, a constant.

5. For $n = 4$: $\dfrac{2h}{45}(7f_0 + 32f_1 + 12f_2 + 32f_3 + 7f_4)$

For $n = 5$: $\dfrac{5h}{288}(19f_0 + 75f_1 + 50f_2 + 50f_3 + 75f_4 + 19f_5)$

6. 0.632722

7. $a_6 = \dfrac{1}{60,480}(12n^7 - 210n^6 + 1428n^5 - 4725n^4 + 7672n^3 - 5040n^2)$

$\displaystyle\int_{x_0}^{x_6} f(x)\,dx$

$= h\left(6f_0 + 18\,\Delta f_0 + 27\,\Delta^2 f_0 + 24\,\Delta^3 f_0 + \dfrac{123}{10}\Delta^4 f_0 + \dfrac{33}{10}\Delta^5 f_0 + \dfrac{41}{140}\Delta^6 f_0\right)$

$= \dfrac{h}{140}(41f_0 + 216f_1 + 27f_2 + 272f_3 + 27f_4 + 216f_5 + 41f_6) - \dfrac{9h^9}{1400}f^{(8)}(\xi_1)$

$= \dfrac{3h}{10}(f_0 + 5f_1 + f_2 + 6f_3 + f_4 + 5f_5 + f_6)$

$\quad - \dfrac{h}{140}(f_0 - 6f_1 + 15f_2 - 20f_3 + 15f_4 - 6f_5 + f_6) - \dfrac{9h^9}{1400}f^{(8)}(\xi_1)$

$= \dfrac{3h}{10}(f_0 + 5f_1 + f_2 + 6f_3 + f_4 + 5f_5 + f_6) - \dfrac{h^7}{140}f^{(7)}(\xi_2) - \dfrac{9h^9}{1400}f^{(8)}(\xi_1)$

8. $A_1 = \dfrac{1}{12}$, $A_2 = -\dfrac{1}{24}$, $A_3 = \dfrac{19}{720}$, $A_4 = -\dfrac{3}{160}$, $A_5 = \dfrac{863}{60,480}$, $A_6 = -\dfrac{275}{24,192}$

9. $\displaystyle\int_{-1}^{1} f(x)\,dx = f\left(-\dfrac{1}{\sqrt{3}}\right) + f\left(\dfrac{1}{\sqrt{3}}\right) + \dfrac{1}{135}f^{(4)}(\xi)$

10. $\displaystyle\int_{0}^{\infty} e^{-x}f(x)\,dx = 0.71140\,f(0.41583) + 0.27852\,f(2.29422)$

$$+0.01038\,f(6.28995) + \dfrac{1}{20}f^{(6)}(\xi)$$

Chapter 5

1. $y(x) = -\frac{49}{10} + \frac{43}{10}x - \frac{1}{2}x^2$ RMS $= 0.6708$

2. $y(x) = -4 + 3x - 2x^2 + x^3$ RMS $= 0$

3. $y(x) = a_0P_0(x) + a_1P_1(x) + a_2P_2(x) + a_3P_3(x)$
$$= 0 \cdot P_0(x) + \tfrac{27}{5}P_1(x) + 1 \cdot P_2(x) + 1 \cdot P_3(x)$$
$$= 0 \cdot 1 + \tfrac{27}{5}(x - 1) + 1 \cdot (x^2 - 2x - 1) + 1 \cdot (x^3 - 3x^2 - \tfrac{2}{5}x + \tfrac{12}{5})$$
$$= x^3 - 2x^2 + 3x - 4$$

4. $f(x) = \dfrac{a_0}{2} + a_1 \cos\dfrac{\pi}{3}x + a_2 \cos\dfrac{2\pi}{3}x + \dfrac{a_3}{2}\cos \pi x + b_1 \sin\dfrac{\pi}{3}x + b_2 \sin\dfrac{2\pi}{3}x$
$$= \dfrac{10}{3} - 3\cos\dfrac{\pi}{3}x - \dfrac{1}{3}\cos\dfrac{2\pi}{3}x + \sqrt{3}\sin\dfrac{\pi}{3}x + \dfrac{\sqrt{3}}{3}\sin\dfrac{2\pi}{3}x$$

5. $y(x') = a_0\phi_0(x') + a_1\phi_1(x') + a_2\phi_2(x')$
$$= 2 \cdot 1 + 0 \cdot x' - 2(2x'^2 - 1)$$
$$= 4 - 4x'^2$$
$y(x) = 0 + 4x - x^2$ (unnormalized)

6. $C_1 = -3$, $C_2 = 1$, $a_1 = 1$, $a_2 = -1$, $A_1 = -3$, $A_2 = 2$
$y(x) = -3e^x + 2e^{-x}$

7. $a_0 = 2$, $a_1 = -2$, $a_2 = 3$, $a_3 = 0$, $a_4 = -5$
$$f(x) = \dfrac{x + 2}{x^2 + 1}$$

8. $\bar{y}_2 = 13.1$, $\bar{y}_3 = 14.8$, $\bar{y}_4 = 16.2$, $\bar{y}_5 = 21.4$, $\bar{y}_6 = 33.8$, $\bar{y}_7 = 44.1$

9. $a_0 = -10.08$, $a_1 = 3.71$, $a_2 = -0.96$, $a_3 = 0.14$
$f(x) = -5.04 + 3.71x - 0.96(2x^2 - 1) + 0.14(4x^3 - 3x)$
$ = 0.56x^3 - 1.92x^2 + 3.29x - 4.08$

Chapter 6

1. See (1.11.6).   **2.** 2.2361   **3.** 1.3247

4. 2.0946   **5.** $z_1 = 2.1$, $z_2 = 2.0946$

6. $p_1 = 2.095$, $q_1 - 2.38$, $x^2 + 2.095x \mid 2.389$

7. -1.414214 **8.** 1.414214

9. $x^2 - 8x + 25$, $x = 4 \pm 3i$

10. $1 \pm i$, $3 \pm 4i$ **11.** 0.3, 1.7, 4.5, 9.4

12. 1, 3, $\pm 2i$

Chapter 7

1.
$$\begin{bmatrix} 3.4 & 1.3 & 0.7 \\ -0.7 & -3.4 & 7.3 \\ 1.5 & 4.9 & 2.1 \end{bmatrix}$$

2.
$$\begin{bmatrix} 2.8 & 4.6 & 7.4 \\ 6.6 & 3.2 & 8.6 \\ 5.0 & 3.8 & 8.2 \end{bmatrix}$$

3.
$$\begin{bmatrix} 10.1 & 1.8 & 2.4 \\ 4.1 & -1.6 & 12.1 \\ 6.7 & -0.3 & 8.1 \end{bmatrix}$$

4.
$$\begin{bmatrix} 8.0 & 2.7 & 9.2 \\ 12.1 & 9.6 & 19.9 \\ -3.5 & 1.3 & -1.0 \end{bmatrix}$$

6. $\{u, v\} = -11$ **7.** $\sqrt{14}$ **8.** $\{u, v\} = 0$ **9.** $|A| = -0.249$

10. $\begin{bmatrix} 6.46633 & 9.63894 & -15.94444 \\ 11.16539 & 14.09702 & -24.86055 \\ -9.11710 & -12.41018 & 21.48689 \end{bmatrix}$

12. $\lambda_1 = -3$, $X_1 = [-3, 1]^t$, $\lambda_2 = 2$, $X_2 = [2, 1]^t$

13. $\lambda_1 = -3$, $Y_1 = [1, -2]^t$, $\lambda_2 = 2$, $Y_2 = [1, 3]^t$

14. $\{X_1^t, Y_2\} = 0$, $\{X_2^t, Y_1\} = 0$

15. $XX^t = I$

16. $\begin{bmatrix} 24 & 0 & 0 & 0 \\ 0 & 12 & 0 & 0 \\ 0 & 0 & 6 & 0 \\ 0 & 0 & 0 & 3 \end{bmatrix}$

17. 1   **18.** 5184

19. Values of principal minors: 11, 76, 792, 5184
      Eigenvalues: 3, 6, 12, 24

20. $\sqrt{765}$ **21.** 45   **23.** See (7.13.12). $|L| = -0.249$, $|U| = 1$

Chapter 8

1. $A^{-1} = \frac{1}{66} \begin{bmatrix} -21 & 9 & 6 \\ 21 & -4 & 12 \\ 51 & -3 & -24 \end{bmatrix}$ $A^{-1}b = \begin{bmatrix} 1 \\ -2 \\ 3 \end{bmatrix}$

2. $x_1 + \frac{3}{2}x_2 + x_3 = 1$
      $x_2 + \frac{1}{2}x_3 = -\frac{1}{2}$
      $x_3 = 3$, $x_2 = -2$, $x_1 = 1$

5. $M' = \begin{bmatrix} 2 & \frac{3}{2} & 1 & 1 \\ 10 & -12 & \frac{1}{2} & -\frac{1}{2} \\ 3 & \frac{3}{2} & -\frac{11}{4} & 3 \end{bmatrix}$

6. $L = \begin{bmatrix} 2 & 0 & 0 \\ 10 & -12 & 0 \\ 3 & \frac{3}{2} & -\frac{11}{4} \end{bmatrix}$, $U = \begin{bmatrix} 1 & \frac{3}{2} & 1 \\ 0 & 1 & \frac{1}{2} \\ 0 & 0 & 1 \end{bmatrix}$

8. See (8.10.7).

Chapter 9

1. $\lambda_1 = 3$, $X_1 = [1, -1, 0, -1]^t$, $\lambda_2 = 6$, $X_2 = [1, 1, -1, 0]^t$.
      $\lambda_3 = 12$, $X_3 = [0, 1, 1, -1]^t$, $\lambda_4 = 24$, $X_4 = [1, 0, 1, 1]^t$

3. $\lambda_1 = -3$, $X_1 = [0, -2, 3]^t$, $\lambda_2 = -2$, $X_2 = [1, 2, -5]^t$,
      $\lambda_3 = 11$, $X_3 = [2, 4, 3]^t$.

Chapter 11

4. $f(z) = -\frac{1}{2}\left\{ \sum_{n=0}^{\infty} \frac{z^n}{3^{n+1}} + \sum_{n=0}^{\infty} z^{-(n+1)} \right\}$

10. a) res $(-1) = -2$, res $(2) = 1$

   b) res $(2) = \frac{1}{12}e^6$

      res $(-1 + i\sqrt{3}) = -(6\sqrt{3}\sin 3\sqrt{3} + 6\cos 3\sqrt{3}) - i(6\sin 3\sqrt{3} - 6\sqrt{3}\cos 3\sqrt{3})$

      res $(-1 - i\sqrt{3}) = -(6\sqrt{3}\sin 3\sqrt{3} + 6\cos 3\sqrt{3}) + i(6\sin 3\sqrt{3} - 6\sqrt{3}\cos 3\sqrt{3})$

c) res $(0) = \frac{1}{2}$,   res $(2) = -\frac{1}{2}$ d) $f(z)$ has a triple pole at $z = 0$.

$$\text{res } (0) = -\frac{4}{3}$$

Chapter 13

1. $y_n = A + B(-1)^n + C(2)^n + D(-2)^n$

2. $y_n = (A + Bn)2^n$

3. $y_n = A(-1 + i)^n + B(-1 - i)^n$

4. $y_n = Aa^n + B(-a)^n + \frac{1}{2}na^{n-2}$

5. $y_n = \begin{cases} Aa^n + \dfrac{b^n - a^n}{b - a}, & a \neq b \\ Aa^n + na^{n-1}, & a = b \end{cases}$

6. $y_n = A(ia)^n + B(-ia)^n + \frac{1}{2}a^{n-2}$

7. $y_n = A2^n + B(-2)^n + \frac{1}{4}n(n - 2)$

8. $y_n = A + B(-1)^n + \frac{1}{6}n(n - 1)(n - 2)$

Chapter 15

1.

$$\begin{bmatrix} q_1(s) \\ q_2(s) \\ q_3(s) \end{bmatrix} = \frac{\begin{bmatrix} s^4 + s^3 + 2s^2 + s & -s^4 + s + 1 & -s^4 - s^3 \\ s^4 - s^3 - s^2 - 1 & s^4 + s^3 & s^4 + s \\ s^4 - s^2 + 1 & -s^4 + s^3 - s & s^4 + s^3 - s^2 + 1 \end{bmatrix} \begin{bmatrix} \dfrac{2}{s^3} \\ \dfrac{1}{s} \\ \dfrac{1}{s^2} \end{bmatrix}}{2s^6 + s^5 + s^3 + s + 1}$$

2. $f(t) = 2e^{-2t} - e^{-3t} \cos 4t$

3. $f(t) = 5e^{-t} + 4e^{-2t} \cos \left(3t + \dfrac{\pi}{6} \right)$

4. $f(t) = \dfrac{1}{2} + \dfrac{\sqrt{2}}{2} e^{-t} \cos \left(t + \dfrac{3\pi}{4} \right)$

5. $T(\omega) = -\dfrac{2}{\omega^4 + 4} + j \dfrac{\omega^2 - 2}{\omega(\omega^4 + 4)}$

Gain $= -20 \log_{10} \omega - 10 \log_{10} (\omega^4 + 4)$

$\theta = 57.29577 \left\{ \text{arc tan} \left| \dfrac{2 - \omega^2}{2\omega} \right| \right\}$

Phase $= \theta - 180°$, $0 < \omega < \sqrt{2}$

$= -180°$, $\omega = \sqrt{2}$

$= -180° - \theta$, $\omega > \sqrt{2}$

AUTHOR INDEX

Aitken, A. C., 40
Anderson, R. L., 310

Babbage, C., 2
Balabanian, N., 162, 170
Bancroft, T. A., 310
Bauer, W. F., 310
Bellman, R., 113
Bendixson, I., 46
Bennett, C., 310
Biot, M., 214
Bishop, R. E., 280
Bodewig, E., 113, 130, 135
Boole, G., 23, 251
Brown, G. S., 214
Brown, T. A., 46
Brownlee, K., 310
Burger, E., 294

Caldwell, G. C., 100
Campbell, D. P., 214
Caratheodory, C., 294
Carslaw, H. S., 76, 238
Cauchy, A. L., 155, 156, 159
Cayley, A., 128
Chebyshev, P. L., 100
Chernoff, H., 294
Churchill, R. V., 162, 170, 238
Cochran, W. G., 310
Cohen, A., 251
Collatz, L., 181, 195, 231
Courant, R., 231, 310
Cox, G. M., 310
Crockett, J. B., 294
Crout, P. D., 119
Cunningham, W. J., 197
Curry, H. B., 294
Curtiss, J. H., 310
Cutkosky, R. E., 310

Davidson, W. C., 294
Davis, H. T., 195, 197
Davis, M., 294
De la Vallée Poussin, Ch.-J., 35, 46, 327
Dirichlet, P. G. L., 215, 232
Dixon, W., 310
Duncan, W., 280

Erdélyi, A., 240, 244
Euler, L., 11

Faddeev, D. K., 113, 141
Faddeeva, V. N., 113, 141
Ferrar, W. L., 35, 46, 327, 329, 330
Forsythe, G. E., 1, 66, 67, 125, 181, 231, 294
Fourier, J. B. J., 73
Fox, L., 113, 125, 181, 270
Franklin, N., 310
Franklin, P., 238
Fredholm, E., 252
Friedrichs, K., 310
Fry, T. C., 310
Fulkerson, D., 149
Fuller, A. T., 207, 214

Gauss, C. F., 42, 57, 118
Givens, W., 142
Gladwell, G. M., 280
Godunov, S., 181
Goldstein, H., 9
Goodwin, E. T., 270
Gorn, S., 90
Guillemin, E. A., 238

Hadamard, J., 215, 231
Hahn, H., 46
Hald, A., 310
Hamilton, W. R., 128
Hamming, R. W., 1, 6, 8, 66, 67, 76
Hardy, G. H., 47
Henrici, P., 141, 181
Hermite, C., 72
Hestenes, M. R., 125
Hilbert, D., 231
Hildebrand, F. B., 6, 8, 16, 17, 46, 67, 76
Hoel, P. G., 310
Hooke, R., 294
Householder, A. S., 67, 113, 139
Hurwitz, H., 207, 243, 244

Irving, J., 270

Jacobi, C. G. J., 113
Jannson, B., 310

347

Jeeves, T. A., 294
Johnson, D. C., 280
Jordan, M. E. C., 109, 123

Kahn, H., 310
Kantorovich, L., 231
Karman, T., 214, 280
Kline, R. C., 294
Knopp, K., 162
Kopal, Z., 1
Krasnosel'skii, M. A., 270
Krein, M. G., 270
Krylov, V., 231
Kunz, K., 289

Lagrange, J. L., 43, 48, 52
Laguerre, E. N., 71
Lanczos, C., 1, 142
Laurent, P. M. H., 158
Lefschetz, S., 197
Legendre, A. M., 71
Levy, H., 310
Luke, Y. L., 244

Magnus, W., 240, 244
Mason, S. J., 289
Massey, F., 310
McCord, J. R., 297
McLachlan, N. W., 196, 197
Metropolis, N., 309, 310
Michaelson, S., 280
Milne, W. E., 67, 181, 188, 195, 231
Minorsky, N., 196, 197
Moler, C., 117, 122, 145
Mood, A. M., 310
Moroney, R. M., 297
Muller, D. E., 89, 133
Mullineux, N., 270
Muskhelishvili, N. I., 270

Newman, M., 332
Newton, I., 20, 36

Oberhettinger, F., 240, 244
Oldenburger, R., 214, 280
Osborne, E. E., 149
Ostle, B., 310
Ostrowski, A. M., 86

Papoulis, A., 310
Parlett, B., 113, 137, 138, 139
Perlis, S., 113, 141
Pipes, L., 280
Poisson, S. D., 296
Price, J. F., 339

Radau, R., 61
Ralston, A., 54, 61
Rich, R. P., 247, 251
Routh, E. J., 207
Runge, C., 46
Ryabenki, V., 181

Samuelson, P., 270
Scarborough, J. B., 18, 46
Scott, E. J., 214, 280
Seshu, S., 162, 170
Shaw, J., 247, 251
Simon, L., 310
Snedecor, G., 310
Spang, H. A., 100
Steffenson, J. F., 47, 327
Stiefel, E. L., 67
Stoker, J. J., 196, 197
Struble, R. A., 196, 197

Taylor, B., 10
Teixeira, F. G., 46
Theis, M., 46
Thompson, W. T., 238
Timoshenko, S., 214, 280
Titchmarsh, E. C., 46, 162
Todd, J., 100, 332
Tompkins, C. B., 294
Tricomi, F. G., 240, 244, 270
Tschebyscheff (*see* Chebyshev)

Ulam, S., 309, 310

Varga, R. S., 113, 125, 195
Volterra, V., 252
Von Mises, R., 129, 142
Von Neumann, J., 9, 310

Wang, H. -H., 332
Ward, J. A., 100
Wasow, W., 310
Watson, C. N., 244
Watson, G. N., 162, 240
Weierstrass, C. T. W., 3
Whittaker, E. T., 35, 46, 76, 162, 214,
    246, 280, 327
Whittaker, J. M., 46, 325
Widder, D. V., 142, 170
Wiener, N., 238
Wilkinson, J. H., 87, 113, 122, 139, 141,
    142, 289
Willers, F. A., 76
Wolfe, P., 149

Zimmermann, H. J., 286
Zweifel, P. F., 243, 244

SUBJECT INDEX

Abstracting journals, 340
Accuracy, 17
Adams' method, 186
  modified, 186
Adams-Bashforth method, 186, 195
Adjoint matrix, 106
Aitken's interpolation, 40
Analysis of variance, 301
Analytic functions, 152
Approximation, 17
  Chebyshev, 76
  exponential, 80
  Fourier, 73
  Hermite, 72
  Laguerre, 71
  Legendre, 71
  Padé, 281
  polynomial, 19, 34, 63, 66
  rational functions, 82
Augmented matrix, 105, 115
Automatic monitoring, 204
Averaging operator, 27

Backward differences, 25, 28
Bairstow's iteration, 94
Bashforth method, 186, 195
Bernoulli's equation, 196
Bessel functions, 239
Bessel interpolation, 46
Binomial, coefficients, 29
  distribution, 296
Bisection method, 88
Bode plots, 209, 249
Boundary-value problems,
  ordinary, 190
  partial, 225
Branch points, 159

Cardinal function, 34, 245
  series, 327
Cauchy's integral formula, 156
Cauchy's integral theorem, 155
Cauchy's problem, 216
Cauchy's residue theorem, 159, 160, 202
Cauchy-Riemann equations, 154
Cayley-Hamilton theorem, 128
Central differences, 13, 25, 29
Central tendency, 295

Characteristics, method of, 230
Characteristic polynomial, 128
Chebyshev, approximation, 76, 234
  polynomials, 76
Chebyshev-Gauss quadrature, 61
Chi-square test, 297, 301
Chrystal's equation, 196
Clairaut's equation, 196
Coefficient matrix, 115
Cofactor, 106
Complex variables, 150
  elementary functions of, 151
  Euler's form, 152
  polar form, 151
  power series, 151
  rectangular form, 151
Computer mathematics, 3
  classical mathematics, 3
  number system, 3
Confidence intervals, 299
Conservative system, 271, 276
Continued fraction, 83
Convergence, 4, 13, 20, 218, 223, 224, 246
Correlation, statistical, 305
Cosine integral, 242
Cotes integration, 54, 55
Cramer's rule, 115
Crank-Nicholson method, 195, 222, 231
Crout reduction, 119
Cubic interpolation, 73
Curve fitting, 63

Data smoothing, 63
Delta function, 233
Derivative, 51
  finite differences, 51
  Lagrangian, 48
Determinant evaluation, 104
  Vandermonde, 323
Difference correction technique, 256
Difference equations, 172
  accuracy, 177
  convergence, 177
  first-order, 174, 177
  higher-order, 178
  order of, 172
  partial, 179
  second-order, 175, 178
  stability, 16, 180, 181

Difference operators, 25
Differences, 23
  backward, 25, 28
  central, 13, 25, 29
  divided, 30
  finite, 23, 183
  forward, 13, 25, 27
  reciprocal, 82
  relationship between, 29, 31
Differential equations, 182, 215
  boundary-value, 190, 225
  characteristic-value, 230
  closed type formulas, 185
  finite difference schemes, 183
  higher-order equations, 188
  open type formulas, 183
  ordinary, 182
  partial, 215
  variable coefficients, 188
Differential operator, 25
Differentiation, 48
  Lagrange formula, 48
Digital filters, 245, 247
Dirichlet conditions, 232
Dirichlet's problem, 215
Dispersion, 295
Dissipation function, 275
Distributions, 296
Divided differences, 30
  differentiation of, 30

Eigenvalue problem, 107, 127, 331, 332
  Givens' method, 131, 132
  Householder's method, 139
  inverse power method, 133
  Jacobi's method, 129
  Laguerre's method, 137
  L. R. algorithm, 141
  Muller's method, 133
  power method, 133
  Q. D. algorithm, 141
  Q. R. algorithm, 141
Electrical vibrations, 275
Elimination, 116
Elliptic equations, 224, 225, 228
Energy, kinetic, 272, 273
  potential, 272, 273, 274
Equations, linear, 115
  nonlinear, 86
  normal, 64
Equations of motion, 273
  Lagrange's, 272, 275
  transformed, 276
Equilibration, 145
Error curve, 9
Errors, 5, 9
  absolute, 17
  generated, 9
  idealized models, 9

measurements, 9
order of, 10
polynomial approximation, 19
relative, 17
roundoff, 9, 11, 13
significant figures, 17
sources and types, 9
in tabular entry, 32
truncation, 9, 10, 11, 13
Euler's constant, 241
Euler's formula, 11, 185
  modified, 185
Everett's formula, 46
Exponential approximation, 80
Exponential integrals, 242

F-test, 297, 301
Factorial function, 24
False position, 89
Filters, 238, 247
  continuous, 249
  discrete analog, 249
Finite differences, 23, 183
  of polynomials, 32
First law of the mean, 321
Fisher's maximum-likelihood, 298
Folding frequency, 246
Formula derivation, 5, 323
Forsythe's method, 68
Forward differences, 13, 25, 27
Fourier approximation, 73, 233
Fourier integral, 234, 237, 242
Fourier transform, 236, 238
Fredholm equations, 252, 253, 262
Free vibrations, 271, 277
  fundamental frequency, 277
  fundamental mode of oscillation, 277
Frequency, folding, 246
  fundamental, 277
  statistical, 295
Frequency response, 204, 208, 238
Full-wave rectification, 171
Functional minimization, 290
  direct, 291
  gradient, 291
  search, 293
Fundamental frequency, 277
Fundamental mode of oscillation, 277
Fundamental statistics, 295

Gain, 238, 251
Gauss elimination, 118
Gauss interpolation, 42
Gauss quadrature, 8, 57
  coefficients and abscissas, 58
Gauss reduction, 118
Gauss-Chebyshev integration, 61
Gauss-Hermite integration, 60
Gauss-Jordan reduction, 123

Gauss-Legendre integration, 59
Gauss-Seidel iteration, 124, 229
Givens' method, 129, 131, 132
Goodness-of-fit parameter, 64, 70
Gradient method, 125
Graeffe's iteration, 97
Gram-Schmidt, 286
Green's function, 253
Green's theorem, 155
Gregory coefficients, 57, 255, 256
Gregory's formula, 57, 253, 254, 256, 262
Gregory-Newton series, 325
Guide, literature, 339

Half-wave rectification, 171
Harmonic analysis, 232
Heat equation, 180
Hermite polynomials, 72
Hermitian matrix, 108
Hessenberg matrix, 112, 129, 137
Heun method, 185
Hilbert matrix, 106
Historical development, 2
    computers, 2
    numerical analysis, 2
Householder's method, 129, 139
Hyperbolic equations, 229
Hypothesis, statistical, 300, 303, 305

Identity matrix, 104
Ill-condition, 106
    singular, 106
Influence function, 252
Initial-value problems, 216
Inner product, 105
Integral equations, 252
    Fredholm, 252, 253, 262
    influence function, 252
    kernel, 252
    nonsingular, 262
    singular, 253
    Volterra, 252
Integral operator, 27
Integration, 48
    finite differences, 55
    Fourier transform, 242
    Gaussian, 57
    Gregory, 57
    Lagrangian, 52
    Lobatto, 61
    Newton-Cotes, 54, 55
    Radau, 61
    Richardson, 61
    Romberg, 61
Interpolation, 34
    Aitken's method, 40
    function theorems, 325
    Gauss, 42

    higher-order, 40
    Lagrange, 43
    linear, 39
    spline, 73
Inverse Laplace transform, 166, 167
Inverse matrix, 106, 122, 331
Inverse power method, 133, 134
Iteration, 20, 87, 117
Iterative improvement, 117
Iterative methods, 87, 123

Jacobi's method, 113, 129
Jordan canonical form, 109
Jordan elimination, 123

Kernel, 252
Kinetic energy, 272, 273
Kutta's methods, 187

Lagrange, differentiation, 48
    coefficient functions, 45
    integration, 52
    interpolation, 43, 229
Lagrange's equation, 272, 275
Laguerre polynomials, 71
Laguerre's method, 129, 137
Laplace transform, 163
    of derivatives, 165
    of differential equations, 166
    differentiation theorem, 168
    division of $f(t)$ by t, 169
    existence of, 163
    final-value theorem, 168
    initial-value theorem, 168
    integration theorem, 168
    inverse, 166, 167
    linearity theorem, 165
    multiplication of $f(t)$ by t, 169
    properties, 168
    shifting theorems, 165, 170
    of simple functions, 164, 169
    tables, 333
Laplace's equation, 154
Laurent series, 157
Law of the mean, first, 321
    second, 321
Least squares, 63
Legendre polynomials, 71
Line integrals, 154
Linear equations, 115
    Cramer's method, 115
    Crout reduction, 119
    Gauss elimination, 118
    gradient methods, 125
    inverse method, 122
    iterative improvement, 117
    Jordan elimination, 123
    orthogonalization methods, 125
Linear interpolation, 39

Linear operators, 27, 323
Linear vibrations, 275
Linearized spline interpolation, 73
Lin's iteration, 92, 93, 101
Literature guide, 339
Lobatto integration, 61
Lower triangular matrix, 105, 111, 121
L. R. algorithm, 141

Maclaurin series, 281, 282
Matrix, 103
    addition and multiplication, 105
    adjoint, 106
    algebra, 103
    augmented, 105, 115
    cofactor, 106
    determinant, 104, 106
    diagonal, 104
    eigenvalues, 107, 331, 332
    eigenvectors, 107
    Hermitian, 108
    Hessenberg, 112
    Hilbert, 106
    inverse, 106, 122, 331
    Jordan canonical, 109
    minor, 106
    norms, 110
    null, 104
    orthogonal, 108
    positive definite, 108
    rank, 106
    root-finding, 101
    scaling, 116, 143
    similarity, 109
    singular, 106
    square, 103
    symmetric, 104
    test, 331
    transpose, 104
    triangular, 111, 121
    tridiagonal, 104, 113
    unit, 104
    unitary, 108
Matrix exponential, 194
Matrix form, 115, 193
Matrix transform equation, 198
Maximum-likelihood, 298
Maximum principle, 222, 224
Mean, 295
Mean value, 321
Median, 295
Milne's methods, 186, 188, 195
Minimax principle, 78
Minimization, functional, 290
    direct methods, 291
    gradient methods, 291
    nonlinear equations, 100

search methods, 293
Minimum phase, 206
Minor, 106
Mode, 295
Monte Carlo techniques, 309
Muller's method, 89, 129, 133

Neumann series, 253
Newton-Cotes integration, 54, 55
Newton-Gauss series, 327
Newton-Raphson iteration, 90
    modified, 97
Newton's backward difference, 38
Newton's divided difference, 36, 328
Newton's forward difference, 37
Newton's fundamental formula, 36
Newton's interation formula, 21
Newton's three-eighths rule, 54
Nichols plots, 209
Nonconservative system, 271, 279
Nonlinear equations, 86
    differential, 195
    systems of, 98, 99
Nonminimum phase, 206
Nordsieck's method, 187
Normal distribution, 297
Normal equations, 64
Normalizing formulas, 69
Norms, matrix, 110
    vector, 110
Numerical analysis, 1
    difficulties, 3
    types of problems, 3
Numerical computation, 1
    art, 2
    science, 2
Numerical differentiation, 48
Nyquist sampling theorem, 246

Operator, averaging, 27
    delta, 23
    difference, 23, 25
    differential, 25
    integral, 27
    shifting, 24
Ordinary differential equations, 182
Orthogonal functions, 65, 66
Orthogonal matrix, 108
Orthogonal polynomials, 67
Orthogonality, 66
    methods, linear equations, 125
    procedure, Gram-Schmidt, 286
Orthonormal functions, 65, 67
Osborne's method, 148
    modified, 149
Oscillations, electrical, 275
    linear, 275
    torsional, 275

Padé approximation, 195, 281
Parabolic equations, 220
Parabolic rule, 6
Partial differential equations, 215
  boundary-value, 190, 225
  Cauchy's problem, 216
  characteristics, method of, 230
  classification of, 216
  convergence, 218, 223
  Crank-Nicholson method, 195, 222, 231
  Dirichlet's problem, 215, 222
  elliptic, 224
  finite difference methods, 218
  hyperbolic, 229, 231
  initial-value problem, 216
  iterative solution, 123, 228
  matrix form, 226
  maximum principle, 222
  parabolic, 220
  stability, 218, 223
  well-posed problem, 215
Periodic, 73, 232
Periodicals, 340
Phase, 238, 251
Picard's method, 182
Pivoting, 116
Poles, 159, 167, 168, 202
Polynomial approximation, 19, 34, 63, 66
Positive definite, 108
Potential energy, 272, 273, 274
Power method, 133
Predicator-corrector methods, 186
Probability distributions, 296
Prony's method, 80

Q. D. algorithm, 141
Q. R. algorithm, 141

Radau integration, 61
Rank, 106
Rational functions, 82
Reciprocal differences, 82
Regression, 301
Relative error, 17
Removable singularities, 159
Residuals, 64
Residues, Cauchy, 159, 167
Riccati's equation, 196
Rich-Shaw method, 100, 247, 251
Richardson extrapolation, 61
Rolle's theorem, 321
Romberg integration, 61
Root-finding methods, 86
  Bairstow's method, 94
  bisection method, 88
  false-position, 89
  Graeffe's method, 97

Lin's method, 92, 93, 101
matrix method, 101
minimizing method, 100
modified Newton-Raphson, 97
Newton-Raphson method, 90, 99
parabolic method, 89
Rich-Shaw method, 100
stability, 87
synthetic division, 91, 93
Root locus, 213
  gain constant, 212, 213
Root mean square, 65, 70
Roundoff errors, 9, 11, 13
Runge-Kutta methods, 187

Sampled data, 245
Sampling noise level, 246
Sampling theorem, 246
Saw-tooth wave, 171
Scalar product, 105
Scaling, 116, 143
  equilibration, 145
  linear program, 145
  modified Osborne, 149
  Osborne's method, 148
Second law of the mean, 321
Second-order reduction, 193
Shifting operator, 24
Significant figures, 17
Simpson's rule, 6, 54, 55, 56
Sine integral, 242
Singularities, 158, 159
  essential, 159
  nonessential, 159
  poles, 159, 167, 168, 202
  removable, 159
Singular matrix, 106
Smoothing formulas, 84
Special functions, 239
Special integrals, 239
Spline interpolation, 73
Square root, 21
Square wave, 169
Stability, 4, 11, 13, 16, 66, 189, 206, 218, 223, 224
Stability-phaseness test, 207
Standard deviation, 296
Static gain, 212, 213
Statistics, elementary, 295
  analysis of variance, 301
  central tendency, 295
  confidence intervals, 299
  dispersion, 295
  distributions, 296
  maximum-likelihood, 298
  Monte Carlo methods, 309
  regression analysis, 301
  testing of parameters, 300

Stirling's formula, 46
Student's t-test, 297, 300
Sturm function, 131
Substitution rule, 247
Symmetric matrix, 104
Synthetic division, 91, 93
System roots, 199

Taylor series, 10, 157
Test matrices, 331
Time response, 202, 247, 248
Torsional vibrations, 275
Transfer functions, 198, 199, 200, 202
Transient response, 202, 247
Transpose, 104
Trapezoidal rule, 54, 55
Triangular matrix, 111, 121
Triangular wave, 171
Tridiagonal matrix, 104, 113, 191
Trigonometric approximation, 73
Truncation errors, 9, 10, 11, 13

Unit impulse function, 170
Unit step function, 169
Upper triangular matrix, 105, 111, 121

Vandermonde, 323
Variance, 296, 297
Vector, column, 104
    norms, 110
    notation, 103
    orthogonalization, 286
    product, 105
    row, 104
Vibration problems, 192, 198, 271
    conservative system, 271, 276
    electrical, 275
    free, 271, 277
    linear, 275
    nonconservative system, 271, 279
    torsional, 275
    types, 271
Volterra equations, 252

Wave equation, 180
Weierstrass theorem, 3, 321
Weighting coefficients, 5, 52, 324
Weighting functions, 63, 67, 68, 71, 72, 73, 78, 79
Well-posed problem, 215

Zeros of functions (*see* root-finding methods)

ABCDE6987